A First Course in
Atmospheric Thermodynamics

Grant W. Petty
ATMOSPHERIC AND OCEANIC SCIENCES
UNIVERSITY OF WISCONSIN-MADISON
MADISON, WISCONSIN

Sundog Publishing
Madison, Wisconsin

Printed and bound in the United States of America.

10 9 8 7 6 5

Library of Congress Control Number: 2008900732

Petty, Grant W., 1958–

A first course in atmospheric thermodynamics - 1st Ed.

Sundog Publishing
ISBN-10: 0-9729033-2-1
ISBN-13: 978-0-9729033-2-5

Cover: A weather observer prepares to release a radiosonde balloon at McMurdo Station, Antarctica. On the back cover in the distance may be seen Discovery Hut, which was built by Robert F. Scott and his crew in 1902 in preparation for their ill-fated expedition to the South Pole. On the hill above and to the left of the hut is Vince's cross, erected in honor of George Vince, who perished in a fall at the site in 1902. Photo courtesy of Alan Robock.

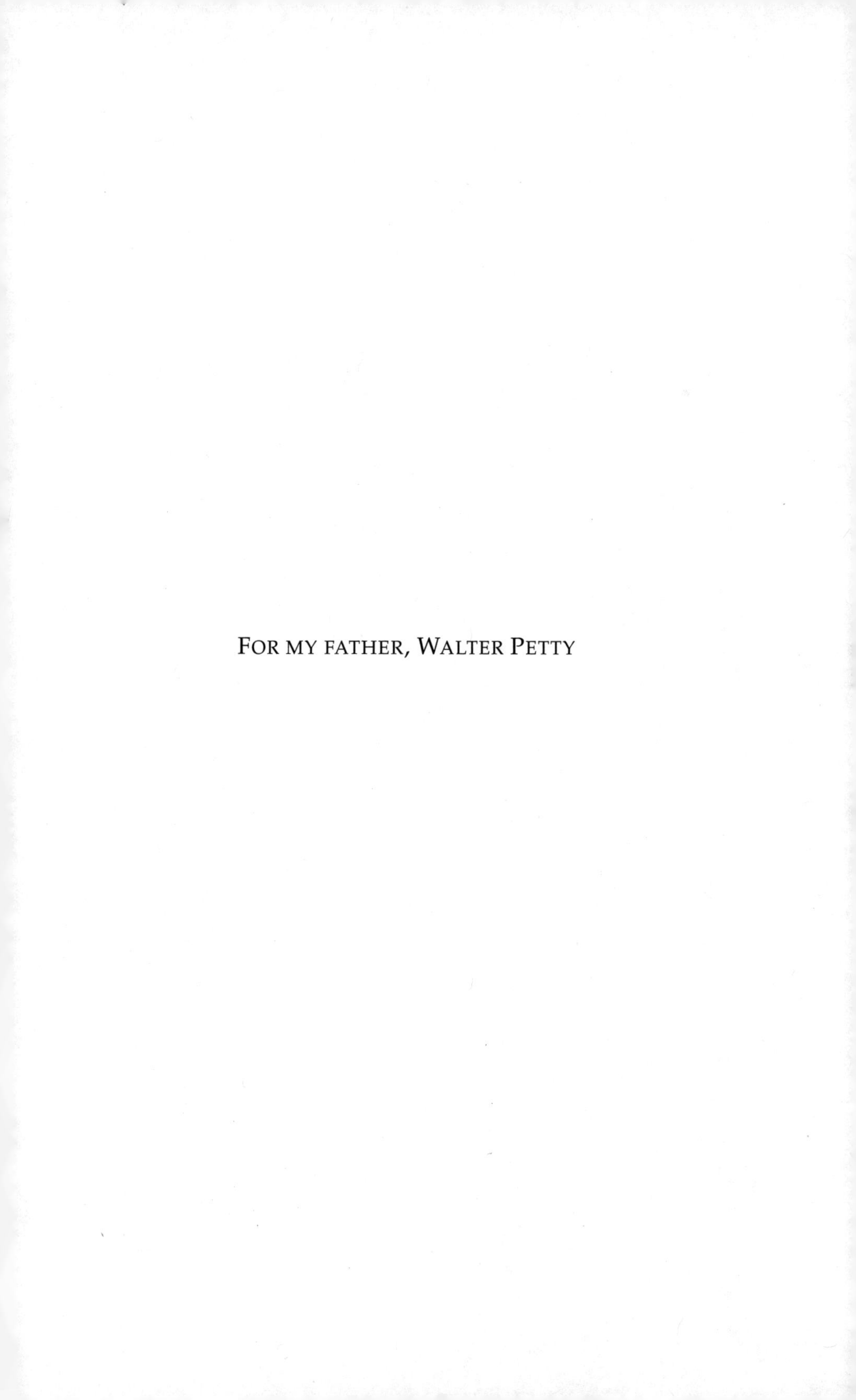

FOR MY FATHER, WALTER PETTY

Contents

Preface

To the student

If you're using this textbook in connection with a college course, there's a good chance that this is your first *quantitative* introduction to the atmospheric sciences. The subject of **atmospheric thermodynamics** concerns the physical behavior of air on a more or less *local* scale — how does an isolated "parcel" of air respond to changes in temperature and pressure, and how do these changes affect its behavior in relationship to the surrounding atmosphere? Atmospheric thermodynamic principles form the foundation for serious study of almost every other major topic in atmospheric science, including **atmospheric dynamics** (the study of the fluid motions of the atmosphere), **cloud and precipitation physics**, and **weather forecasting**, especially the forecasting of thunderstorms and severe weather.

It's fairly likely that this course, along perhaps with one in dynamics, will be your first occasion to begin routinely *using* differential and integral calculus and principles of basic physics to solve real-world problems. As you progress through this book, take time to review the relevant mathematical and physical principles as needed, and persuade yourself that you can correctly apply these principles to the problem at hand. To assist you with this review, I have included some reference material in an appendix.

I have found that a student's success in a course like this one is often directly related to their willingness to move beyond "blind" application of memorized formulas and to develop a good feel for how the mathematical relationships relate to the physical process, and vice versa. I encourage you to strive for this insight at all times; it will serve you well not only in this course but also in future atmospheric science courses.

In Appendix B, I offer a number of specific suggestions on how to solve and write up your problem solutions the way a professional scientist would. In my own courses, they're not suggestions but requirements! I require them not because I'm cruel and capricious but because good problem solving skills make life much easier for both the grader *and the student* in the long run. Even if your own instructor is less demanding about this, there is nothing to stop you from adopting these techniques voluntarily. Your goal should be to move away from the tedious and error-prone "high school" habits of manipulating *numbers* and *units* and to cultivate instead the more efficient and reliable habit of manipulating algebraic *symbols* and *physical dimensions.*

To the instructor

Atmospheric thermodynamics is often the first quantitative atmospheric science course encountered by new meteorology majors. It serves as a natural bridge between the generic principles of physics and calculus (energy and work, differentiation and integration) acquired in the lower division years and the more specialized knowledge and methods associated with atmospheric dynamics and the analysis of weather systems. For these reasons, there are also special pedagogical challenges in the teaching of atmospheric thermodynamics — one must give due attention not only to the core subject matter but also provide meteorological context and further reinforce newly acquired math and physics skills.

This book is therefore not *just* about atmospheric thermodynamics, and that is perhaps the most important distinction from other excellent texts on the subject. It reviews in some detail the application of basic calculus concepts and skills to physical problems. It also gives new majors a basic grounding in the observed composition and structure of the atmosphere as well as in how routine meteorological measurements are made. Wherever possible, it highlights connections between abstract theoretical concepts and easily observable properties and behavior of the atmosphere. The appendix includes a substantial, self-contained review of "mature" problem solving skills in the physical sciences.

Although you would never guess it by reading most meteorology textbooks, the evolution of modern operational meteorology owes more to the emergence and growth of aviation throughout the 20th century than to any other single technological development. A great many meteorologists are employed in jobs that directly or indirectly support civilian and military air operations. How many of the thousands of surface and upper air stations that cover the globe are *not* located at airports? Many of the basic properties of the atmosphere introduced in this book — especially the relationships among pressure, density, temperature, and altitude — are literally of life-and-death importance to pilots. In my opinion, a meteorologist's undergraduate training cannot be considered complete without explicit reference to these applications.

Notwithstanding the above ways in which I have added to the scope of a traditional thermodynamics text, I have consciously resisted the temptation to include lengthy chapters on topics whose relevance to applied meteorology is more obscure. Relatively few undergraduate meteorology majors are ready to ponder the meaning of entropy, the deeper implications of the Second Law of Thermodynamics, or the theoretical properties of heat engines and refrigeration cycles. I therefore introduce these and similar topics only in passing, often as a waypoint to something more "useful." Those students requiring a more sophisticated understanding will almost certainly have another shot at it in graduate school, where they will undoubtedly also use a more advanced textbook than this one.

Homework problems are interspersed throughout each chapter rather than being grouped at the end in the traditional manner. These exercises are designed not to stump the student but rather to facilitate his/her internalization of the immediately preceding material. Complete solutions for most exercises are available to instructors upon request (`feedback@sundogpublishing.com`). Numerical answers are provided at the end of selected problems. A strategy I have found effective is to assign problems from the book, but with modified parameters. Students can independently verify their method using the original values and then turn in for grading their solution for the modified problem. Once they master the art of deriving reusable symbolic solutions, very little additional effort is needed to obtain a second numerical result.

Central to any course in atmospheric thermodynamics is the thermodynamic diagram, of which the skew-T $\log p$ chart is perhaps the most popular. In my own experience, keeping students supplied with fresh skew-T charts for use in homework and lab exercises was a logistical challenge. The original government-issue charts are relatively expensive to keep stocked today, not to mention large and unwieldy. Home-made alternatives, while more compact, typically suffer from poor precision and/or legibility. I therefore set out to create skew-T charts that combine the best of both worlds and that can be downloaded for free and printed as needed by students and instructors alike. These and other resources may be found on the publisher website at `www.sundogpublishing.com`.

As was the case for my first book, *A First Course in Atmospheric Radiation,* I intend to undertake revisions and corrections with each new print run, following a model more nearly resembling that of regular software updates rather than traditional textbook publishing. Comments, corrections, and suggestions for future revisions are encouraged and may be sent to the author at `feedback@sundogpublishing.com`.

Acknowledgments

This book is the outgrowth of course notes developed and refined over 17 years of teaching junior level courses in atmospheric thermodynamics and physics at Purdue University and the University of Wisconsin-Madison. The raw material was drawn from, or at least inspired by, a variety of published and unpublished sources, including all of the textbooks cited in Appendix A, as well as the unpublished lecture notes by Brian C. Weare that served as the text for my own first exposure to atmospheric thermodynamics when I was a senior at the University of California at Davis in 1983.

As my own rough notes evolved into this book, I was alerted to omissions and outright errors by the students taking my courses and by the graduate teaching assistants whose thankless job it was to serve as interpreter. In the final stages of writing, I received helpful comments and suggestions from Ankur Desai, Ralf Bennartz, and David Dempsey. Amy Curl gave invaluable proofreading assistance on an exceptionally tight deadline. Robert L. Street, David Emory Stooksbury, Leigh Orf, and Karen Russ are gratefully acknowledged for pointing out significant errors that made it into the first printing.

I have made extensive use of photographs drawn from U.S. government sources, in particular the NOAA Photo Library and the National Severe Storms Laboratory. In addition, a number of photographs have been generously placed in the public domain by weather enthusiasts like Alan Sim, Adrian Pingstone, and Greg Keefer. For all of these contributions I am grateful; this book is considerably more interesting to look at as a result.

Above all, I would like to thank Professor Alan Robock of Rutgers University for his meticulous and insightful review of what I had thought at the time was a near-final draft. In addition to addressing specific issues, his comments and suggestions helped raise my own overall standards for completeness, clarity, and pedagogical value, which in turn inspired me to add a number of new sections and figures. For any remaining deficiencies, I am, of course, solely responsible.

GRANT W. PETTY

Do not write so that you can be understood, but so that you cannot be misunderstood. — Marcus Fabius Quintilianus

CHAPTER 1

Atmospheric Composition and Structure

In simplest terms, the atmosphere is nothing more than an "ocean" of fluid covering the entire surface of the Earth. Like any ocean, it is bound to the Earth by gravity. The most important distinction between the atmosphere and a real (liquid) ocean is that the atmosphere's fluid is a highly compressible *gas* (air) rather than a relatively incompressible *liquid* like seawater. It is for this reason that the atmosphere has no clearly defined "top," unlike the ocean. The ability of air to compress or expand substantially in response

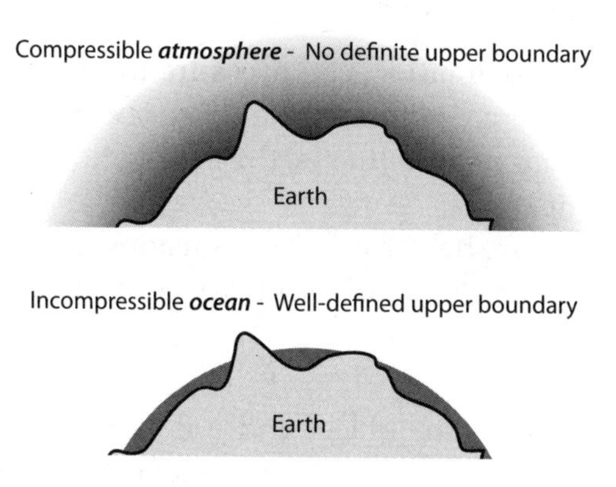

Fig. 1.1: The similarities and differences between an atmosphere and an ocean.

to changes of pressure is also directly or indirectly responsible for a variety of atmospheric phenomena that have no direct analogs in the ocean, such as clouds, precipitation, hurricanes, and thunderstorms.

Like any fluid, the atmosphere flows horizontally under the influence of gravity to maintain a more or less uniform distribution of mass, as measured above any fixed altitude above sea level. Left to its own devices, the atmosphere would quickly equalize *all* horizontal differences and settle down to a stagnant state with no fluid motions whatsoever. There would be no weather.

It is only because of the uneven addition and subtraction of heat energy to and from the atmosphere—for example, by way of the absorption of solar energy and the emission of infrared radiation to space—that no such equilibrium is ever reached. The atmosphere remains in a perpetual state of both horizontal and vertical motion, not unlike a pot of water on a hotplate.

Although the atmosphere is constantly evolving in its details, some aspects of its observed composition and gross vertical structure are observed to be relatively constant. This "typical" structure, which we review in this chapter, provides the larger context for most of what goes on in the atmosphere and therefore for our discussion of atmospheric thermodynamic processes.

1.1 Pressure and Density

1.1.1 Hydrostatic balance

To an excellent approximation, the **pressure** measured at any point within the atmosphere is equal to the *weight per unit area* of the atmosphere above that point—that is, the atmosphere is essentially in **hydrostatic balance.**[1]

Recall that pressure has physical dimensions of *force per unit area.* Recall also that the *weight* of an object is a force and is given by

$$F_g = mg, \tag{1.1}$$

where m is the mass of the object and g is the acceleration due to gravity (approximately 9.81 m s^{-2} at sea level). It follows that the

[1]We will examine the finer details of hydrostatic balance in Chapter 4 .

pressure at any point is equal to the *mass per unit area* of the atmosphere above that point times the average value of g (because g decreases slightly with altitude).

The SI unit for pressure is the **pascal** [Pa], which is equal to one newton per square meter (N m^{-2}; see Appendix D for a review of SI dimensions and units). Before the widespread adoption of the SI system of units, meteorologists traditionally used a different unit called the **millibar** [mb] for atmospheric pressure. Fortunately, there is a simple conversion—one mb is equal to 100 Pa, or one **hectopascal** (hPa; the prefix **hecto-** means 100). A pressure of 1000 mb is therefore the same as a pressure of 1000 hPa or, equivalently, 1.000×10^5 Pa.

Key fact: Hectopascals and millibars are synonymous and may be used interchangeably, though "hectopascal" is now preferred by many (but by no means all) meteorologists. "Millibar" is certainly easier to say than "hectopascal," but the latter unit is more likely to be understood by a non-meteorologist. In this book, we prefer the hectopascal to the millibar for one practical reason: to constantly remind you that it represents 100 times the MKS unit pascal and that it must almost always be converted to pascals before performing physical calculations.

Problem 1.1: The average atmospheric pressure p_0 on the surface of Mars is 6.0 hPa. The radius of the planet is $r_M = 3400$ km. The acceleration due to gravity g_M is 3.7 m s^{-2} (ignore variations with altitude). Compute the total mass M of the Martian atmosphere. Here, and throughout this book, start by finding a valid *symbolic* solution (i.e., express M as a self-contained function of the other relevant variables). Then (and only then!) substitute numerical values to obtain the value of M in kilograms. Before starting this problem, please carefully review Appendix B.

1.1.2 Pressure as a vertical coordinate

Because the pressure at a point is proportional to the mass of the atmosphere *above* that point, it follows that the pressure decreases *monotonically* as you move upward from the surface. The pressure will continue to decrease until you have left the entire mass of the atmosphere below you, i.e., until you are in outer space, at which point the pressure is extremely close to zero. (Even outer space is not a *perfect* vacuum!)

If the surface pressure p_0 at your location on a particular day is, say, 1010 hPa, then there is guaranteed to be one (and only one) altitude above you where the pressure is, say, 850 hPa. In fact, you could get into a balloon or airplane with a barometer in hand and find the altitude z corresponding to *any* particular pressure p I might care to name, as long as $p < p_0$.

In meteorology, it is common to use pressure p rather than geometric altitude z as a vertical coordinate—that is, as a measure of where you are vertically in the atmosphere. This is partly because it is easier to directly measure pressure on a weather balloon or an aircraft than it is to measure altitude; pressure is also more directly relevant to most atmospheric processes.

The geometric altitude z associated with a particular pressure p is not constant but varies somewhat from time to time and place to place. We will examine the precise relationship between z and p in a later chapter. However, the *typical* (approximate) relationship between p and z is shown in Fig. 1.2.

Problem 1.2: From Fig. 1.2, estimate the pressure at 10,000 m altitude, which is a typical cruising altitude for transcontinental airliners. About what fraction of the atmosphere's mass is below you when you are at that altitude, given that average sea level pressure is 1013 hPa?

Problem 1.3: In Fig. 1.2a, the relationship between pressure and altitude is well approximated by a straight line. Because the pressure axis is logarithmic and the altitude axis is linear, this implies a mathematical relationship of the form $p(z) \approx p_0 \exp(-z/H)$, where p_0 is the surface pressure and H is called the *scale height*. From the figure, use the endpoints of the shaded area to estimate the average scale height.

1.1.3 Atmospheric density

Near sea level, a typical value for the density of air is about 1.25 kg m^{-3}, give or take a few percent. This is only about 1/800th of the density of water, which is about one kilogram per liter, or 1000 kg m^{-3}.

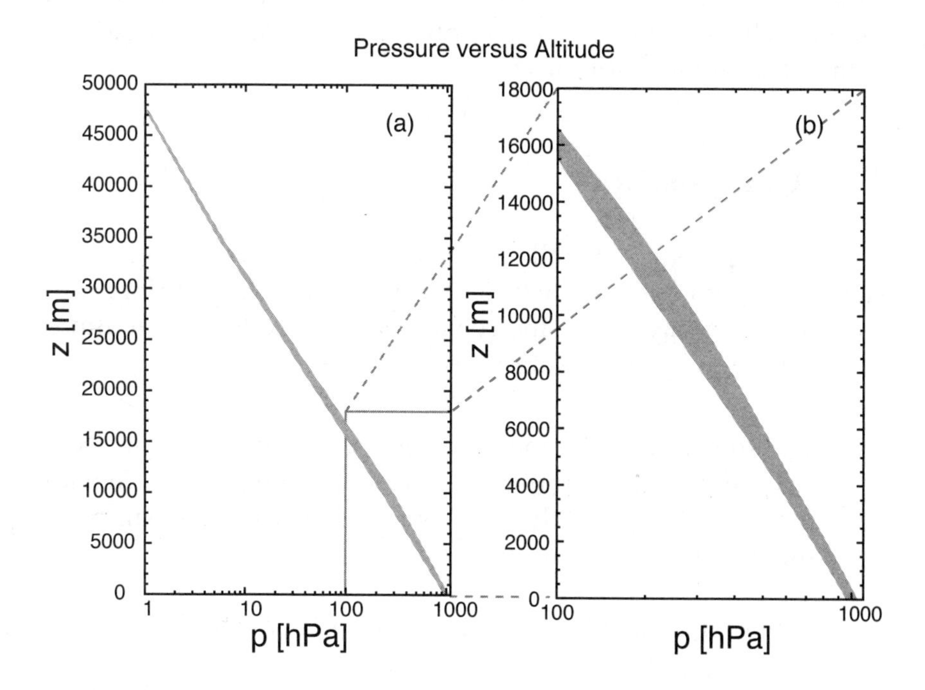

Fig. 1.2: Relationship between pressure p and altitude z in the free atmosphere. Gray shaded area represents the approximate range of values of z corresponding to a given value of p, and vice versa. (a) Pressure range is from 1100 hPa down to 1 hPa. (b) Expanded view from inset in (a), covering the range down to 100 hPa.

We have already seen that the pressure decreases as one moves upward through the atmosphere. I also pointed out at the beginning of the chapter that air, unlike seawater for example, is very compressible. This fact implies that air at higher pressures (i.e., near the surface) will be compressed to a greater density than is the case at low pressures (high altitudes), where it should exhibit a lower density, all other factors being equal. That is, the same mass of air should occupy a smaller volume at low altitudes than it does at high altitudes.

This is indeed what is observed. The air is noticeably "thinner" at the top of a high mountain than it is at sea level, and at altitudes much above 5000 m it is too thin to support human life without supplemental oxygen or a pressurized cabin.[2]

Later, we will look at the precise mathematical relationship between density, pressure, altitude, and temperature. For now, we simply note that the decrease in density with altitude explains why pressure changes much more sharply with altitude near the surface than it does at high altitudes.

1.2 Composition

Although we frequently talk about "air" as if it were a single substance, it is of course a mixture of a wide variety of distinct constituents. We may group the constituents of the terrestrial atmosphere into the following four categories:

1. The so-called "permanent" gases: principally nitrogen (N_2), oxygen (O_2), and argon (Ar), plus traces of other inert (noble) gases. Collectively, these gases make up what we will commonly refer to as "dry air."

2. Water (H_2O) in all three of its phases (vapor, liquid, ice).

[2]A very few expert mountain climbers have trained themselves to be able to survive and function without supplemental oxygen at the summit of Mt. Everest — altitude 8,848 m, where the pressure is about one-third that at sea level. Almost anyone else would fall unconscious and die of hypoxia within minutes of being exposed to the low air density at that altitude.

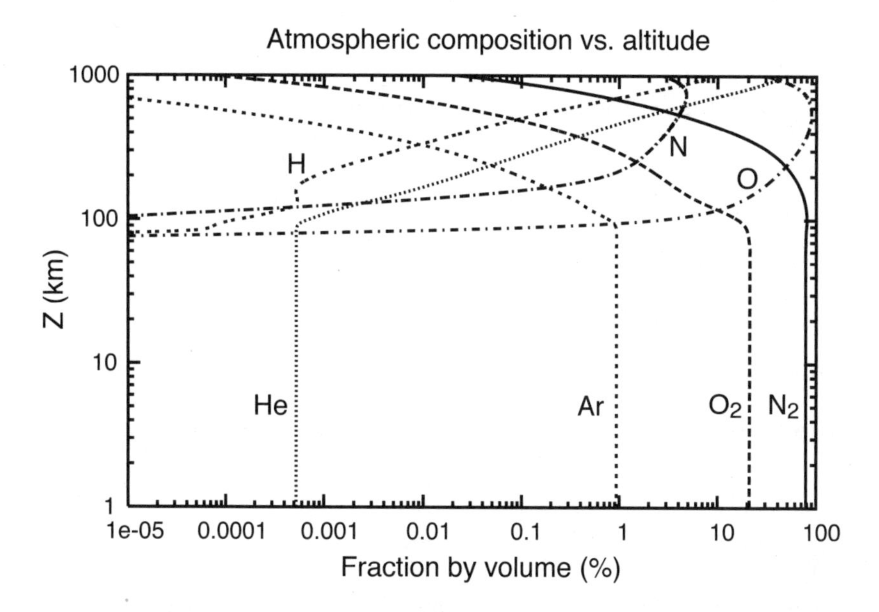

Fig. 1.3: Typical proportions of selected gases in dry air as a function of altitude. Note the fairly abrupt transition from constant proportions below 100 km to variable composition above this level (Data source: the NRLMSIS-00 model by Mike Picone, Alan Hedin, and Doug Drob.)

3. Variable gaseous constituents other than water: e.g., carbon dioxide (CO_2), ozone (O_3), nitrous oxide (N_2O), and methane (CH_4).

4. Aerosols—i.e., solid and liquid particles other than water.

For the most part, we are concerned in this book mainly with (1) and (2). The constituents falling in categories (3) and (4) are often of great interest *chemically*, *radiatively*, or as *pollutants*, but these have a negligible influence on the bulk *thermodynamic* properties of air. Nevertheless, I will highlight a few key facts about the trace gases carbon dioxide and ozone for the sake of your general education in meteorology.

1.2.1 The permanent gases

Below about 100 km altitude, the permanent gases are found in nearly fixed proportions. This is because (1) the processes that add

Table 1.1: Key constituents of air in the atmosphere below 100 km.

Constituent	Fraction by volume in (or relative to) dry air	Remarks
Nitrogen (N_2)	78.1%	
Oxygen (O_2)	20.9%	
Water vapor (H_2O)	(0–5%)	highly variable in time and space
Argon (Ar)	0.93%	inert
Carbon dioxide (CO_2)	383 ppm	concentration as of 2007; increasing 1.6 ppm per year
Neon (Ne)	18 ppm	inert
Helium (He)	5 ppm	inert
Methane (CH_4)	1.7 ppm	increasing due to human activities
Krypton (Kr)	1 ppm	inert
Nitrous Oxide (N_2O)	0.35 ppm	
Carbon Monoxide (CO)	0.07 ppm	
Ozone (O_3)	0–12 ppm	highly variable concentration; high in stratosphere and in polluted air
Chlorofluorocarbons ($CFCl_3$,CF_2Cl_2, etc.)	$\sim 10^{-10}$	industrial origin

and remove these gases from the atmosphere (**sources** and **sinks**, respectively) are both very slow and closely in balance over long periods of time, and (2) the stirring action of wind and turbulence is efficient enough to keep the lower atmosphere "well mixed," so that no significant differences in concentration can arise at different locations or altitudes.

Table 1.1 gives the volume (molar) fractions of the most important permanent constituents, as well as a few variable constituents. Nitrogen (N_2) and oxygen (O_2) together make up just about 99.0% of the total, with Argon (Ar) contributing most (but not quite all) of the remaining 1%, for a total of 99.97% of the permanent gases in the atmosphere. Every other permanent gas is present in only trace amounts.

Above about 100 km, air stops behaving like a well-mixed fluid; instead, individual molecules follow long ballistic trajectories without colliding very often with other molecules. Gravity therefore tends to prevent heavier molecules from reaching the highest altitudes, and there is an increasing predominance of lighter molecules like H and He. In addition, intense solar radiation breaks up diatomic molecules like N_2 and O_2, so that monoatomic species are increasingly prevalent with altitude (Fig. 1.3).

1.2.2 Variable components

Water vapor

Unlike the permanent gases, water is a substance that is constantly being added to and removed from the atmosphere. These exchanges occur primarily by way of evaporation or transpiration from surface water and vegetation (a *source* for the atmosphere) and condensation and fallout as rain or snow (a *sink*). Because these processes occur relatively rapidly and depend strongly on local conditions, the distribution of water in the atmosphere is highly variable in both time and space.

Water vapor in the lower atmosphere may be present in a fraction varying from almost zero in cold, dry air to as much as 3% by mass, or 5% by volume, in warm, very humid air. As we shall see later, the temperature of the air determines the *upper limit* on how much vapor can be present. That limit increases sharply with increasing temperature.

Despite its relatively small fractional contribution relative to oxygen and nitrogen, water in all of its phases is by far *the* most important constituent from a meteorological point of view. This is because of its central role in the thermodynamics and energy balance of the atmosphere, as well as in the formation of clouds, rain, and snow.

A substantial portion of this book will be devoted to describing the thermodynamic properties of water in the atmosphere.

Carbon dioxide

Carbon dioxide makes up less than 0.04% of the atmosphere by volume but is nevertheless an important gas. For one thing, it plays a crucial role in terrestrial life. Plants take up CO_2 from the air, photosynthesize organic compounds from the carbon, and release oxygen back into the air. In fact, all free oxygen in the atmosphere

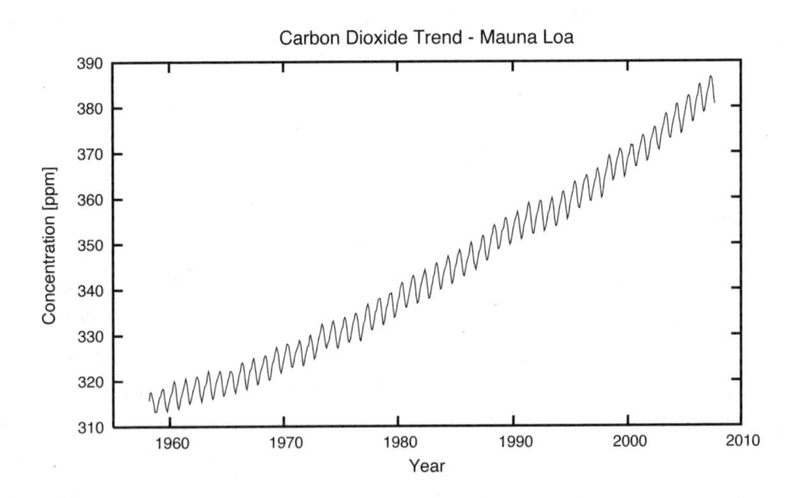

Fig. 1.4: Measurements of atmospheric carbon dioxide concentration at Mauna Loa Observatory, Hawaii. Annual fluctuations are due to seasonal variations in biomass, mainly in the northern hemisphere. The longer-term trend is apparently the result of the heavy use of fossil fuels by the industrialized parts of the world. (Data source: C.D. Keeling and T.P. Whorf, Scripps Institute of Oceanography, University of California.)

results from photosynthesis by green plants and algaes. The subsequent oxidation of organic matter, whether by animal respiration, combustion, or decay, returns CO_2 to the atmosphere, where it is quickly taken up by plant life again and converted to new biomass.

Vast amounts of carbon dioxide present in the Earth's early atmosphere were extracted by organisms that manufacture calcium carbonate shells. Much of this carbonate is now locked up in limestone deposits in the Earth's crust. Some carbon dioxide is released back into the atmosphere via processes such as volcanic eruptions and weathering of exposed limestone.

In addition to the importance of carbon dioxide for biogeochemical cycles, it plays a major role in the atmospheric energy balance due to its ability to strongly absorb and emit infrared radiation with wavelengths near 15 μm while being transparent to most solar radiation. For this reason, carbon dioxide is known as a **greenhouse gas**—that is, it has a net warming effect on the Earth's climate. While this greenhouse effect has always been present, the burning of fossil fuels (petroleum, coal, and natural gas) has steadily elevated carbon dioxide concentrations in the atmosphere (Fig. 1.4). The evidence is now compelling that this increase has been responsible for a measurable increase in global temperature, especially in the polar regions. A continuation of this trend, along with continued emissions of other greenhouse gases, will likely cause unprecedented warming during this century.

Ozone

Ozone (O_3) is a highly variable trace constituent that is either harmful or beneficial, depending on where in the atmosphere it is found. When it occurs in near-surface air as one of many components of **photochemical smog**, it is a pollutant that is damaging to human tissues and organic materials such as rubber and plastics. On the other hand, it is a natural constituent of the atmosphere above about 20 km altitude—in the **ozone layer**, where it shields the surface of the Earth from harmful shortwave ultraviolet radiation.

In both cases, ozone results from the breakdown and recombination of molecular oxygen (O_2). At very high altitudes, highly energetic ultraviolet photons from the sun can directly break the bond of the O_2 molecule according to the reaction

$$O_2 + \text{photon}\ (\lambda < 0.2423\ \mu\text{m}) \rightarrow O + O. \tag{1.2}$$

The free oxygen atoms from the above reaction then can combine with O_2 to form ozone according to the reaction

$$O + O_2 + M \rightarrow O_3 + M, \tag{1.3}$$

where M is any third molecule or atom (required in order to carry away the energy released by the above reaction).

Ozone has the property of efficiently absorbing ultraviolet radiation with wavelengths between 0.24 and about 0.31 μm. As a result of both reactions above, most radiation from the sun having wavelengths shorter than about 0.32 μm never reaches the Earth's surface. This is fortunate, because it is precisely these wavelengths that are most hazardous to life. We literally owe our existence to the ozone layer.

Although ultraviolet radiation with wavelengths between 0.32 and 0.4 μm is not directly harmful to life (apart from the sunburn we can get from radiation with wavelengths at the short end of this range), it triggers photochemical reactions involving organic molecules (e.g., unburned fuel vapors) and nitrogen oxides (produced by high temperatures in automobile engines), leading to the formation of ozone as a serious pollutant in surface air. The location in the U.S. most stereotypically associated with photochemical smog is the Los Angeles basin, with its high quota of sunshine, high concentration of automobiles and, commonly, a shallow pool of cool, stagnant marine air hemmed in by mountains.

Problem 1.4: For the following calculations, assume a classroom with dimensions 6 m by 10 m by 3 m, or substitute the actual dimensions of your classroom if so instructed.

a) You have a one-liter flask containing, at room temperature and pressure, a harmless gas not normally found in air, such as sulfur hexafluoride (SF_6). If the gas in the flask is released and mixed thoroughly throughout the classroom, what is the final concentration of the gas in parts per million by volume? *Answer: 5.6 ppmv*

b) Using the data given in Table 1.1, express the equivalent pure volumes of pure carbon dioxide, krypton, carbon monoxide, and chlorofluorocarbons found in the classroom, using common units such as liters, cubic centimeters, or others as appropriate.

1.3 Temperature

Most of us do not find the concept of temperature mysterious — after all, it is the temperature we pay attention to first when we decide how to dress before going outside. Nevertheless, it is surprisingly difficult to give a nontechnical explanation of what temperature *is* or to tell *without a thermometer* whether the temperature of one material body is greater or less than that of another.

For example, water in a hot tub is normally heated to about 40°C (104°F). Heating it further to 43°C (110°F)—a mere 6°C above normal body temperature (37°C) would put the temperature near the very upper limit of what you are likely to find bearable, whereas you can tolerate a few minutes in a dry sauna heated to 93°C (200°F) without ill effect.[3] Likewise, I routinely venture out in temperatures of −5°C (23°F) or less without a jacket to fetch a newspaper, but I would not dream of jumping into water colder than, say, 15°C (59°F). Clearly, the human sensation of hot and cold is a poor basis for estimating temperature.

One useful (though incomplete) definition of temperature is that *it is that quantity that determines the direction in which thermal energy ("heat") will flow when two objects are brought into contact with one another.* Thus, if a particular object has a temperature of 30°C and is

[3]Those hardy souls who winter over at Amundsen-Scott South Pole Station have a rite of passage known as the Three Hundred Club. Prospective members of this most exclusive club must wait for a time in the dead of winter when the outside temperature is expected to fall below −100°F. For the occasion, the station sauna is heated to +200°F. After preheating in the sauna for a while, the candidate runs unclothed except for shoes from the sauna to the outdoors, takes a lap around the ceremonial South Pole and returns posthaste to the sauna. If all goes well, they thereby experience a full 300°F (167°C) change of temperature!

brought into contact with another object having a slightly warmer temperature of 31°C, heat will *conduct* from the latter to the former and tend to reduce the difference in temperature. In fact, left to its own devices, heat conduction will always act to reduce temperature differences.

On a microscopic level, the temperature of a particular substance[4] is proportional to the *average kinetic energy* of its molecules. In a solid or liquid, this kinetic energy is associated with chaotic vibrations of the molecules about some mean position; in a gas, it is associated with the translational motion of the molecules as they follow ballistic trajectories.

1.3.1 The Zeroth Law of Thermodynamics

If two objects are in thermal contact[5] with one another and there is no heat flow, then they are at **thermal equilibrium**, which is another way of saying they have the same temperature. We may further invoke the so-called **Zeroth Law of Thermodynamics**, which states that if object A is in thermal equilibrium with object B, and object B is in thermal equilibrium with object C, then object C is also in thermal equilibrium with object A.

An important implication of the Zeroth Law is that temperature is an unambiguous property that does not depend on one's choice of reference body. In other words, it is not only possible to construct a thermometer, but any thermometer worthy of the name will reach the same conclusion about whether two objects have the same temperature.

1.3.2 Temperature and molecular kinetic energy

Temperature is ultimately a measure of the kinetic energy associated with the chaotic motions of molecules. A substance in which the molecules are flying around madly has a higher temperature than the same substance when the molecules are more or less at rest.

---

[4]When comparing the temperatures of different substances, what matters is the average kinetic energy *per degree of freedom*, which may include not only translational velocity but also vibrational and rotational motions.

[5]Such "contact" can include the opportunity to exchange energy via the emission and absorption of electromagnetic radiation.

If a body with more energetic molecular motion is brought into contact with one in which the molecules have little energy, collisions will transfer energy from the higher temperature object to the lower temperature object until equilibrium is established, in which case they wind up with the same temperature. This is the nature of thermal conduction.

Heat

The energy exchanged between the two bodies via conduction, as described above, is what we call **heat**. Note that an object cannot *have* heat; heat exists only in the form of *exchanges* between two objects or *conversions* of energy within an object. Moreover, heat generally refers to what can be thought of as *undirected* or *chaotic* energy at the molecular level. It is thus distinguished from other mechanisms of energy exchange involving mechanical **work**—e.g., a directed (i.e., vector) force $\vec{\mathbf{F}}$ coupled with a directed (vector) displacement $\vec{\mathbf{x}}$.

Absolute temperature

For an ideal gas, we may define **absolute temperature** as proportional to the **mean translational kinetic energy** $\overline{K}_E$ of the constituent molecules. For a gas whose molecules have mass m, the translational kinetic energy of a single atom is

$$K_E = \frac{1}{2}mv^2, \tag{1.4}$$

where v is its speed. Thus, the absolute temperature

$$T \propto m\overline{v^2}, \tag{1.5}$$

where the bar over v^2 indicates the average of that quantity for all atoms in the sample.

Keep in mind that the molecules in any gas will have a wide variety of speeds; it is the **mean squared speed** that is relevant to temperature. The above relationship implies that a temperature of **absolute zero** is reached when all molecular motion has decreased to its minimum possible level. The kinetic energy cannot decrease any further; therefore, absolute zero represents a fundamental lower bound on the temperature that our gas can achieve.

Because the mass m of the molecule also appears in (1.5), it follows that, for any given temperature, light molecules will have a higher average speed than heavy molecules.

1.3.3 Temperature scales

The conventional temperature scale used by scientists everywhere, as well by the lay public in almost every country *except* the United States, is the **Celsius scale**.[6] The Celsius scale sets 0°C at the freezing point of pure water and 100°C at the boiling point at standard sea level pressure. It used to also be called the *centigrade* scale.

More directly relevant for most physical calculations is the *absolute* temperature described in the previous subsection. For this purpose, the Kelvin scale[7] is used by most scientists. It employs temperature units that are the same *size* as Celsius degrees, but the zero point of the scale is absolute zero rather than the freezing point of water.

When specifying temperatures on the Kelvin scale, the temperature unit *Kelvin* is abbreviated simply as "K", without a degree symbol. Moreover, many scientists say "three hundred Kelvins," not "three hundred degrees Kelvin."

For non-scientific purposes, the Fahrenheit[8] temperature scale remains in wide use in the United States. The origin of the zero point on this scale is the subject of conflicting accounts, though it is widely believed that it corresponds to the coldest temperature that Fahrenheit was able to achieve with a mixture of ice, water, and salt. The 100-degree point was apparently based on what Fahrenheit took to be body temperature, though we now know that normal body temperature is closer to 98.6°F (37.0°C).

[6]Named after its inventor, Anders Celsius (1701–1744), a noted Swedish astronomer.

[7]William Thomson, 1st Baron Kelvin (or Lord Kelvin; 1824–1907) was a mathematical physicist, engineer, and outstanding pioneer in the physical sciences of the 19th century.

[8]Daniel Gabriel Fahrenheit (1686–1736) was a German physicist and engineer. His temperature scale was in use long before the Celsius scale became popular.

The following table gives the correspondence between key temperatures on the three different scales:

Kelvin	Celsius	Fahrenheit	Remarks
0 K	−273.15°C	−459.7°F	Absolute zero
273.15 K	0°C	32°F	Freezing point of water
373.15 K	100°C	212°F	Boiling point of water

From the above correspondences, we obtain the following conversions between different scales:

- To convert from Celsius to Kelvin, *add* 273.15.
- To convert from Kelvin to Celsius, *subtract* 273.15
- To convert from Celsius to Fahrenheit, first *multiply* by 9/5, and then *add* 32.
- To convert from Fahrenheit to Celsius, first *subtract* 32, and then *multiply* by 5/9.

If you do not plan to live in the United States, you can pretty much forget about the Fahrenheit scale. Otherwise, it is probably worth memorizing the following pairs of values, which are based on the rule that for every 5°C degree change in temperature, there is exactly a 9°F change. Once you have these "marker" values in your head, it is straightforward to mentally interpolate (at least approximately) to any intermediate value.

°C	°F
40	104
35	95
30	86
25	77
20	68
15	59
10	50
5	41
0	32
−10	14
−20	−4
−30	−22
−40	−40

1.3.4 Atmospheric temperature profiles

Now that you have a somewhat clearer physical understanding of temperature, let us examine the temperature structure of the atmosphere. The *details* of this structure, which vary from place to place and from day to day, play an important role in many atmospheric processes, including thunderstorm occurrence, the evolution of weather systems, and the large-scale circulation. For now, we will concentrate only on the *typical* features found in atmospheric temperature profiles.

Fig. 1.5 gives an example of an actual atmospheric temperature sounding for Dodge City, Kansas on September 8, 2004. The profile was obtained by an instrument package called a **radiosonde** car-

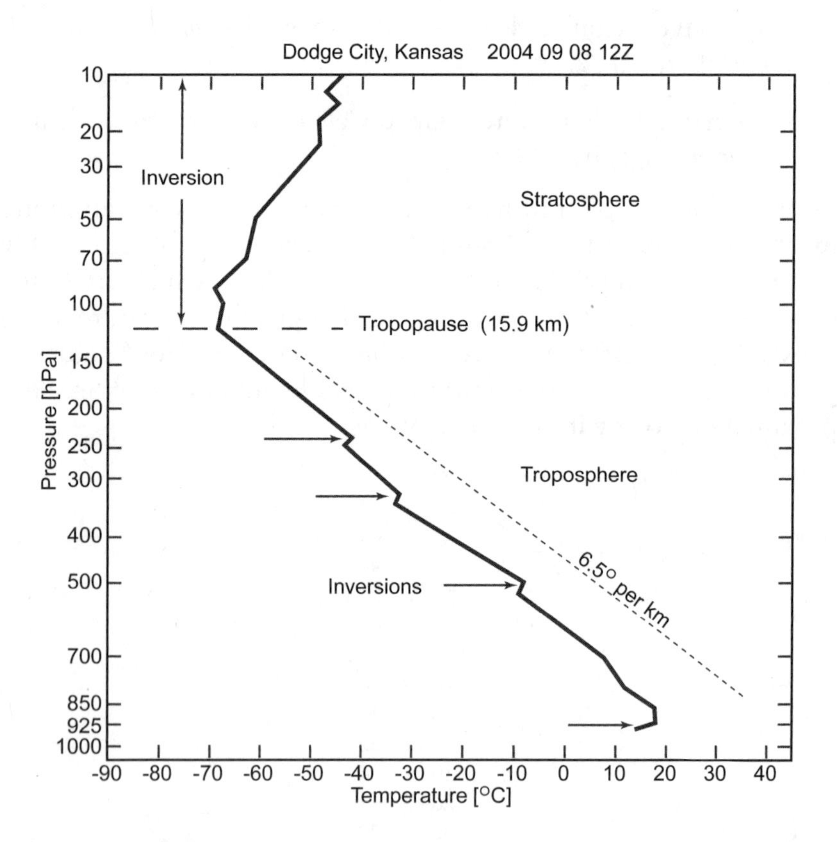

Fig. 1.5: An example of a typical atmospheric temperature profile at a midlatitude station during autumn.

ried aloft by a weather balloon. Radiosondes are launched routinely twice a day at thousands of stations around the world and provide meteorologists with an up-to-date snapshot of the temperature, humidity, pressure, and wind structure of the atmosphere.

Graphical depiction

The horizontal axis in Fig. 1.5 represents temperature, of course, with warmer temperatures falling to the right. The vertical axis on this plot is labeled not with altitude in meters but rather with pressure in hPa (or millibars). In meteorology, pressure is often the preferred vertical coordinate. Not only is it the variable related to altitude that is most easily and directly measured by a radiosonde instrument package, it is also the variable that is most directly relevant to most thermodynamic processes. Because pressure is greatest (close to 1000 hPa) near ground level, we have set up our diagram to be more visually intuitive by showing the pressure as *decreasing*

Fig. 1.6: A weather observer prepares to release a radiosonde at McMurdo Station, Antarctica. *(Photo: Alan Robock)*

toward the top of the plot, so that the surface is found near the bottom.

The ticks of pressure p are more closely spaced near the surface on this diagram than at high altitudes. This convention accounts for the fact that pressure decreases less rapidly with height at higher altitudes and doesn't approach zero until an extremely high altitude (basically, outer space). A diagram that used a vertical axis that is linear in pressure would have a point on the axis corresponding to zero pressure, which does not exist in the real atmosphere.

Figure 1.5 is a known as a *Stüve* diagram. The vertical axis is proportional to p^k, where $k = 0.286$. We've chosen to use a Stüve diagram here because it works well for the large pressure range spanned (1000–10 hPa). Later, we will switch to a vertical coordinate system proportional to $\ln p$, which has the advantage of making vertical distance on the plot roughly proportional to geometric altitude z. It also has other theoretical advantages (section 5.8.3). A chart whose horizontal axis is temperature and whose vertical axis is proportional to $\ln p$ is called an **emagram.** The closely related skew-T diagram facilitates visual interpretation of temperature profiles.

The troposphere, tropopause, and stratosphere

You have probably known since grade school that the atmosphere is generally cooler at higher altitudes than it is near sea level. Our example sounding in Fig. 1.5 confirms that idea, at least up to a point. The temperature near the surface is near 13°C. Moving up to the 600 hPa pressure level, we find that the temperature falls to around the freezing point (0°C). By the time we get to the 120 hPa level, at an altitude of just under 16 km, the temperature is a bitterly cold −70°C!

The layer between the surface and the point where the temperature stops generally decreasing with height is called the **troposphere.** We live in the troposphere. Almost everything that we regard as "weather," including almost all clouds, takes place in the troposphere.

The top of the troposphere is called the **tropopause**. In the middle latitudes, the tropopause is usually found somewhere between the 300 and 100 hPa levels, or between about 10 and 16 km altitude.

It is often (though not always) the coldest point anywhere in the atmospheric temperature profile below at least 50 km.

The next layer up, in which the temperature either increases with height or at least ceases to decrease rapidly, is called the **stratosphere.** The stratosphere is usually free of both clouds and significant weather disturbances. The cruising altitude for most medium- and long-range jet airliners (typically between 10 and 13 km) is often within the lower stratosphere, depending on the tropopause height along the flight path.[9]

Environmental lapse rate

The environmental **lapse rate** Γ at any given altitude is defined as the *local rate of decrease of temperature with altitude.*

$$\boxed{\Gamma = -\frac{\partial T}{\partial z}.} \tag{1.6}$$

In practice, rather than trying to take mathematical derivatives of the observed temperature profile $T(z)$, we usually can only estimate an *average* lapse rate by looking at the temperature change $T_2 - T_1$ between two fairly closely spaced levels z_1 and z_2:

$$\Gamma \simeq -\frac{T_2 - T_1}{z_2 - z_1}. \tag{1.7}$$

The lapse rate is defined to be *positive* for the usual situation (in the troposphere) in which the temperature *decreases* with height. It is *negative* when the temperature *increases* with height, a condition called a temperature **inversion**. Several shallow inversions are indicated in the Dodge City sounding.

Occasionally, the temperature is approximately the same throughout a given layer and it is called **isothermal.** In this case, $\Gamma \approx 0$.

Although the lapse rate in the troposphere varies from place to place and day to day, we often assume a typical value for Γ of about

[9]The tropopause height of 15.9 km observed in our Dodge City sounding is higher than average for a location in the middle latitudes. A jetliner cruising at 40,000 feet, or about 13 km, on this particular day would still be in the troposphere.

6.5°C per kilometer. This **standard lapse rate** is indicated in the plot as a straight dashed line. You can see that this is only an average: there are some layers within which the temperature decreases more slowly with height, or even increases, and others where it decreases more rapidly.

Problem 1.5: On a particular day over Wisconsin, the pressure levels of 850 hPa and 700 hPa are found at altitudes of 1425 m and 2982 m, respectively, and the corresponding temperatures are 3.8°C and −2.9°C. Determine the average lapse rate in degrees (to the nearest tenth) per kilometer.

Inversions

Temperature inversions represent such a marked contrast from the usual decrease of temperature with height that they deserve special comment. Here are just some of the many different reasons why inversions form:

Radiation inversions form as the result of radiational cooling of the ground at night and consequently of the layer of air directly in contact with the ground. This effect is most pronounced when the atmosphere is relatively transparent to infrared radiation—for example, when the sky is clear and the humidity is low. The wind must also be relatively calm in order to prevent the cold surface air from getting mixed upward into the warmer air above it. Except in polar regions during wintertime, radiation inversions are generally quite shallow—only a few meters in depth—and quickly disappear once the sun comes up.

Subsidence inversions may form when air sinks from a higher altitude, warming by compression as it goes. This mechanism is discussed further in Section 5.8.1.

Frontal inversions may appear in a sounding taken on the cold side of a surface front (warm or cold). This is because the frontal discontinuity between the cold and warm air masses slopes sharply back toward the cold air, over the position where the radiosonde was released.

Boundary layer inversions frequently delimit the top of the surface mixed layer, which may be anywhere from a few tens of meters to several kilometers deep. The primary physical mechanism behind the appearance of inversions at the top of a mixed layer is discussed in Section 7.10.5. Boundary layer inversions often develop in conjunction with a preexisting subsidence or radiation inversion, in which case the resulting strength of the inversion is that much greater.

Marine layer inversions are an especially strong type of boundary layer inversion that develops when warm, subsiding continental air overruns cool, humid air formed from contact with a relatively cold ocean surface. This is a frequent occurrence on and near the California coast, among other locations. When the marine layer pushes inland and is then hemmed in by mountains (e.g., in the Los Angeles basin), the strong inversion can trap pollutants in a shallow layer near ground level.

1.3.5 Mean thermal structure of the atmosphere

The profile we examined in Fig. 1.5 revealed the presence of a well-defined troposphere and stratosphere. Routine radiosonde balloons often reach altitudes of 30 km or more, or pressures as low as 10 hPa, before bursting, but they remain well within the stratosphere. Nonroutine measurements at extremely high altitudes, using rocketsondes and other specialized instruments, reveal that the lapse rate changes again not once but twice in the rarefied air above the stratosphere.

A schematic depiction of the "typical" atmospheric temperature structure up to an altitude of 100 km, as exemplified by the **U.S. Standard Atmosphere**, is given in Fig. 1.7. We see that the atmosphere actually can be divided into four distinct layers based on thermal structure. As already noted, the lowest layer is the **troposphere**, which extends from the surface to around 11 km, give or take a few km. Within the troposphere, the temperature generally decreases with height (i.e., $\Gamma > 0$).

The top of the troposphere is defined by the **tropopause**, which marks the beginning of a sharp reduction in the lapse rate, as compared with that prevailing within the troposphere. For reasons that will become clearer in the chapter on stability, the tropopause often serves as a "lid" on vertical motions and therefore confines much of what we describe as "weather" to the troposphere.

The next layer is the **stratosphere**, which extends upward to around 40–50 km. Within the stratosphere, the temperature is generally either nearly isothermal or increases with height. At the top of the stratosphere (the **stratopause**), atmospheric temperatures may approach the freezing point again.

In the **mesosphere**, the temperature generally decreases with height again until around 80 km or so. The temperatures found at the **mesopause** are quite cold—as low as −93°C in the U.S. Standard Atmosphere.

The **thermosphere** consists of very thin, hot, ionized gases and has no well-defined upper boundary. It basically continues indef-

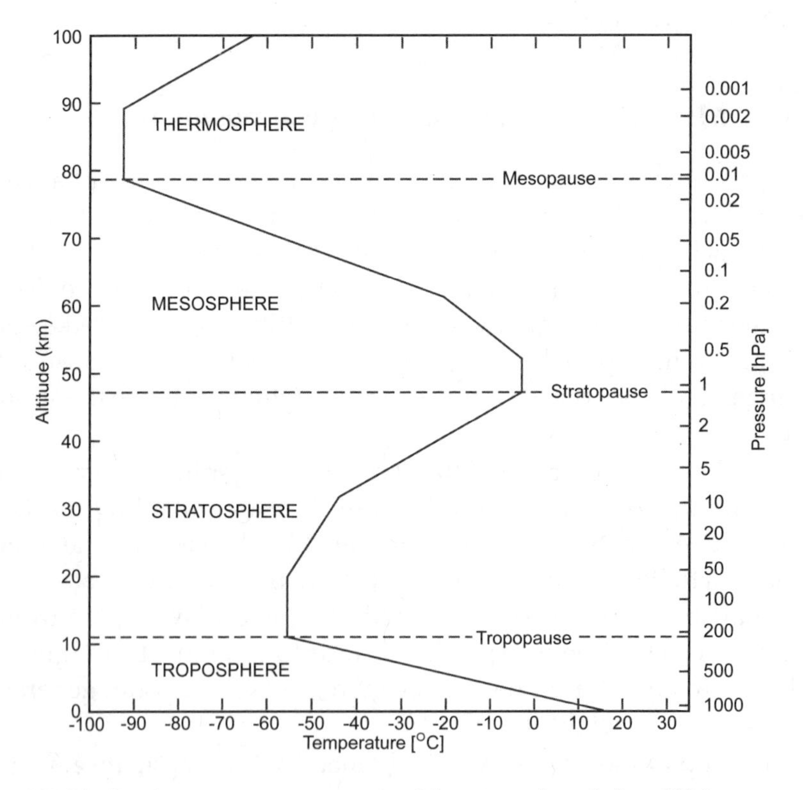

Fig. 1.7: Idealized temperature structure of the atmosphere below 100 km, as represented by the U.S. Standard Atmosphere.

initely, merging seamlessly with the near-perfect vacuum of outer space. The temperature in the upper thermosphere (not shown) depends strongly on solar activity; it may be as "cool" as 600 K when the sun is quiet or may increase in temperature to 2000 K under the influence of a sun that is particularly active, as indicated by the presence of numerous sunspots. Because solar activity is associated with the quasi-periodic 11-year sunspot cycle, the average temperature of the thermosphere also varies with this period.[10]

Geometrically, the above layers range in thickness from $\sim$10 km for the troposphere to hundreds of kilometers for the thermosphere. However, because of the very low air densities found at higher altitudes, most of the *mass* of the atmosphere is found in the troposphere. Indeed, the troposphere has 70–90% of the total mass, and the stratosphere has almost all of the remaining 10–30%. The mesosphere and thermosphere account for only about 0.1% and 0.001%, respectively.

The troposphere is the most interesting layer for most meteorologists (and for us), not only because it contains the lion's share of the mass of the atmosphere, but also because we live in it, and it is in the troposphere that most weather occurs. As we shall see later, the difference between the characteristic lapse rates in the stratosphere and the troposphere help explain why there is so much more "action" in the troposphere.

You might ask why the temperature structure of the atmosphere is so complicated. Why does the temperature first decrease with height, then increase in the stratosphere, then decrease in the mesophere again, and finally increase in the thermosphere? It is in fact the ozone layer that is primarily responsible for the existence of a distinct stratosphere and the mesosphere. By absorbing shortwave ultraviolet radiation from the sun, the ozone heats the atmosphere between roughly 20 and 50 km and gives rise to the local maximum in atmospheric temperature found at the stratopause.

[10]The temperature of the thermosphere, and therefore the activity of the sun, plays a crucial role in the drag experienced by satellites in low Earth orbit and therefore in how quickly they expend their limited onboard fuel. Specifically, high temperature causes the atmospheric density within the thermosphere to decay more slowly with height than would otherwise be the case (see Section 4.2.2), leading to markedly higher air densities, and therefore greater drag, at orbital altitudes.

1.3.6 Latitudinal and seasonal variations

So far, we have looked at a single example of a typical midlatitude temperature profile in the lower atmosphere (Fig. 1.5), as well as at idealized profiles from the troposphere into the lower thermosphere (Fig. 1.7). While significant variations in temperature structure occur from day to day, they also have a systematic seasonal and regional component. In particular,

- The tropopause is generally lower and warmer near the poles than it is near the equator.
- In the middle and high latitudes, the tropopause is generally lower and warmer in wintertime than it is in the summertime.
- The seasonal difference in height is generally greater at middle and high latitudes than in the tropics.
- There is a pronounced semi-permanent inversion near the surface at high latitudes, particularly in the wintertime.

An example of the seasonal difference at a midlatitude location (Dodge City again) is shown in Fig. 1.8. Not surprisingly, the lower atmosphere was considerably colder on January 27 than it was on July 4. On the other hand (and as predicted by the rules of thumb given above), the tropopause is considerably lower and warmer in the wintertime sounding. Interestingly, in the January case, the tropopause is not at the base of a deep inversion but rather a layer in which the lapse rate is still generally positive but much lower than in the tropopause.[11]

Figure 1.9 gives an example of the difference between a sounding in the deep tropics (in this case, the island of Borneo, which straddles the equator in the western Pacific) and a wintertime arctic sounding (Resolute, in far northern Canada). You will seldom see a colder, higher tropopause than the one in the tropical sounding. The temperature at a height of 18 km is a frigid −90°C, in contrast to the surface temperature of 26°C. The arctic sounding, on the

[11]The precise rules used by observers to define the height of the "official" tropopause are somewhat arcane and involve tests on the average lapse over some minimum depth of the atmosphere.

other hand, reveals a very low tropopause with a temperature of "merely" −57°C, only 15 degrees colder than the surface temperature of −42°C. Note also the very strong near-surface inversion in the arctic sounding. This feature is very common at high latitudes during the wintertime, because of the loss of heat from the surface in the form of infrared radiation to space without compensating heating from the sun.

Of course, the above descriptions are only examples. At any given instant in time and at any given location, an actual profile and/or cross-section of the atmosphere may look quite different from the profiles shown. One of the most important objectives of a course in atmospheric thermodynamics is to explain how these

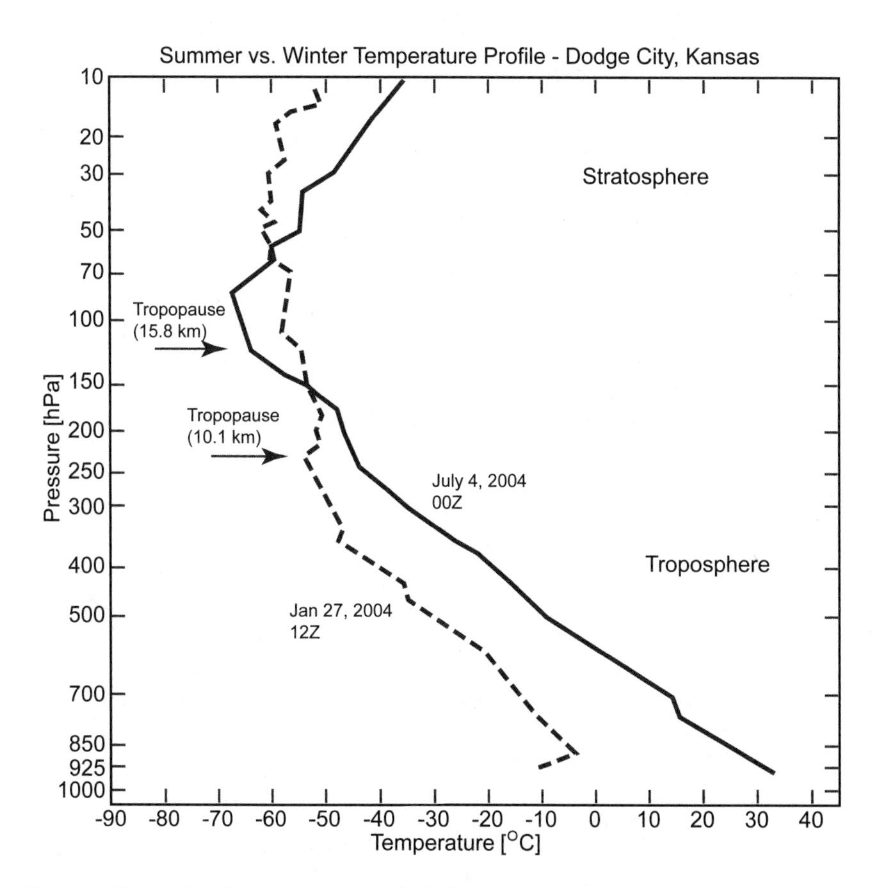

Fig. 1.8: Example of a summertime (solid) and wintertime (dashed) temperature profiles at a midlatitude station.

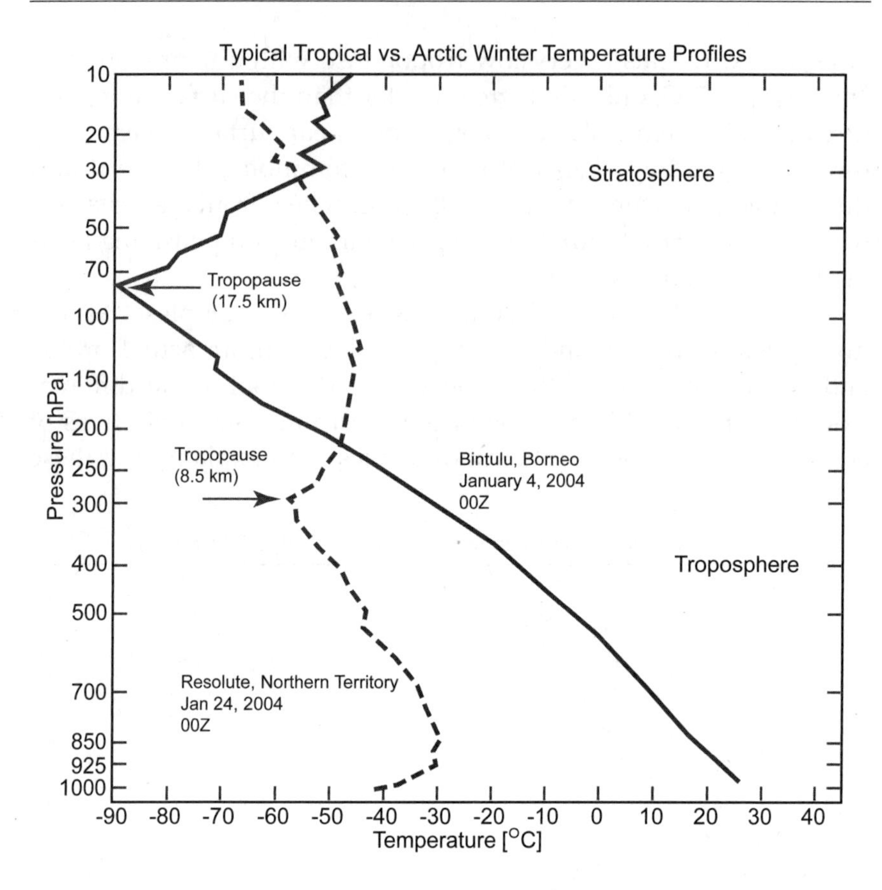

Fig. 1.9: A typical tropical (solid) and wintertime arctic (dashed) sounding.

daily variations influence the likelihood of vertical air currents associated with a variety of weather phenomena.

Problem 1.6: For this exercise you will need to access the University of Wyoming's "Atmospheric Soundings" website at `http://weather.uwyo.edu/upperair/sounding.html`. (The following instructions assume not only that the website is still available but also that the interface has not changed significantly since early 2008.)

From the menus, choose the region appropriate to your location, and then locate (but don't click on) the nearest upper air station. Leave the date and time set to the most recent observation time.

a) Record the date, time, and station ID you will be using.

b) Select "`GIF: to 10 mb`" as the type of plot. Click on your chosen station and view the profile of temperature (heavy line on the right). Visually attempt to identify the tropopause, and estimate its height to the nearest 0.1 km from the height labels appearing just inside the left border of the plot. If the sounding terminates before reaching an obvious tropopause, then choose a different station or time for this exercise and note the change.

c) Return to the main page, and this time select "`Text: List`" as the type of plot. Find the height and temperature at the surface level in the sounding. Also find the height and temperature at the 500 hPa level, if present; otherwise, use the highest available level. Use these data to determine the average lapse rate to the nearest 0.1 K/km between the two levels.

d) Determine whether any inversions are found within the troposphere. If so, give their altitude and the magnitude of the temperature increase.

1.4 In Practice

Although this book is not intended as a substitute for a course in atmospheric instruments, measurements, or observations, it is worthwhile to tie abstract principles to the actual practice of meteorology whenever possible. I will therefore conclude most chapters with a brief overview of some practical tools, techniques and concepts utilized by working meteorologists, as well as some examples of real-world applications.

1.4.1 Measurement of temperature

As everyone knows, temperature is measured with **thermometers.** Less well known, perhaps, is how many distinct *types* of thermometers exist, each with its own advantages and disadvantages.

Liquid-in-glass thermometers

Most laypeople are familiar with **liquid-in-glass thermometers**, such as those used to take a person's temperature (Fig. 1.10). In this type, a liquid (usually either mercury or colored alcohol) is contained in a reservoir (the bulb) connected to a long, thin tube. When

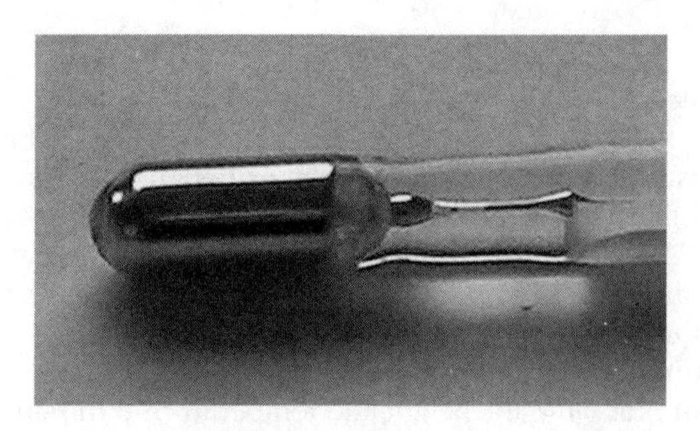

Fig. 1.10: Closeup of the reservoir of a common liquid-in-glass thermometer designed to measure a patient's temperature. In this case, the liquid is mercury. The constriction in the channel at the exit from the reservoir prevents the mercury from automatically returning to the reservoir when the temperature decreases. It therefore allows the maximum temperature achieved to be read at leisure. The thermometer is vigorously "shaken down" by hand to reset the mercury column.

the temperature goes up, the liquid expands to a greater degree than the surrounding glass, driving the column of liquid further up the tube. The temperature is read visually by way of a calibrated scale.

Liquid-in-glass thermometers are still widely used in meteorology, laboratories, cooking, and swimming pools, to give just a few examples. They are stable, sensitive, and relatively inexpensive. Major drawbacks include their relatively slow response, their fragility (unless encased in sturdy housing, in which case their response time becomes even slower), and the need to read them visually, which rules out the possibility of automated measurements.

Bimetallic strips

The other type of thermometer most of us depend on in daily life (whether we realize it or not) is based on **bimetallic strips**. Two dissimilar metal strips are bonded together in a spiral coil. Because of the different coefficients of expansion of the two metals, the coil winds or unwinds in response to changes in temperature. A needle connected to the coil may then be read against a scale. These dial-type thermometers are common for outdoor and indoor temperature measurements because they are inexpensive and easy to read. They are also commonly used as oven and refrigerator thermometers. If the bimetallic strip is connected to an electrical switch instead of a dial, it can serve as a *thermostat* to control air condi-

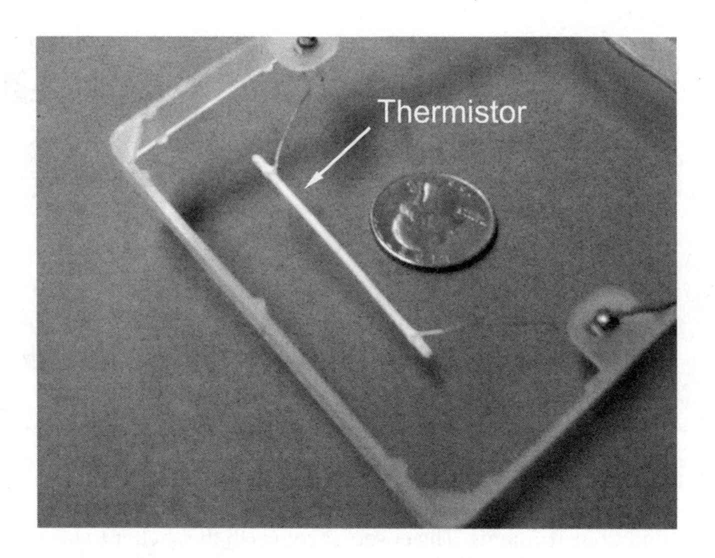

Fig. 1.11: A thermistor used as the temperature sensor on an older model of radiosonde.

tioning, refrigerators, or heaters. Bimetallic thermometers have the drawback that they are not terribly accurate, and calibration may change over time due to metal fatigue. They also tend to have a fairly slow response time, like liquid-in-glass thermometers.

Thermistors and thermocouples

In addition to the above, there exists a variety of thermometers based on electrical temperature sensors. The two most common types are **thermistors** and **thermocouples.** A thermistor is a conductor whose electrical resistance goes up sharply with increasing temperature (Fig. 1.11). A thermocouple is a junction between two dissimilar metals that produces an electrical voltage that is proportional to temperature. There are also other solid-state devices that control electrical current or some other parameter. By measuring the relevant property electronically, one may monitor and digitally record temperature automatically at any desired time interval.

One of the key advantages of thermistors is that they are very small and inexpensive. Good thermocouples aren't quite as inexpensive but can be made *extremely* small—some are almost as small as the period at the end of this sentence. Small is good not only for

Fig. 1.12: Standard instrument shelter, called a Stevenson screen, still used at many non-automated weather stations. The shelter houses temperature, pressure, and relative humidity instruments. The observer comes to the shelter to take readings. The shelter is a wooden box painted white with double-louvered sides to ensure ventilation and to reduce heating by the sun. *(Photos by Alan Sim)*

portability but also for the ability to respond very rapidly to changes in ambient temperature. In fact, in studies of turbulent energy fluxes in the atmosphere, thermocouples are often used to measure fluctuations in temperature lasting only a fraction of a second!

Siting

Regardless of the technology employed, the goal (for meteorologists) is usually to obtain a measurement that is representative of the free atmosphere. You would not try to monitor the outdoor temperature in your neighborhood using a device left on the back seat of your car parked in the sun. In general, the correct siting of a meteorological thermometer requires that it be

- shielded from direct heating by the sun and/or radiated heat from nearby objects,
- well-ventilated, so that it measures the temperature of the free atmosphere,
- situated in location that is representative of the surrounding area (i.e., not in a wind-sheltered courtyard or right next to a building), and

- a standard distance above the ground, usually between 1.2 and 1.8 meters.

The standard instrument shelter used at countless official and unofficial weather observing sites around the world for many decades is shown in Fig. 1.12. As is often the case, there has recently been a rapid trend toward replacing such manually operated shelters and equipment with automated electronic stations, though the need for correct siting and ventilation remains the same. The precise rules governing the placement of instruments at official weather stations are quite detailed and picky. The point is to ensure that temperature measurements can be meaningfully compared when taken from weather stations scattered over a wide area.

1.4.2 Wind chill

By definition, temperature is that thermodynamic quantity that determines the *direction* in which heat flows when body is brought into thermal contact with a second body. If a jug of milk is taken out of the refrigerator and left on the kitchen table, heat *will* flow into the bottle from the warmer surrounding air until it has the same temperature as the air. If you step out into a snowstorm, heat *will* be drawn out of your body by the colder air.

Although the difference in temperature determines the direction in which heat flows and therefore which body will warm and which will cool, it does not, by itself, tell you *how fast* the heat will flow. All we can normally say is that, *all other factors being equal*, the larger the temperature difference, the faster the heat will flow. If the temperature difference is eliminated, the heat will cease to flow.

A major function of clothing (besides fashion and modesty) is to reduce the *rate* of heat loss from the body when exposed to colder temperatures. Other factors play an important role in that rate as well. For example, water at 15°C will chill your body (clothed or not) much more rapidly than air at the same temperature, because water has a much higher thermal conductivity and a higher heat capacity. This is one reason why you can't reliably estimate the temperature of an unfamiliar object just by touching it—your sense of hot and cold is far more attuned to the *rate* of heat gain or loss than it is to actual temperature.

Table 1.2: Wind chill temperature T_{wc} for indicated air temperature T in degrees Celsius and wind speed U in km/hr.

U	T [°C]										
[km/hr]	10	5	0	−5	−10	−15	−20	−25	−30	−35	−40
5	10	4	−2	−7	−13	−19	−24	−30	−36	−41	−47
10	9	3	−3	−9	−15	−21	−27	−33	−39	−45	−51
15	8	2	−4	−11	−17	−23	−29	−35	−41	−48	−54
20	7	1	−5	−12	−18	−24	−30	−37	−43	−49	−56
25	7	1	−6	−12	−19	−25	−32	−38	−44	−51	−57
30	7	0	−6	−13	−20	−26	−33	−39	−46	−52	−59
35	6	0	−7	−14	−20	−27	−33	−40	−47	−53	−60
40	6	−1	−7	−14	−21	−27	−34	−41	−48	−54	−61
45	6	−1	−8	−15	−21	−28	−35	−42	−48	−55	−62
50	5	−1	−8	−15	−22	−29	−35	−42	−49	−56	−63
55	5	−2	−8	−15	−22	−29	−36	−43	−50	−57	−63
60	5	−2	−9	−16	−23	−30	−36	−43	−50	−57	−64
65	5	−2	−9	−16	−23	−30	−37	−44	−51	−58	−65
70	5	−2	−9	−16	−23	−30	−37	−44	−51	−58	−65
75	5	−3	−10	−17	−24	−31	−38	−45	−52	−59	−66
80	4	−3	−10	−17	−24	−31	−38	−45	−52	−60	−67
85	4	−3	−10	−17	−24	−31	−39	−46	−53	−60	−67
90	4	−3	−10	−17	−25	−32	−39	−46	−53	−61	−68
95	4	−3	−10	−18	−25	−32	−39	−47	−54	−61	−68
100	4	−3	−11	−18	−25	−32	−40	−47	−54	−61	−69

When a body having one temperature is immersed in a fluid (like air) having a different temperature, the other major factor controlling the rate of heat gain or loss is the rate of flow of that fluid past the body. If the air is dead calm, then you can tolerate rather cold ambient air temperatures, because the thin film of air in direct contact with your skin quickly approaches equilibrium with the skin's temperature and the heat flow is then greatly reduced. When there is even a light breeze, on the other hand, that warmed air is quickly stripped away and replaced with fresh, colder air.

It is the latter phenomenon that led to the definition of **wind chill temperature** as a way of predicting the rate of loss of heat by exposed skin. Basically, it purports to tell you, based on the actual temperature and wind speed, how cold the air would have to be *without any wind* in order to rob your body of heat at a similar rate.

The stronger the wind, the colder the wind chill temperature and thus the more rapid the heat loss. The wind chill temperature is therefore an important predictor of the risk of hypothermia and/or frostbite.

Unfortunately, there is no unique basis for defining wind chill temperature, as the effects of wind are strongly dependent on the shape and insulating properties of the thing being chilled. Nevertheless, in 2001 the U.S. National Weather Service devised a new official formula that is now used in both the U.S. and Canada. It is based on measured heat loss from the bare face when a 1.5 m (5 ft.) tall person walks directly into a steady wind at about 5 km/hr (3 mph) and assuming that the wind speed is measured at the standard height above ground level of 10 m. The formula is

$$T_{wc} = 13.12 + 0.6215T - (11.37 - 0.3965T)U^{0.16} \quad , \tag{1.8}$$

where T is the air temperature in degrees Celsius and U is the wind speed in km/hr. Representative values of T_{wc} are given in Table 1.2.

As a very rough rule of thumb, frostbite on exposed skin becomes a significant risk after less than 30 minutes of exposure when wind chill temperatures drop below −25°C. Hypothermia, on the other hand, can occur even at wind chill temperatures well above freezing — all that is required is for an individual's core body temperature to fall a few degrees below the normal body temperature of 37°C.

Before we leave this subject, let me reiterate that the wind chill temperature is *not* in any sense a measure of the effective thermodynamic temperature of the environment. If it were, then Table 1.2 would suggest that we could freeze water in a sealed jar by setting it outside when the air temperature is +5°C and the wind is blowing at speeds greater than 40 km/hr, because the computed wind chill temperature is then negative. On the contrary, the equilibrium temperature of the water in the jar is still the same as the air temperature. Indeed, a block of ice set out under those conditions would still quickly melt — even more quickly, perhaps, than if there were no wind.

Key fact: Wind chill temperature is *only* meaningful as a predictor of the *rate* of heat loss from exposed human skin.

Problem 1.7: On a particular day in International Falls, Minnesota, the temperature is $-4°F$ and the wind speed is 10 knots (see Appendix D for unit conversions). Determine the wind chill temperature in degrees Fahrenheit, to the nearest degree.

1.4.3 Upper air observations

As will become quite clear as you continue with this book, the vertical temperature, humidity, and pressure structure of the atmosphere are extremely important factors in day-to-day weather. Students of meteorology should have a basic understanding of how this structure is observed.

Upper air observations are taken by a network of over 800 stations worldwide, typically twice a day at 00 and 12 UTC.[12] These observations are used to create maps of upper level conditions as well as to initialize numerical weather prediction models. Upper observations are sometimes also taken specifically for research purposes, usually in connection with a regional field experiment.

As already noted, the basic instrument package used in upper air observations is an expendable unit called a *radiosonde*. Radiosonde observations, or **soundings**, are often called **raobs** for short. When, as is often the case, a radiosonde package is also capable of observing upper level winds, it may be called a **rawinsonde**. If the instrument package is dropped from an aircraft rather than lofted by a balloon, it is called a **dropsonde.**The latter are often deployed during hurricane penetrations over the ocean or as part of a

[12]Coordinated Universal Time, formerly known as Greenwich Mean Time (GMT). Also known as Zulu (Z) time.

Fig. 1.13: Two of the mainstays of airborne meteorological research by NOAA: one of two P-3s converted for meteorological research and hurricane surveillance (foreground) and a converted C-130 cargo plane (background). Both aircraft are equipped with a variety of sophisticated instrumentation, including dropsondes, for observing the thermodynamic and microphysical environment within and near hurricanes and other storm systems. As a graduate student, the author spent many hours over the East China Sea in the the above-pictured P-3. *(Courtesy of the NOAA Photo Library.)*

meteorological field experiment where no surface-based radiosonde stations are available (Fig. 1.13).

The radiosonde

A conventional radiosonde (or rawinsonde) measures vertical[13] profiles of temperature, humidity, and wind. A barometric sensor inside the package allows the other variables to be recorded as functions of pressure as the balloon ascends.

[13]Weather balloons often drift horizontally at speeds of many tens of meters per second or more, as compared with an ascent rate of only about 5 m/sec. The profile they measure is therefore not actually *vertical*. However, because horizontal variations in atmospheric temperature and humidity are almost always far weaker than vertical variations, even a rapidly drifting balloon usually obtains a good *approximation* to a true vertical profile.

Fig. 1.14: Although radiosonde observations still form the backbone of the upper-air observing network, considerable progress is being made in the remote measurement of atmospheric temperature and humidity profiles and cloud properties based on ground-based and satellite-based observations of microwave and/or infrared emission by the atmosphere. Pictured here is a microwave radiometer.

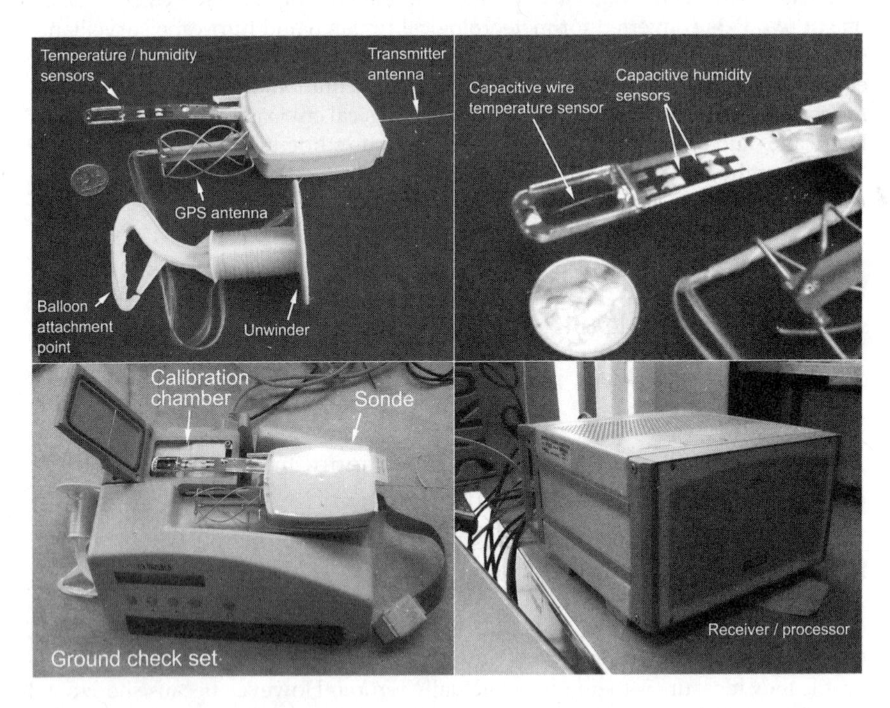

Fig. 1.15: Selected components of the current-generation Vaisala RS92-SGP radiosonde package and associated calibration and receiver equipment.

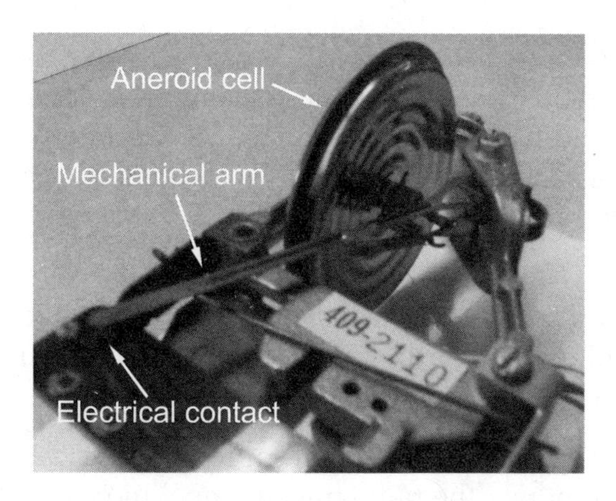

Fig. 1.16: Example of a typical aneroid pressure cell, in this case found inside an older model radiosonde.

An example of a modern radiosonde package is shown in Fig. 1.15. Key components include the following:

Temperature sensor: Temperature is measured by a small rod thermistor (e.g., Fig. 1.11) or capacitive wire sensor. The small size ensures that it can respond very quickly (within a few seconds or less) to changes in ambient temperature as the balloon ascends.

Humidity sensor: Most operational radiosonde systems use a carbon hygristor or, more recently, a thin-film electrical capacitance sensor to measure relative humidity. The sensor may be shielded inside a ventilated duct within the sonde's enclosure to minimize exposure to solar radiation and precipitation.

Pressure sensor: Pressure is measured by a small sensor inside the radiosonde package whose electrical properties are a function of the ambient pressure. Until recently, the most common example was an *aneroid cell* like that pictured inFig. 1.16. Now there are also silicon-based solid-state pressure transducers in use.

Navigation unit: For a radiosonde to be used to obtain upper-level winds, there must be some way to track its horizontal position as it ascends. Although it is possible to do this using external methods, such as optical tracking or radar, most modern radiosondes are now equipped with an internal navigation system, such as an Omega LORAN (Long Range Navigation) receiver or, more recently a GPS (Global Positioning System) unit.

Transmitter: The measurements made by the above sensors are transmitted to Earth via a coded radio signal, usually at around 404 MHz or 1680 MHz.

Battery: Radiosondes need a good source of electrical power, especially to power the radio transmitter, which must be effective over a range of 100 km or more. The most common power supply is a disposable chemical battery that is activated by immersing it briefly in water.

The balloon

The balloon used to carry a radiosonde package is commonly made of latex rubber or similar material and is usually inflated with helium.[14] The size of a balloon is conventionally specified in terms of its uninflated mass. A 10 gm, 30 gm, or 100 gm balloon is relatively small and usually carries no payload. It may be used as a **ceiling balloon** (Fig. 1.17) to observe cloud base height or visually tracked as a **pilot balloon** (**pibal** for short) to observe wind drift aloft. Balloons designed to carry radiosonde packages range from 200 gm to 3000 gm, the latter being suitable for carrying fairly heavy payloads[15] (1 kg or more) to altitudes above 38 km.

[14]Hydrogen is often preferred at remote locations, because it can be generated from easily transported chemicals, unlike helium, which always requires heavy pressurized tanks. Hydrogen is also less expensive than helium. However, hydrogen is also highly inflammable and potentially explosive. It therefore requires extremely careful handling, a fact that discourages more widespread use.

[15]Throughout much of the latter half of the 20th century, radiosonde packages were much bulkier and heavier than they are today. They not only required fairly large balloons to carry them aloft at an acceptable ascent rate (around 300 meters per minute is considered optimal), but they had to be equipped with parachutes to protect people and property on the ground from the falling sonde. As radiosondes have shrunk in size and weight, it has become possible to eliminate the need for parachutes and to employ smaller, less expensive balloons.

Fig. 1.17: A ceiling balloon ready to be taken outside for release. Ceiling balloons are inflated to achieve a known ascent rate. They are released without a payload and are tracked visually until they disappear into the base of the cloud layer. The elapsed time from launch allows the height of the cloud base to be estimated with reasonable accuracy. *(Photo: Alan Sim)*

As the balloon ascends through the troposphere and eventually into the lower stratosphere, it expands in response to the reduction in pressure. Because the thin latex stretches so easily, the difference between the internal and external pressure remains small. Also, the internal temperature adjusts fairly quickly, via conduction, to that of the environment.

Eventually, the balloon reaches an altitude where it cannot expand any further, and it bursts. This event effectively terminates the sounding, and the radiosonde package falls back to Earth, though it will often continue to transmit data on the way down. The altitude at which the balloon bursts can be very sensitive to how it is stored and handled before launch. Even invisible scuffs can lead to premature bursting, as can prolonged exposure to air pollution and ultraviolet rays.

Table 1.3: Typical balloon performance. *Reprinted from the WMO Guide to Meteorological Instruments and Methods of Observation (CIMO Guide) Seventh Ed. (2006).*

Weight (g)	10	30	100	200	350	600	1000	1500	3000
Initial diameter (cm)	30	50	90	120	130	140	160	180	210
Typical payload (g)	0	0	0	250	250	250	250	1000	1000
Free lift (g)	5	60	300	500	600	900	1100	1300	1700
Ascent rate (m/min)	60	150	250	300	300	300	300	300	300
Max. height (km)	12	13	30	21	26	31	34	34	38

The ground station

While the expendable radiosonde makes the actual measurements and transmits them via radio waves back to Earth, the most expensive part of the radiosonde system remains on the ground. Key components include the following:

Antenna subsystem: Responsible for reliably capturing the ever-weaker signal of the radiosonde as it climbs to high altitude and drifts downrange, the antenna system typically has two modes of operation. One mode is **omnidirectional**, which means that it picks up signals equally well from all directions. Its overall sensitivity is low, however, meaning that this mode is most useful during the early part of the sounding. Once the signal becomes too weak for omni mode, the operator will switch the antenna system to a more sensitive **directional mode**. The antenna must then be kept pointed more or less at the sonde while it continues to drift. Some equipment can track the sonde automatically; in other cases, the operator must manually adjust the direction of the antenna in order to keep the incoming signal at optimum strength. Usually, as long as the sonde remains above the horizon relative to the ground station, a directional antenna will continue to pick up its signal, even if it has drifted a considerable distance from the launch point.

Receiver and data processing subsystem: The radio signals must be received and decoded into raw engineering units. Based on calibration information either supplied by the manufacturer or obtained during prep, the sensor values are then converted to accurate meteorological values in standard units. Part of the processing also includes applying the hypsometric equation (4.30) to the measurements of temperature, humidity, and pressure to obtain the geopotential height Z at each sounding level.[16] Finally, if a navigation or tracking subsystem provides the horizontal position, the change of position with time is used to calculate the drift velocity and, thus, the wind direction and speed as a function of altitude.

Display and output subsystems: A measurement serves no purpose unless it is made available in some form to prospective users. There may be a real-time graphical display of the sounding-in-progress on a computer screen; this display usually serves mainly to let the operator know that everything is working properly. The raw data, often consisting of thousands of individual readings, will usually also be written to a file on hard disk or other storage device, as well as perhaps a paper printer. Last, but not least, there is usually an onboard program that can condense the raw sounding down to a very concise upper air report suitable for transmission to a central authority.

The preparation, launch, and tracking

At most official upper air stations, a radiosonde is launched twice each day, usually at 00Z and 12Z. For each launch, one or two meteorological technicians perform the following steps:

- prepare the radiosonde (e.g., connect the battery, deploy the sensors);
- activate the data acquisition system;
- enter the radiosonde calibration information, either manually or using a coded data tape from the manufacturer;
- inflate the balloon and attach the sonde;

[16]During the author's tour of duty as a Navy weather observer in the late 1970s, these calculations had to be performed manually for each level using cumbersome paper charts and slide rules.

Fig. 1.18: This pressure regulator valve (black knob and gauge in the foreground) is used to control the flow of helium from the high pressure tank into a radiosonde balloon or other weather balloon. The pressure gauge behind it is used to monitor the amount of remaining helium. *(Photo: Alan Sim)*

- obtain baseline measurements of local temperature, humidity, and pressure;
- release the balloon and activate the tracking system;
- monitor the data during the ascent;
- perform post-sounding procedures, such as completing local sounding documentation, encoding the sounding for worldwide transmission, and transferring the coded report to a central data processing facility.

The entire pre-launch procedure typically requires 30 minutes, while the sounding itself may require 1.5 hours or more.

1.4.4 Skew-T diagrams

In this chapter, we already discussed *emagram*-style depictions of atmospheric temperature profiles in which the horizontal axis is temperature T and the vertical axis is pressure p, with pressure decreasing upward. An example is shown again in Fig. 1.19 (top). In this

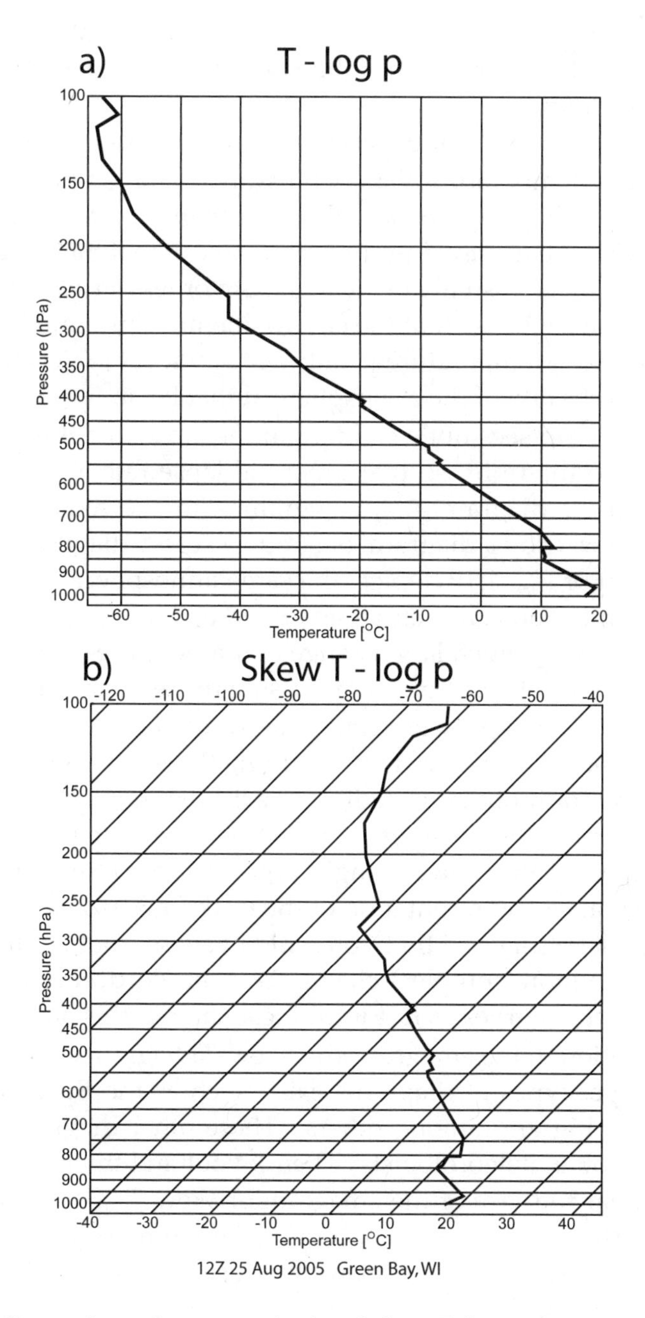

Fig. 1.19: Comparison of emagram (top) and skew-T (bottom) representations of of the same atmospheric temperature profile.

plot, the horizontal reference lines are lines of constant pressure and are called **isobars**. The vertical lines are lines of constant temperature, or **isotherms**.

While an emagram is a perfectly valid way to display plots of atmospheric temperature versus pressure, there is one refinement that makes such a diagram *visually* easier to interpret without otherwise altering the *physical* interpretation. Recall that the temperature in the atmosphere usually decreases more or less steadily with altitude. Later we will see that the environmental lapse rate Γ—that is, the slope of the temperature profile—at any level is closely related to the local *stability* of the atmosphere at that level.

It is easier to see subtle changes in the lapse rate if we *skew* the isotherms to the right, so that a normal lapse rate appears nearly vertical on the diagram. An emagram with skewed isotherms is called a skew-T log p diagram, or simply skew-T diagram for short. The bottom of Fig. 1.19 depicts the same atmospheric sounding in skew-T form. You can see that an added advantage of the skew-T diagram is that a much larger range of temperatures may be represented comfortably without compressing the temperature scale.

So far, we have presented the skew-T with only isotherms and isobars depicted. Later, we will be adding three other sets of curves. While these additions admittedly make the diagram quite confusing to the beginner, they also make the skew-T infinitely more useful to the expert. I therefore strongly urge you to memorize the general appearance and orientation of the isotherms, isobars, and their numerical labels *now* so that you will have less trouble identifying them on the more complete charts. You should do the same with each new set of curves as it is introduced later in this book.[17]

In addition to the emagram and skew-T diagrams already mentioned, other types of diagrams exist, such as the **Stüve diagram** and the **tephigram**, among others. These other diagrams remain in use by some meteorologists. Their layout and interpretation are quite similar to those of the emagram or skew-T. For various reasons, the skew-T diagram has come to be the most popular of the bunch. That is therefore what we will use exclusively throughout the remainder of this book.

---

[17] A helpful introductory tutorial on the use of the skew-T diagram can be found at `www.meted.ucar.edu/mesoprim/skewt/`

Problem 1.8:

Obtain a blank skew-T chart from your instructor or download and print one (see Appendix F). Identify the isobars and isotherms, and ignore all other lines and curves for now. On your diagram, plot the following simplified temperature profile, where the data for each level are given as (pressure in hPa, temperature in degrees Celsius): (1014, 20.0), (980, 20.3), (878, 17.6), (830, 19.0), (500, −11.5), (400, −25.1), (267, −46.1), (213, −49.1), (142, −67.5), (100, −72.7).

CHAPTER 2

Thermodynamic Systems and Variables

The previous chapter gave a brief *descriptive* survey of the chemical, temperature, pressure, and density structure of the atmosphere. We will soon turn to the question of how these properties are related to one another *physically* and *quantitatively*.

We will launch this discussion by introducing some definitions related to the description of thermodynamic systems in general and atmospheric **parcels** in particular. We will then introduce some definitions and techniques relevant to the mathematical analysis of thermodynamic systems.

2.1 Air Parcels

2.1.1 Definition

The concept of an air parcel plays a central role in much of the material covered by this book. A parcel is simply an imaginary sample of air, often taken to be representative of a particular location in the free atmosphere. We assume that the properties of the air are uniform throughout the parcel. We can always get away with this simply by defining our parcel to be small enough.

We pretend that we can follow the same parcel of air around as it experiences changes in pressure and temperature almost as if it were loosely confined in a sealed plastic bag or balloon.

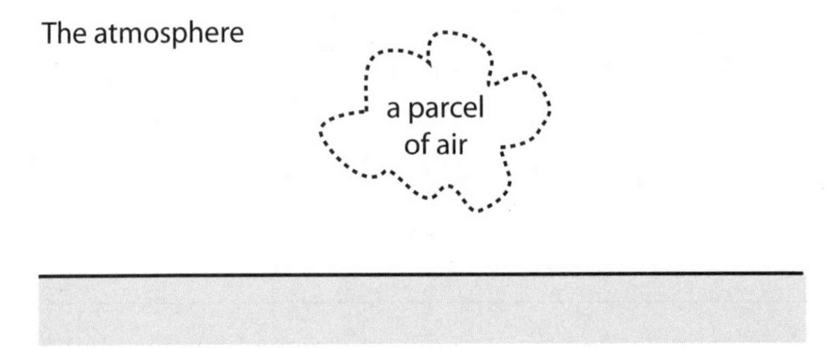

Of course, this is an idealization. We can no more track a single parcel of air as it travels through the atmosphere than we can keep track of a single drop of water in the ocean. Things quickly get mixed up and lose their identity. Nevertheless, it is a useful idealization because it allows us to unambiguously predict the changing properties of our chosen sample of air without worrying about the effects of dilution by the surrounding environmental air.

2.1.2 Air parcel as a thermodynamic system

In thermodynamics, it is convenient to divide the universe into two chunks. One is the chunk we are specifically interested in, which we will call the **system**. The other chunk (i.e., everything else) we call the **environment.** In this book, we will usually think of a parcel of air as "the system" and the atmosphere within which it is embedded as "the environment." The rest of the universe, while technically part of the environment, plays no active role in the processes we care about here.

Thermodynamic systems are classified according to how they do or do not interact with the environment (i.e., their surroundings). The principle types of interactions we care about are exchanges of *energy* and exchanges of *matter*. We then have the following possibilities:

Isolated system: A system that exchanges neither matter nor energy with the environment. Apart from a system consisting of the entire universe, an isolated system is *always* an idealization. However, we can get away with treating some systems as *approximately* isolated, at least for short periods of time.

Closed system: A system that exchanges no matter with its surroundings but which may exchange energy in various forms. A sample of air enclosed in a sealed jar or plastic bag is effectively a closed system. A system that exchanges matter very slowly with its surroundings (i.e., it leaks!) might be considered effectively "closed" on short time scales but "open" over longer time scales. A parcel of the air in the free atmosphere might also be treated as a closed system on short time scales, before it has had an opportunity to mix significantly with the surrounding air.

Open system: A system that exchanges both matter and energy with its surroundings. A parcel that mixes with the surrounding atmosphere is an open system, as is a cloud from which mass exits the cloud in the form of rainfall. In fact, the entire atmosphere is an open system because it exchanges both matter and energy with land and ocean surfaces, as well as exchanging energy (in the form of solar and infrared radiation) with outer space.

Unless otherwise stated, we will normally idealize an air parcel as a closed thermodynamic system.

Problem 2.1: For each case, state whether the system in question can be regarded as approximately "isolated," "closed," or "open" over time periods of an hour or less: (a) the Earth, (b) the gas in an inflated weather balloon, (c) the same balloon with a leak, (d) a sealed jar of pickles, (e) the coffee in an uncovered mug, (f) the coffee in a sealed Thermos® bottle, (g) the human body.

2.2 Working With System Variables

2.2.1 State variables and process variables

Any quantitative analysis of the behavior of a system (e.g., our air parcel) requires us to identify and manipulate relevant physical variables. Broadly speaking, we may group such variables into two categories: those that describe the **state** of the system at any instant in time and those associated with a **process** such as an exchange of energy between our system and its environment.

Thus, for any given physical system, **state variables** are those variables that are uniquely determined by the current state of the system. By definition, your ability to measure the value of a particular state variable cannot require you to also know the history of the system. In other words, state variables tell you what the properties of a system *are* at a point in time, *not* how it arrived at that state.

For an isolated sample of dry air, the best-known examples of state variables include pressure, temperature, density, and volume. Any one of these tells you something specific about the state of your air sample; each one is uniquely defined at a given point in time without reference to the prior history of the air sample.

Where state variables are involved, the net effect of a particular process may be characterized entirely by the starting and ending values of the state variable, such as the starting temperature T_0 and the ending temperature T_1. There is therefore also a well-defined *change* in that variable, given in this example by $\Delta T \equiv T_1 - T_0$.

A good example of a variable that is *not* a state variable is the amount of heat energy Q that was added to your air sample to bring it to its current temperature. You cannot determine "heat added" as a unique function of the starting and ending states of the sample; rather it depends on the details of how the system evolved from one state to the other. Because there are no unique starting and ending values Q_0 or Q_1, it makes no sense to try to define a $\Delta Q \equiv Q_1 - Q_0$, and we will therefore avoid Δ-notation in such cases.

Problem 2.2: Indicate which of the following variables can be viewed as state variables: (a) your weight W, (b) the volume V of gasoline burned by your car on the way home from college, (c) the volume V of gasoline remaining in your tank at any particular time, (d) the position in space of a weather balloon, (e) the distance traveled by the weather balloon after launch.

2.2.2 Differentials

Regardless of the type of variable we are concerned with, it is common to begin our analysis of a particular problem by looking at how an infinitesimal increment, or **differential**, in one variable is related to differentials in the other relevant variables. A differential is simply an arbitrarily small change in the variable in question; what matters is not the absolute magnitude of the change (as long as it is sufficiently small) but rather the functional relationship between it and other differentials.[1]

To take a very simple example from high school physics, velocity v is defined as the time rate of change of position x:

$$v = \frac{dx}{dt} \quad . \tag{2.1}$$

The ordinary derivative on the right may be interpreted quite literally as the *ratio* of the position differential dx to the corresponding time differential dt. If we multiply through by dt, we then have

$$dx = v\,dt \quad . \tag{2.2}$$

In words, the incremental change in position x is given by the instantaneous velocity v times the increment of time t elapsed. Neither dx nor dt has any particular fixed size; we only require that the differentials be "small enough" that v can be regarded as effectively constant during the time interval dt for (2.2) to be valid.

[1] BA98 argue that differentials are mythical creatures having no real mathematical meaning and that they should therefore be avoided in physical derivations. Their solution is to introduce time as an explicit variable in every thermodynamic process, so that time derivatives replace differentials. This author remains unpersuaded of the pedagogical or theoretical superiority of their approach. Like many other useful concepts, differentials must be used and interpreted with care and common sense.

Once we have established the mathematical relationship between *differentials*, the next step is to generalize to **macroscopic** changes in the relevant variables. In this example, we might want to find the change in position Δx associated with a *finite* elapsed time Δt (we use Δ to indicate a *finite* difference between a specific starting point and a specific ending point). We therefore integrate by prepending an integral sign with appropriate limits:

$$\int_{x_0}^{x_1} dx = \int_{t_0}^{t_1} v \, dt \quad . \tag{2.3}$$

Of course, you must *always* choose the limits so that they match between both sides of the equation: x_0 and x_1 are synonyms for $x(t_0)$ and $x(t_1)$, respectively (alternatively, t_0 and t_1 could be considered functions of the corresponding values of x).

We then have the *formal* solution

$$\Delta x \equiv x_1 - x_0 = \int_{t_0}^{t_1} v \, dt \quad . \tag{2.4}$$

This is as far as we can get until we state precisely how v varies as a function of t. For example, if $v(t) = at$, with a denoting a constant acceleration, then

$$\Delta x = \int_{t_0}^{t_1} at \, dt = \frac{1}{2} a \left(t_1^2 - t_0^2 \right) \quad . \tag{2.5}$$

Alternatively, we might want to specify the position x as a continuous function of some arbitrary elapsed time t, given an initial position x_0 at time $t = 0$. Instead of (2.3), we would then write

$$\int_{x_0}^{x} dx' = \int_0^t v(t') \, dt' \quad , \tag{2.6}$$

yielding

$$x(t) = \int_0^t v(t') \, dt' + x_0 \quad , \tag{2.7}$$

$$x(t) = \int_0^t at' \, dt' + x_0 \quad , \tag{2.8}$$

$$x(t) = \frac{1}{2} at^2 + x_0 \quad . \tag{2.9}$$

We changed the symbol representing the variable of integration from t to t'. Why? Because we are reserving the symbol t for the elapsed time that appears as the upper limit of integration and that will remain as an explicit variable in the resulting equation after integration. The variable t' is a "dummy" variable that is eliminated by the process of integration. It is always a good idea to use different symbols to represent limits of integration (which persist) from those symbols used to represent variables of integration (which disappear), because they play different roles in the integral.

Last, but not least, imagine that we are given the velocity v not as a function of time t but rather as a function of position x. In this case, we would rearrange (2.2) to get everything involving x on one side of the equation and everything involving t on the other, i.e.,

$$\frac{1}{v(x)}\,dx = dt \quad . \tag{2.10}$$

We then integrate as before to find the macroscopic relationship between Δx and elapsed time t. For example, if $v(x) = \sqrt{2a(x - x_0)}$, then

$$[2a(x - x_0)]^{-1/2}\,dx = dt \quad , \tag{2.11}$$

$$\int_{x_0}^{x} [2a(x' - x_0)]^{-1/2}\,dx' = \int_0^t dt' \quad . \tag{2.12}$$

Evaluating the integrals and solving for $x(t)$ yields

$$x(t) = \frac{1}{2}at^2 + x_0 \quad . \tag{2.13}$$

which, not coincidentally [because we chose $v(x)$ to make it so], is the same as (2.9).

2.2.3 Separable first-order differential equations

Equation (2.1) is an example of a very simple **first-order linear differential equation**. In this case, v is prescribed as a function of either x or t, and $x(t)$ [or, alternatively, $t(x)$] is the unknown function to be found.

The vast majority of the differential equations we will encounter in this book can be written in the slightly more general form

$$dy = f(x,y)\,dx \quad . \tag{2.14}$$

If we are fortunate enough that $f(x, y)$ can be factored as follows,

$$f(x,y) = \frac{g(x)}{h(y)} \quad , \tag{2.15}$$

then (2.14) is said to be **separable** because we can rewrite it as

$$g(x)\,dx = h(y)\,dy \quad , \tag{2.16}$$

so that x and dx appear only on the left-hand side, and y and dy appear only on the right. It is then straightforward to find the relationship between y and x by integrating both sides with appropriate limits:

$$\int_{x_0}^{x} g(x')\,dx' = \int_{y_0}^{y} h(y')\,dy' \quad . \tag{2.17}$$

Key fact: Many problems and derivations in this book entail the following general steps: (1) set up a first-order linear differential equation relating two or more variables of interest, (2) use additional information, if needed, to eliminate all but two variables, (3) separate variables according to (2.16), and, finally, (4) integrate with appropriate limits to establish the functional relationship between the two variables.

Problem 2.3: The rate of growth of the mass M of a spherical raindrop falling through a particular cloud is given by $\frac{dM}{dt} \approx Cr^3$, where $M = \rho_l \frac{4}{3}\pi r^3$ and C is a constant.

a) Eliminate M from the above equation, so that the size of the drop is expressed solely in terms of the radius r.

b) Separate variables and integrate to find an expression for $r(t)$, given an initial radius r_0 at time $t = 0$.

c) If $r_0 = 0.1$ mm and $C = 30$ kg/(sec m^3), find the radius after the drop has grown for 10 min. *Answer: 0.42 mm*

Hint: You don't need to know anything about the physics of raindrop growth to solve this problem.

Exact and inexact differentials

As noted in Section 2.2.1, we are interested in both state variables and process variables. Pressure p is an example of a state variable; heat Q and work W are examples of process variables. The former have uniquely defined values for any given "snapshot" of our system; the latter are meaningful only in connection with the evolution of our system from one state to another.

A differential associated with a state variable is known as an **exact differential**. By definition, the value of an integral of an exact differential over some arbitrary path between two states depends on the value of the endpoints only, i.e.,

$$\int_C dv = v_B - v_A \quad , \tag{2.18}$$

where the C indicates any path between endpoints A and B, and v_A and v_B are the values of the state variable v associated with those endpoints.

It follows that for an exact differential the line integral around an arbitrary closed path *must* equal zero, i.e.,

$$\oint_C dv = 0 \quad . \tag{2.19}$$

Any differential that does not satisfy the above description is an **inexact differential**. Process variables like work and heat are always associated with inexact differentials.

We will use the following notational convention to distinguish between the exact and inexact differentials:

Key fact: If x is a state variable, then its differential is exact and will be written as dx. If it is not a state variable, then its differential is inexact and will be written as δx.

Furthermore, when we are dealing with finite changes, a state variable can be expressed as a difference between two endpoints:

$$\Delta x \equiv x_2 - x_1 = \int_{x_1}^{x_2} dx \quad , \tag{2.20}$$

where the Δ denotes the difference between the ending and starting state.

With an inexact variable, we cannot speak of a difference between starting and ending values, so we will not use Δ-notation nor will the associated integral have limits. Rather, we will write things like

$$Q = \int \delta Q \quad . \tag{2.21}$$

Later, it will sometimes be useful to invent new variables that are defined in terms of existing state and/or process variables. The above tests for inexact and exact differentials give us a way to tell whether the new variable is a state or process variable. That is, for an arbitrary closed path,

$$\begin{array}{|lcl|} \oint \delta q \neq 0 & \rightarrow & q \text{ is process variable} \\ \oint dx = 0 & \rightarrow & x \text{ is state variable} \end{array} \tag{2.22}$$

2.2.4 Conserved variables

An important characteristic of any state variable is the set of conditions under which it does or does not remain constant. If a physical process has no influence on the value of a particular state variable, then we say that the variable is **conserved** for that process. Some variables we encounter will be conserved under a wide range of conditions, others only under the most restrictive conditions. As I introduce new state variables, I will often point out any particular conservation properties you should be aware of.

Of the variables we have considered so far, the only one that is always conserved in any closed system (one that does not exchange matter with its surroundings) is mass. Temperature, pressure, and density, on the other hand, are all readily altered by a wide variety of processes.

In the latter case, however, we sometimes have occasion to *force* one of those variables to remain constant (and therefore be conserved) for a particular process. For example, if we put a fixed mass of air into a sealed container whose volume does not change, then the volume of the air in the container remains constant no matter what else we do to it. Similarly, we might control the temperature of a sample of air so that it does not change. The following definitions will prove quite handy later in this book, and I encourage you to memorize them now:

Key fact:

An isothermal process is one in which temperature is held constant

An isobaric process is one in which pressure is held constant

An isochoric process is one in which volume is held constant.

2.2.5 Extensive and intensive variables

We further distinguish between **extensive** variables and **intensive** variables. An extensive variable is one that depends on the size of the sample or system under consideration; an intensive variable is one that does not. For example, **volume** is an extensive variable; *volume per unit mass* (or **specific volume**) is an intensive variable.

Unlike chemists and other laboratory scientists who work with well-defined quantities of materials (a liter of water, a gram of ammonium chloride, for example), meteorologists usually prefer to work with intensive variables. This is because a sample of air in the free atmosphere can represent an arbitrary quantity—our ability to describe its motion and physical behavior shouldn't depend on whether we assume that we are dealing with a mere liter or rather a thousand cubic meters or more.

Some intensive variables, such as pressure and temperature, have no extensive counterparts. On the other hand, all extensive variables have intensive counterparts—all we need to do is divide the extensive variable by the mass of the assumed sample, as we saw in the case of *volume* versus *specific volume*. Of course, any function of only intensive variables is also an intensive variable. For example, density (mass per unit volume) is the reciprocal of specific volume and is therefore also intensive.

The distinction between "extensive" and "intensive" applies to both state variables and process variables. For example, a process variable such as "heat added" may be expressed either as joules (extensive) or joules per kilogram (intensive).

In this book, we will often use upper-case symbols (W, Q, Φ) for extensive variables and lower-case symbols (w, q, ϕ) for their intensive counterparts. This rule does not necessarily apply to variables that have no extensive form, such as pressure (p) and temperature (T).

CHAPTER 3

Physical Properties of Air

Having dispensed with basic definitions, we can now undertake a quantitative description of the behavior of air in terms of relevant state variables. We will develop these ideas first for dry air and then generalize them to air with variable water vapor content.

3.1 Equation of State

For a **homogeneous**[1] parcel of dry air, the state variables (intensive form) we will consider first include pressure p, temperature T, specific volume α, and density ρ. The last two are related as

$$\boxed{\alpha \equiv \frac{1}{\rho}} \tag{3.1}$$

and are therefore not independent—if you know the value of one of these, you automatically know the value of the other, by definition. Of the four variables mentioned, therefore, only three are in-

[1] *Homogeneous*: Exhibiting uniform properties throughout. Pronounced with five syllables, not four.

dependent: (1) pressure, (2) temperature, and (3) density or specific volume.

Furthermore, even these three are related to one another by an **equation of state**. An equation of state is an experimentally or theoretically derived relationship that ties the value of any one state variable (e.g., density) to the values of all the other relevant state variables (e.g., temperature and pressure). Equations of state exist, at least in principle, for everything from gases to the molten rock in the interior of the Earth.

Strictly speaking, any equation of state will be valid only for a restricted range of conditions. For example, the equation of state we will introduce shortly for air is accurate enough under all conditions encountered in the free atmosphere, but it fails to make useful predictions about the properties of air at extremely high pressures or cold temperatures.

We will now briefly review some of the early experimental results that ultimately led to the formulation of an equation of state for air (and other gases) called the **Ideal Gas Law**.

3.2 Experimental Properties of Gases

3.2.1 Boyle's Law

In 1662, the Anglo-Irish natural philosopher Robert Boyle[2] (1627–1691) undertook a series of careful experiments to determine how the volume of a gas changes in response to changing pressure, while keeping the temperature constant (isothermal). His results are now summarized in **Boyle's Law**, which states that *at constant temperature, the volume of a given sample of gas varies inversely as the pressure.* That is,

$$p \propto \frac{1}{V} \quad \text{or} \quad p = \frac{C_1}{V} \quad \text{or} \quad pV = C_1 \tag{3.2}$$

where C_1 is a constant of proportionality [Note: $C_1 = f(T)$].

[2]Boyle is widely regarded as the first modern chemist.

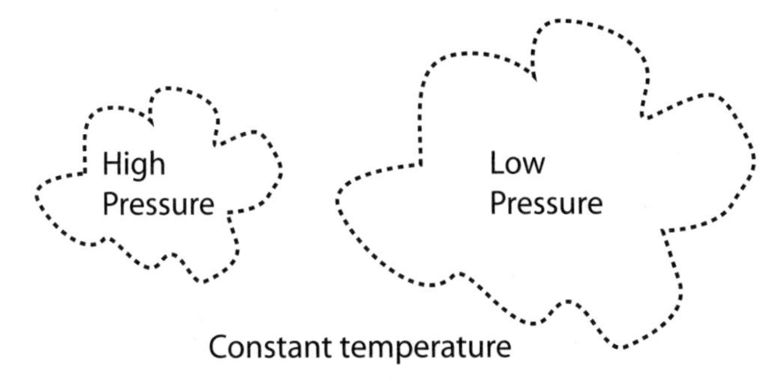

For example, if you double the pressure of a gas while keeping the temperature constant, the volume will be reduced by half. Likewise, if you compress the gas isothermally to 1/3 of its original volume, the final pressure will be three times as great.

3.2.2 Charles' Law

It was 125 years later before the next key property of gases was explored, namely their response to changes in temperature. Jacques Charles[3] (1746–1823) and Joseph-Louis Gay-Lussac (1778–1850), two prominent French scientists, had become interested in the buoyancy of balloons and undertook a series of experiments in which the pressure of a gas was held constant while the temperature was varied. Although the main work was done by Charles and led in 1787 to what is now known as **Charles' Law**, it was first actually published by Gay-Lussac only in 1802.

Charles' Law states that *at constant pressure, the volume of a given sample of gas is proportional to absolute temperature.* That is,

$$\frac{V_T}{T} = \frac{V_0}{T_0} = C_2 \quad \text{or} \quad V = C_2 T \tag{3.3}$$

where C_2 is a constant of proportionality [Note: $C_2 = f(p)$]. For example, if the absolute temperature of a gas is increased isobarically from 200 K to 300 K, that is, by a factor of 1.5, then the volume will also increase by the same factor of 1.5.

[3]Charles created the first manned balloon filled with hydrogen, with which he ascended to a height of around 3 km in 1783. On one demonstration flight, the launch of which was witnessed by the American ambassador to France, Benjamin Franklin, Charles and his balloon landed in a field after about 45 minutes in the air. There, terrified farmers attacked the "monster" with shovels and pickaxes, and Charles barely escaped with his life.

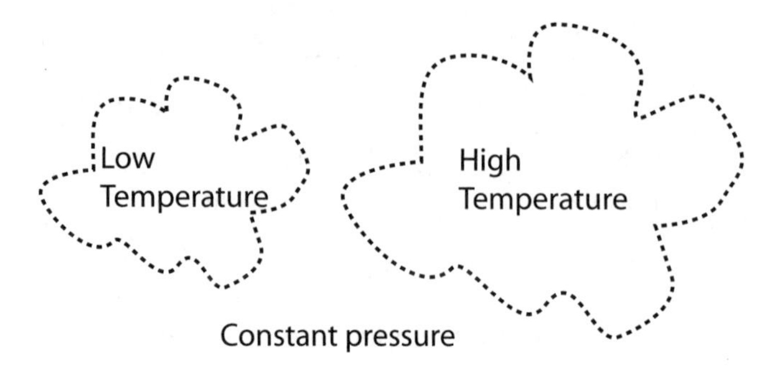

Problem 3.1: A kitchen oven has an interior volume V of 0.12 m^3. The initial pressure p_0 inside the oven equals the outside pressure of 1000 hPa. The air in the oven is then heated from an initial temperature T_0 of 20°C to a baking temperature T_1 of 175°C.

a) If the oven were perfectly sealed so that no air escaped (this would be a very bad idea for real ovens!), what would the pressure be inside the oven when it reached its final temperature? *Answer: 1530 hPa*

b) If the door has an area of 0.25 m^2, what would the *net* force acting on the door be if someone opened it without relieving the pressure first? *Answer:* 1.32×10^4 *N*

c) If the oven is not sealed (the normal case), air will leak out as the air expands from heating, so that inside pressure always equals the outside pressure. Assuming that the air leakage is one-way (no outside air enters the oven), what fraction of the original mass of air in the oven is lost due to expansion? *Answer: 35%*

3.2.3 Avogadro's Law

Charle's Law and Boyle's Law are thus given by the following pair of equations:

$$pV = C_1(T) \tag{3.4}$$

$$V = C_2(p)T \tag{3.5}$$

These can both hold true only if there is another constant C such that

$$pV = CT \tag{3.6}$$

Note that C is actually constant only for a particular gas sample, as it depends on both the mass and composition of the sample.

It was the Italian scientist Count Amedeo Avogadro[4] (1776–1856) who, in 1811, found experimentally that *for fixed pressure and temperature, the number of molecules per unit volume of a gas is a constant, irrespective of the chemical composition.*

By that time, the concept of atomic and molecular mass was understood, and Avogadro therefore originated the concept of a **mole** of a compound, which is the actual mass of the sample in grams divided by its standard molar mass m. A mole therefore represents a fixture *number* of molecules, which we now know as **Avogadro's number** $N_A = 6.022 \times 10^{23}$ mole^{-1}.

Because we now prefer to work in the SI system of units, the preferred way to express the above constant is in terms of the number of molecules per **kilomole** [kmole], which is given by the mass of the sample *in kilograms* divided by m. Thus, we will express Avogadro's number as $N_A = 6.022 \times 10^{26}$ kmole^{-1}.

3.2.4 The Ideal Gas Law

Derivation

In view of fact that volume, pressure, and temperature of an ideal gas are tied uniquely to the *number* of molecules in the sample, not to its composition, the equation of state, known as the **Ideal Gas Law** can now be written as

$$pV = nR^*T \tag{3.7}$$

where n is the number of kilomoles in the sample and R^* is known as the **Universal Gas Constant.** The value of R^* was originally determined experimentally by noting that at 0°C and standard atmospheric pressure of 1013.25 hPa, the volume of one mole of an ideal gas is 22.414 liters (1000 liters = 1 m^3). This corresponds to a value for R^* of

$$R^* = 8314.5\,\mathrm{J\,K^{-1}kmol^{-1}} \tag{3.8}$$

Problem 3.2: Verify that the units given for R^* are dimensionally correct in light of (3.7).

[4]Full name: Lorenzo Romano Amedeo Carlo Avogadro di Quaregna e Cerreto!

Validity

Under what conditions does the Ideal Gas Law give an accurate description of the behavior of a gas? In general, the Ideal Gas Law is valid whenever the density of the gas is low enough (due to a suitable combination of low pressure and high temperature) that individual molecules do not experience significant attractive forces, nor does the space occupied by the molecules represent a significant fraction of the total volume. At ordinary atmospheric pressures, air obeys the Ideal Gas Law quite closely for almost all meteorological purposes.

For specialized applications in which the Ideal Gas Law is not accurate enough, scientists and engineers usually use a more complicated equation of state known as Van der Waal's Equation:

$$\left[p + a\left(\frac{n}{V}\right)^2\right](V - nb) = nR^*T \quad . \tag{3.9}$$

The coefficient a characterizes the relative importance of attractive forces between the molecules; the coefficient b is a measure of the effective volume occupied by the molecules. For dry air, $a = 1.358 \times 10^5$ J m^3/kmol^2 and $b = 3.64 \times 10^{-2}$ m^3/kmol. When nb is vanishingly small compared to V, and when $a(n/V)^2$ is vanishingly small compared to p, then (3.9) reverts to (3.7).

For dry air at 200 K and 300 K, respectively, the above values of a and b imply that the Ideal Gas Law will be in error by 1% or more only for pressures exceeding 3.6 atmospheres and 13.6 atmospheres, respectively. Thus, the error at normal atmospheric pressures is negligible for most purposes.

The meteorological form

Equation (3.7) is probably the form of the Ideal Gas Law you learned in freshman chemistry. It is *not* the form that is most convenient for meteorologists. Instead of working with kilomoles and cubic meters of a gas (both extensive variables), we prefer to work with specific volume or density, which are intensive.

Let us assume that we have a mixture of k gases, the ith of which contributes n_i kmoles to the total. Thus

$$n = \sum_{i=1}^{k} n_i \quad . \tag{3.10}$$

The **molar fraction** of each constituent, which is also the *fraction by volume* according to Avogadro's Law, is then

$$f_i = \frac{n_i}{n} \quad , \tag{3.11}$$

and

$$\sum_{i=1}^{k} f_i \equiv 1 \quad . \tag{3.12}$$

The total mass of our sample (in kg) is

$$M = \sum_{i=1}^{k} n_i m_i \quad , \tag{3.13}$$

where m_i is the molar mass (units kg kmol^{-1} = "atomic mass units" or amu) of each constituent. We now convert the Ideal Gas Law (3.7) to intensive units by dividing through by M:

$$\frac{pV}{M} = \frac{n}{M} R^* T \quad . \tag{3.14}$$

We can rewrite this as

$$\boxed{p\alpha = RT \quad ,} \tag{3.15}$$

where

$$\boxed{R \equiv \frac{R^*}{\overline{m}} \quad ,} \tag{3.16}$$

and the **mean molar mass** of the mixture is

$$\overline{m} \equiv \frac{M}{n} = \frac{\sum_{i=1}^{k} n_i m_i}{n} \quad , \tag{3.17}$$

or

$$\overline{m} \equiv \sum_{i=1}^{k} f_i m_i \quad . \tag{3.18}$$

The coefficient R is thus the gas constant *for a particular mixture of gases.* Its units are J/(kg K). Because it depends on the mean molar mass of the gas, the value of R is not a universal constant, unlike R^*. However, the above form of the Ideal Gas Law (3.15) is very convenient in meteorology because we can normally consider dry air to be a constant mixture of the so-called permanent gases, and it is referenced to the familiar meteorological state variables pressure p, specific volume α, and absolute temperature T. Alternatively, we can write it in terms of density ρ as

$$p = \rho R T \quad . \tag{3.19}$$

3.2.5 Dalton's Law of Partial Pressures

In deriving a form of the Ideal Gas Law that accounts for mixtures of gases of different molar masses, we exploited the fact that it is *the number of molecules per unit volume* in a gaseous system that determines the pressure p, given the volume V and temperature T. This fact is implicit in **Dalton's Law of Partial Pressures.**[5], which states that *the total pressure exerted by a mixture of gases is equal to the sum of the partial pressures that would be exerted by each constituent alone if it filled the entire volume at the temperature of the mixture.* That is, for a mixture of k components

$$p = \sum_{i=1}^{k} p_i \quad , \tag{3.20}$$

where p is the total pressure and the p_i are the partial pressures of each gas. These may be assumed to obey the Ideal Gas Law (3.7)

[5]John Dalton (September 6, 1766 – July 27, 1844) was a British chemist and physicist best known for his advocacy of the atomic theory.

separately, so that

$$p_i V = n_i R^* T = \frac{M_i}{m_i} R^* T \quad , \tag{3.21}$$

where V is the total volume of the mixture, M_i is the mass (kg) of the ith constituent, and m_i is the molar mass. Thus

$$p_i = \rho_i R_i T \quad , \tag{3.22}$$

where $R_i \equiv R^*/m_i$ is thus the gas constant specific to the ith constituent.

Problem 3.3: A previously evacuated tank with a capacity of 0.1 m^3 is pressurized with one kilogram each of helium (molar mass 4.0) and nitrogen (molar mass 28.0). What is the final pressure of the mixture?

3.3 Gas Constant for Dry Air

Armed with the knowledge of the composition of dry air, we may compute an average molar mass m_d and a specific gas constant R_d for dry air. We will not include the contribution of water vapor at this point because it is so variable in space and time. Later, we will look at the many ways in which water vapor complicates (and thus makes more interesting!) the thermodynamic behavior of air.

Taking the volume fractions of only the top four constituents N_2, O_2, Ar, and CO_2 we find that

$$\begin{aligned} m_d \approx & 0.7808(28.013) + 0.2095(31.999) \\ & + 0.0093(39.948) + 0.000383(44.010) = 28.966 \end{aligned} \tag{3.23}$$

A more accurate value accounting for all permanent constituents is

$$m_d = 28.9655 \text{ kg/kmol} \tag{3.24}$$

We then have the gas constant for dry air

$$R_d \equiv \frac{R^*}{\overline{m}_d} = \frac{8314.472 \text{ J/(kmol K)}}{28.9655 \text{ kg/kmol}} = 287.047 \text{ J/(kg K)} \quad , \tag{3.25}$$

or, to the four significant figures of precision needed for exercises in this book,

$$R_d = 287.0 \text{ J}/(\text{kg K}) \tag{3.26}$$

We will require this value of R_d so often that you will probably soon know it by heart!

Problem 3.4: a) Standard sea level pressure is approximately 1013 hPa and standard surface temperature in the U.S. Standard Atmosphere is 15°C. What is the density of dry air under these conditions? *Answer: 1.23 kg* m^{-3}

b) A sample of dry air has a pressure of 400 hPa and a density of 0.7 kg m^{-3}. What is its temperature in degrees Celsius?

c) A sample of dry air has a temperature of 30°C and a specific volume of 2.0 m^3 kg^{-1}. What is its pressure?

d) The record low observed surface pressure (in Typhoon Tip, 1979) was 870 hPa; the record high (Mongolia, 2001) was 1087 hPa. Air temperature at the surface can easily vary between −40°C and +50°C. Find the densities of air corresponding to all four possible combinations of the above extremes.

e) Based on your answers to (b), which of the two variables, pressure or temperature, is typically responsible for the most pronounced variations in the density of air at sea level?

Problem 3.5: a) Determine the mean molar mass of the atmosphere of Venus, which consists of 95% CO_2 and 5% N_2 by volume. *Answer: 43.2 kg* $kmol^{-1}$

b) What is the corresponding gas constant? *Answer: 192.5 J* kg^{-1} K^{-1}

c) The mean surface temperature T on Venus is a scorching 740 K as compared to only 288 K for Earth; the surface pressure is 90 times that on Earth. By what factor is the density of the near-surface Venusian atmosphere greater or less than that of Earth? *Answer: factor of 52 greater*

Problem 3.6: Two sealed containers with volumes V_1 and V_2, respectively, contain dry air at pressures p_1 and p_2 and room temperature T. The containers are connected by a thin tube (negligible volume) that can be opened with a valve. When the valve is opened, the pressures equalize, and the system reequilibrates to room temperature. Find an expression for the new pressure.

3.4 Equation of State for Moist Air

We previously calculated the gas constant R_d for perfectly dry air—that is, air that contains absolutely no water vapor, only the permanent gases that are always present in constant proportion. Perfectly dry air does not exist in the atmosphere; moreover, a dry atmosphere would be extremely uninteresting meteorologically. Let us therefore see how the presence of water vapor affects the equation of state.

3.4.1 Ideal Gas Law for water vapor

First, let us consider water vapor in isolation, that is, without the added complication of other gases. If we can treat water vapor as an ideal gas, then the Ideal Gas Law is just as valid here as it was earlier for dry air:

$$p\alpha = RT \quad . \tag{3.27}$$

For water vapor, however, it is conventional to identify the **vapor pressure** with the symbol e rather than p. We will use the symbol ρ_v to denote the water vapor density, more commonly known to meteorologists as the **absolute humidity**.

We can thus write the Ideal Gas Law for water vapor as

$$\boxed{e = \rho_v R_v T \quad ,} \tag{3.28}$$

where R_v is the gas constant for pure water vapor. What is the value of R_v? We can calculate this just as before, using

$$R_v = \frac{R^*}{m_w} \quad , \tag{3.29}$$

where m_w is the molar mass of H_2O and equals about 18.016 kg/kmol. Therefore,

$$\boxed{R_v = 461.5 \text{ J kg}^{-1} \text{ K}^{-1} \quad .} \tag{3.30}$$

The gas constant for water vapor and the corresponding form of the Ideal Gas Law (3.28) will prove very useful. However, do not make the common beginner mistake of trying to use either one for a *mixture* of water vapor and dry air! We will soon have other ways of dealing with that more general case.

Problem 3.7: The density ρ_l of liquid water at the boiling point (100°C) is 958 kg m^{-3}. By what factor does the volume of the water increase when it changes from liquid to steam at that temperature?
Answer: 1628

Is the Ideal Gas Law as good an approximation for water vapor as it is for dry air? Not quite, because water vapor at typical atmospheric temperatures and pressures is usually much closer to condensation than is the case for dry air. This implies that attractive forces between the molecules are significant. Nevertheless, the inaccuracy in assuming that water vapor behaves as an ideal gas is not enough to worry about for most meteorological applications.

Now let us generalize to the case in which water vapor and the permanent gases of the atmosphere coexist in the same volume. Can we still use the relationship $e = \rho_v R_v T$? Of course, because we recognize that the vapor pressure e represents the **partial pressure** of vapor in the air and that the *total* pressure is given by Dalton's Law as

$$\boxed{p = p_d + e \quad .} \tag{3.31}$$

Here p_d is the partial pressure of the dry air in the mixture and is related to the dry air density ρ_d and temperature T by the familiar gas constant for dry air $R_d = 287.0\,\mathrm{J/(kg\,K)}$:

$$p_d = \rho_d R_d T \quad . \tag{3.32}$$

Combining the Ideal Gas Laws for the two components, we have that the total pressure of a moist volume of air is given by

$$p = (\rho_d R_d + \rho_v R_v)T \quad . \tag{3.33}$$

Also, the combined density of moist air is obviously just the sum of the densities of the dry air and water vapor

$$\rho = \rho_d + \rho_v \quad . \tag{3.34}$$

3.4.2 Mixing ratio and specific humidity

It is often inconvenient to use water vapor density ρ_v or vapor pressure e to express the relative vapor content of a mass of air because these quantities are not conserved. That is, the vapor pressure and the density each increase or decrease when the air containing the vapor is compressed or expanded, respectively. By contrast, the **mixing ratio** w of an air mass is conserved as long as there is no condensation or evaporation taking place. The mixing ratio is defined by

$$\boxed{w \equiv \frac{M_v}{M_d} = \frac{\rho_v}{\rho_d} \quad ,} \tag{3.35}$$

where M_v is the mass of water vapor mixed into a mass M_d of dry air. Because there is usually much more dry air than vapor in given volume of the atmosphere, it is often convenient to express w in units of grams vapor per kilograms dry air. For example, in a warm tropical air mass, the mixing ratio may be as high as 20 g/kg. In cooler air masses, w is typically only a few grams per kilogram.

Closely related to the mixing ratio w is the **specific humidity** q, which is defined as

$$\boxed{q \equiv \frac{M_v}{M_d + M_v} = \frac{\rho_v}{\rho} = \frac{\rho_v}{\rho_d + \rho_v} \quad .} \tag{3.36}$$

In words, q gives the mass of water vapor per unit mass of *moist* air, so that the mass contribution by the water vapor is included in the denominator.

Because the mass of water vapor is typically no more than one or two percent of the total mass, the numerical values of w and q also differ by no more than one or two percent. For applications in which high precision is not important, w and q are effectively interchangeable. If an exact conversion is required, the following relationships may be used

$$w = \frac{q}{1-q} \quad , \tag{3.37}$$

and

$$q = \frac{w}{1+w} \quad . \tag{3.38}$$

Problem 3.8:

a) Show the steps leading to the above two equations.

b) Show that, for realistic values of either w or q in the free atmosphere (e.g,. $w < 20$ g/kg), the difference between the two, expressed as an absolute value, is indeed small.

Often, it is necessary to convert between mixing ratio w or specific humidity q and vapor pressure e. For w, this can be accomplished by noting that

$$w = \frac{\rho_v}{\rho_d} = \frac{e/R_v T}{p_d/R_d T} = \frac{\varepsilon e}{p-e} \approx \frac{\varepsilon e}{p} \quad , \tag{3.39}$$

where

$$\varepsilon \equiv \frac{R_d}{R_v} = \frac{m_w}{m_d} = 0.622 \quad . \tag{3.40}$$

Similarly,

$$q = \frac{\rho_v}{\rho_v + \rho_d} = \frac{\varepsilon e}{p-(1-\varepsilon)e} \approx \frac{\varepsilon e}{p} \quad . \tag{3.41}$$

In summary, to a good approximation

$$\boxed{q \approx \frac{\varepsilon e}{p} \approx w \quad .} \tag{3.42}$$

You may use the above approximation in all problems arising in this book, unless otherwise instructed.

3.4.3 Virtual temperature

We already saw that the total pressure of moist air is given by

$$p = p_d + e = (\rho_d R_d + \rho_v R_v)T \quad . \tag{3.43}$$

We can factor out the moist air density ρ and the gas constant for *dry* air R_d by writing

$$p = \rho R_d \left(\frac{\rho_d R_d + \rho_v R_v}{\rho R_d} \right) T = \rho R_d \left(\frac{\rho_d}{\rho} + \frac{\rho_v}{\rho} \frac{R_v}{R_d} \right) T \quad . \tag{3.44}$$

Using the definitions of specific humidity $q = \rho_v / \rho$ and $R_d / R_v = \varepsilon$, it is easy to show that

$$p = \rho R_d \left[1 + \left(\frac{1}{\varepsilon} - 1 \right) q \right] T \quad . \tag{3.45}$$

Problem 3.9: Show the steps used to derive the above equation.

This is identical to the Ideal Gas Law for dry air, except for the appearance of the factor in brackets on the right hand side. How should we interpret this factor? We start by recalling that the Ideal Gas Law for moist air can be written

$$p = \rho R_m T \quad , \tag{3.46}$$

where the gas constant R_m reflects the mean molar mass of the air, *including not only the permanent gases but also the variable contribution by water vapor.* Because humid air at normal atmospheric temperatures invariably consists of a lot of dry air and only a little water vapor, we expect that R_m will be much closer to R_d than it is to R_v.

Clearly, R_m is also not a constant but depends on the moisture content of the air. While we could calculate the mean molar mass directly using the same formula we used much earlier in getting R_d, it is easy to see by comparing the last two equations that

$$R_m = R_d \left[1 + \left(\frac{1}{\varepsilon} - 1\right) q\right] \quad . \tag{3.47}$$

In other words, the term in brackets gives us a convenient means to adjust the gas constant for dry air in order to account for the presence of water vapor.

However, people don't usually have an instinctive feel for the physical meaning of a given value of the gas constant R. As a result, the approach just described for interpreting the water vapor correction term is not the most common one. Instead, we define a new quantity called the **virtual temperature** as

$$\boxed{T_v \equiv \left[1 + \left(\frac{1}{\varepsilon} - 1\right) q\right] T \quad ,} \tag{3.48}$$

so that the Ideal Gas Law may then be written for moist air as

$$\boxed{p = \rho R_d T_v \quad .} \tag{3.49}$$

The virtual temperature is simply the temperature a dry parcel of air would have to have in order that the parcel's density equal the density of the moist parcel, assuming equal pressures. That is, if a dry parcel of air has temperature T_0 and a nearby moist parcel of air has a virtual temperature T_v which happens to be equal to T_0, then both parcels have the same density.

The quantity $1/\varepsilon - 1$ is a constant with the approximate value 0.61; consequently, a convenient expression for T_v is just

$$\boxed{T_v \approx (1 + 0.61q)\, T \quad .} \tag{3.50}$$

By substituting q equal to 0.03 kg/kg (a rough upper limit for q in the atmosphere), one finds that

$$0 < T_v - T \lesssim 5\ \mathrm{K} \quad . \tag{3.51}$$

The practical value of T_v is most obvious when the hydrostatic law comes into play (next chapter), which relates the local density of air to the local rate of change of pressure with height. It is also relevant to the buoyancy of air parcels—a humid parcel of air is less dense, and therefore more likely to rise, than a dry parcel having the same temperature and pressure.

From this point onward, anytime you solve problems that depend in some way on the density of air, you should remember that it is the *virtual* temperature that determines this density, not the *actual* temperature, except when $q = 0$. In many cases, the difference between T_v and T is small enough that we will ignore that difference and use T in place of T_v. Nevertheless, you should always be at least aware of the difference and know when it is likely to be worth taking into account.

To summarize, we have the following two equivalent versions of the Ideal Gas Law for moist air:

$$\boxed{\begin{gathered} p\alpha = R_d T_v \\ \text{or} \\ p = \rho R_d T_v \end{gathered}} \tag{3.52}$$

where the virtual temperature T_v is given by (3.50). Whenever the humidity is not specified (or if it is low), you can simply assume $T_v \approx T$. You should memorize these relationships.

Problem 3.10: a) If the specific humidity q in a sample of air is 20 g/kg at 30°C, find the virtual temperature T_v expressed in both Kelvins and degrees Celsius. *Answer: 306.8 K*

b) If the pressure p is 1020 hPa, find the density ρ.

c) By what percentage is the above density greater or less than that for dry air at the same pressure and temperature? (Be careful with significant figures here!)

Problem 3.11: On a summer day, the air conditioning breaks down and the air in your classroom becomes very warm and muggy with a vapor pressure of 20 hPa and a temperature of 25°C.

a) If the volume of the classroom is 40 m^3, how much water is present in the room in vapor form? Express your answer both as a mass in kg and a liquid-equivalent volume in liters, assuming that the density of liquid water is 1000 kg/m^3. *Answer: 0.58 kg*

b) If the pressure in the room is 900 hPa, what is the virtual temperature of the air? Express your answer both in K and degrees C. *Answer: 300.7 K*

3.5 In Practice

From a meteorologist's perspective, the Ideal Gas Law (3.52) is of value primarily as the basis for determining the effects of pressure and temperature, and, to a lesser extent, humidity, on atmospheric density. As we shall see later, density variations in the atmospheric column are directly responsible for variations in atmospheric pressure at the base of the column.

Density also has practical implications of a more local nature, namely for the **buoyancy** of an object immersed in a fluid. Later on, we will look at the buoyancy of air parcels in the context of atmospheric stability. For now, let's consider applications of the Ideal Gas Law to very simple buoyancy problems.

3.5.1 Buoyancy calculations

Archimedes' Principle

Archimedes' Principle states that the upward force exerted on an object immersed in a fluid is equal to the weight of the displaced fluid. The *net* downward force on the object is then of course the object's own weight minus the above buoyant force.

For example, a ship floating on the surface of a body of water experiences no net downward force (i.e., it does not sink) because the weight of the water displaced by the ship's hull exactly balances the weight of the ship itself. Any object whose average density

$$\rho = \frac{M}{V} \tag{3.53}$$

is greater than the density of the surrounding fluid *cannot* displace enough fluid to equal its own weight; therefore, it sinks.

The net upward force experienced by a stationary object immersed in a fluid is thus given by the following:

$$F_B = (\rho' V - M)g \quad , \tag{3.54}$$

where ρ' is the density of the surrounding fluid, V is the total volume displaced by the object, and M is the object's total mass.

Problem 3.12: A non-elastic Mylar balloon weighs 2.0 grams and has negligible volume when empty. It has a fixed capacity of 5.0 liters when inflated at normal pressure. The ambient temperature and pressure of the atmosphere at ground level are 15°C and 1000 hPa, respectively. The balloon is filled with pure helium (He; molar mass 4.0) at the same temperature and pressure as the environment (i.e., the helium fills the balloon but is not under pressure relative to the outside air).

a) What is maximum payload in grams (in addition to the mass of the balloon itself) that the balloon could barely lift when released at ground level? *Answer: 3.2 gram*

b) If it carries no payload and does not burst, estimate (to within about 10%) the maximum altitude to which it will rise. You should start by using information in tables and/or figures depicting the temperature and pressure structure of the atmosphere to construct a rough sketch of how density changes with altitude (high accuracy is not required!).

You may use Fig. 1.2 together with the Ideal Gas Law and/or Appendix E.2 to find reasonable estimates of the density at various altitudes.

Problem 3.13: When filling a weather balloon, the operator ideally stops when the balloon has achieved the desired free lift as determined using a calibrated weight and a special nozzle. Sometimes this is not possible, in which case the next best method is often to observe the pressure drop in the tank supplying the helium. A standard large tank of helium contains 6.8 m^3 of the gas (measured at 1 atmosphere pressure) compressed to about 2000 pounds per square inch (psi) or 13.8 MPa.

a) Calculate the volume of helium required in order for a 200 g balloon to achieve the proper free lift (i.e., the net buoyancy without a payload) according to the information in Table 1.3. Helium has a molar mass of 4.0 kg/kmol.

b) By how many psi should the pressure in the tank drop to achieve the target volume? *Answer: 266 psi*

c) Based on conditions in a U.S. Standard Atmosphere (see Appendix E.2), what is the approximate diameter of the balloon when it bursts?

d) An impatient operator wants to get the sounding over more quickly by overinflating the balloon by 50% (by volume) and thereby increasing its ascent rate. Estimate the new altitude at which the balloon will burst, assuming that the balloon's maximum diameter before bursting does not change. How much altitude is lost?

e) Explain why either overinflating or underinflating the balloon might be a bad idea, even if data at higher altitudes are not needed.

Vertical acceleration

From (3.53) and (3.54), we can write

$$F_B = (\rho' - \rho)Vg \quad . \tag{3.55}$$

Being meteorologists, however, we prefer to express the buoyant force F_B in intensive units by dividing through by the mass of the object, in which case we have the net buoyant force per unit mass

$$f_B = \frac{F}{M} = \frac{(\rho' - \rho)Vg}{\rho V} \quad , \tag{3.56}$$

which simplifies to

$$\boxed{f_B = \left[\frac{\rho' - \rho}{\rho}\right] g} \quad . \tag{3.57}$$

Absent other forces (e.g., fluid drag on moving objects), f_B is also the vertical acceleration of the object.

Buoyancy of air parcels

If the object we are considering is a parcel of air, we can use the Ideal Gas Law to express the densities in terms of more commonly measured meteorological variables

$$\rho = \frac{p}{R_d T_v} \qquad \rho' = \frac{p}{R_d T_v'} \quad , \tag{3.58}$$

substitute these into our expression for f_B, and cancel variables appearing in both the numerator and denominator to get

$$\boxed{f_B = \left[\frac{T_v - T_v'}{T_v'} \right] g \quad .} \tag{3.59}$$

We have exploited the fact that the pressure p of the parcel is the same as that of the environment at the same level. This *must* be true if the parcel is not confined, as it would otherwise expand or compress until the pressures were equal.

Not surprisingly, the buoyant force is upward when $T_v > T_v'$ and downward when $T_v < T_v'$. When the two virtual temperatures are equal, there is no net force, and the parcel is said to be **neutrally buoyant**.

Problem 3.14: A parcel of air has a temperature of 29°C and a specific humidity of 24 g/kg. It is embedded in an environment having a temperature of 30°C and a specific humidity of 5 g/kg.

(a) What is its vertical acceleration?

(b) If there are no other forces acting on it, how long would it take for the parcel to rise 10 m from its starting position?

CHAPTER 4

Atmospheric Pressure

4.1 Hydrostatic Balance

With the Ideal Gas Law at our disposal *and* knowing something about how temperature varies with height in the atmosphere, we are finally equipped to consider in detail how and why atmospheric pressure varies throughout the atmosphere.

4.1.1 The hydrostatic equation

Imagine a rectangular slab of air having vertical thickness dz and horizontal area A. Assume that the bottom is positioned at altitude z; it follows that the top is at $z + dz$ (see Fig. 4.1). There are three vertical forces acting on this slab. The first is the downward force of gravity, which is given by

$$F_g = mg = (\rho dV)g = \rho(Adz)g \quad , \tag{4.1}$$

where $dV = Adz$ is the volume of the slab and ρ is its density. We are assuming that dz is small enough to ignore variations of ρ within the volume.

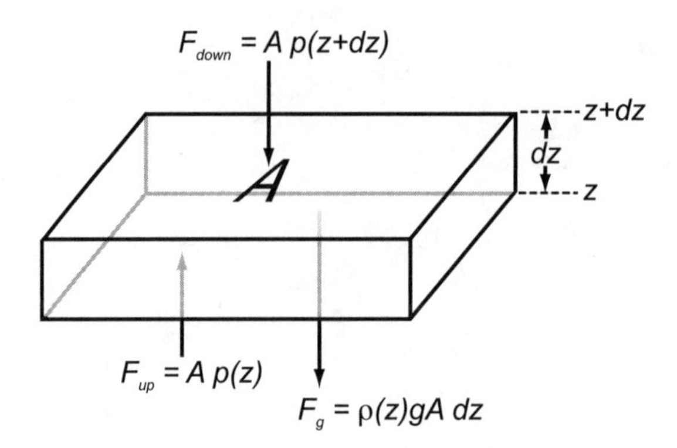

Fig. 4.1: Vertical forces acting on a thin slab of air with vertical thickness dz and horizontal area A.

The second is the upward force due to the atmospheric pressure acting on the bottom of the slab. That force is given by

$$F_{\mathrm{up}} = Ap(z) \quad . \tag{4.2}$$

The third is the downward force due to the pressure acting on the top of the slab. It is given by

$$F_{\mathrm{down}} = Ap(z+dz) \quad . \tag{4.3}$$

The *net* upward force is therefore

$$F = F_{\mathrm{up}} - F_{\mathrm{down}} - F_g \quad , \tag{4.4}$$

or

$$F = Ap(z) - Ap(z+dz) - \rho(Adz)g \quad , \tag{4.5}$$

and its upward acceleration a is obtained by dividing by the mass as follows:

$$a = \frac{F}{\rho Adz} = \frac{Ap(z) - Ap(z+dz) - \rho(Adz)g}{\rho Adz} \quad , \tag{4.6}$$

which simplifies to

$$a + g = -\frac{1}{\rho}\frac{[p(z+dz) - p(z)]}{dz} \quad . \tag{4.7}$$

In the limit as $dz \to 0$, the quantity on the right becomes, by definition, the vertical derivative of pressure, so

$$-(a+g) = \frac{1}{\rho}\frac{\partial p}{\partial z} \quad , \tag{4.8}$$

which we can rearrange to get

$$\frac{\partial p}{\partial z} = -\rho(a+g) \quad . \tag{4.9}$$

Problem 4.1: Consider a rectangular object of density ρ and dimensions X, Y, and Z (total volume $V = XYZ$) immersed in a uniform fluid of density ρ'. Use reasoning similar to that given in this section to derive Archimedes' Principle (3.54).

So far, we have made no approximations. Now we will: It is observed that under all but the most extreme meteorological conditions the vertical acceleration a of air parcels in the free atmosphere is generally much, much smaller than g. This assumption is known as the **hydrostatic approximation**.

Consider, for example, a typical thunderstorm, in which vertical velocities near the middle of the troposphere (say, near 3-4 km altitude) may be of order 10 m s^{-1}. In such a storm, it is observed that a buoyant parcel of air rising from the surface and accelerating steadily will require on the order of 10 minutes to reach that speed if it starts out from a standstill. This implies an average acceleration a of only about 0.02 m s^{-2}, or only 0.2% of g! Most vertical motions in the atmosphere involve smaller accelerations still.

It follows that we may ordinarily neglect a relative to g, in which case we are effectively assuming a perfect balance between the upward pressure gradient force and the downward force of gravity. This balance is given by the **hydrostatic equation**,

$$\boxed{\frac{\partial p}{\partial z} \approx -\rho g \quad .} \tag{4.10}$$

The hydrostatic equation is valid not only in the atmosphere but in any fluid that experiences only weak vertical accelerations. This includes the ocean, the Earth's mantle, and the water in your fish tank.

The hydrostatic equation gives the *derivative* of pressure with altitude in terms of local density. We can integrate downward from the top of the atmosphere to obtain the pressure at any chosen level z. We take $z = \infty$ to place us outside any vestige of the Earth's atmosphere; at that altitude the pressure $p(\infty) = 0$. These values will therefore serve as the upper limits of our integrals. The lower limits correspond to our chosen level, so the limits must be $p(z)$ and z, respectively:

$$-\int_{p(z)}^{p(\infty)} dp = \int_{z}^{\infty} g\rho \, dz \quad , \tag{4.11}$$

or

$$p(z) = \int_{z}^{\infty} \rho g \, dz \quad . \tag{4.12}$$

The product ρg is just the weight per unit volume of the air at a given level. Therefore, the integral is just the combined weight of the entire column of air above altitude z.

Key fact: If we ignore minor variations in g with altitude, the mass of air per unit horizontal area in a fluid layer bounded by two arbitrary pressure levels $p_1 > p_2$ is just $\Delta M = (p_1 - p_2)/g$.

Problem 4.2:

a) By setting up and solving the relevant integrals, prove the above "key fact."

b) How deep would a freshwater lake have to be for the mass of water in a vertical column to be equal to the mass of the entire atmosphere above the lake's surface? Refer to Appendix E for the typical values of relevant parameters. *Answer: 10.3 m*

Application to the atmosphere

We can now use the Ideal Gas Law (3.52) to eliminate ρ and arrive at an expression for the rate of change of pressure with height as a function of virtual temperature in the atmosphere:

$$\boxed{\frac{\partial p}{\partial z} = -\rho g = -\frac{pg}{R_d T_v}} \quad . \tag{4.13}$$

If we are dealing with a reasonably dry atmosphere, then $T_v \approx T$. Substituting standard sea level values of $g = 9.81$ m s^{-2}, $p =$ 1013 hPa and $T = 288$ K, we find that $\frac{\partial p}{\partial z} \approx 12$ Pa/m. This translates into a one-hPa change in pressure per 8.3 m change in elevation. Of course, at higher altitudes you have to change altitude by much more than this to achieve the same change in pressure because the air is less dense.

A convenient transformation of the above equation may be obtained simply by dividing both sides by the pressure p. We then have

$$\frac{1}{p}\frac{\partial p}{\partial z} = -\frac{g}{R_d T_v} \quad . \tag{4.14}$$

Recalling that $d(\ln p) = \frac{1}{p}dp$, the above can be rewritten as

$$\boxed{\frac{\partial \ln p}{\partial z} = -\frac{g}{R_d T_v}} \quad . \tag{4.15}$$

In words, the rate of change of the *logarithm* of pressure with height is inversely proportional to the absolute temperature *and does not depend on p*. As we shall see shortly, this is the same as saying that pressure generally falls off *exponentially* with height.

4.1.2 Gravity and geopotential height

We are now seeing the acceleration due to gravity g cropping up repeatedly, and we would do well to take a closer look at this important parameter. We already know that g is close to 9.81 m s^{-2} at sea level. For some purposes, this is a sufficiently accurate value for g. However, we should not forget that g is *not* constant—it *does* vary slightly with both altitude and geographic location. Small as those differences are, they do sometimes matter. We will therefore take a quick look at the source of the most important variations and then introduce a convention that will allow us to sweep them back under the rug.

Altitude dependence

The actual acceleration due to gravity is a function of the distance r from the center of mass of the Earth. Specifically,

$$g(r) = \frac{GM_E}{r^2} \quad , \tag{4.16}$$

where M_E is the mass of the Earth ($M_E = 5.977 \times 10^{24}$ kg), and G is the so-called Universal Gravitation Constant and has a value of 6.6720×10^{-11} N m^2 kg^{-2}. If we wish to consider gravity as a function of the altitude z above the surface, we can substitute $r = r_E + z$ in the above equation, where r_E is the mean radius of the Earth and is equal to about 6370 km. In this case, we have

$$g(z) = \frac{GM_E}{(r_E + z)^2} \quad . \tag{4.17}$$

Employing a power series expansion in (z/r_E) and discarding higher-order terms (see Appendix C.3), we can write

$$g(z) \simeq g_0 \left[1 - 2\left(\frac{z}{r_E}\right)\right] \quad , \tag{4.18}$$

where

$$g_0 = \frac{GM_E}{r_E^2} \tag{4.19}$$

is the standard acceleration due to gravity at sea level. According to the above formula, for $z = 10$ km above sea level (i.e., near the top of the troposphere), g decreases to about 9.78 m s^{-2} or about 0.3% less than its sea level value.

Problem 4.3: Show the mathematical steps leading from (4.17) to (4.18).

Latitude dependence

Two things complicate the picture somewhat further. First, the Earth bulges somewhat at the equator, so that r_E is different for the equator (6378.1 km) than it is for the poles (6356.9 km). For this reason alone, the sea level value of g is slightly lower (about 0.7%) at the equator than at the poles.

Second, we have not considered the minor difference between the true (or "pure") gravity g and the **apparent gravity** g', which includes an outward centrifugal force (really an *apparent* force, not a real one!) due to the rotation of the Earth. An adequate approximation for the apparent acceleration due to gravity is given by

$$g' = g - \Omega^2 r \cos\theta_{\text{lat}} \quad , \tag{4.20}$$

where Ω is the angular velocity of the Earth and equals 2π (radians) per 23.9 hr or $7.29 \times 10^{-5}\ \text{s}^{-1}$, and θ_{lat} is the latitude.[1] One can easily calculate that the difference between g' and g amounts to only about $0.03\ \text{m s}^{-2}$ at the equator.

Clearly, the range of variability of g due to the oblateness of the Earth and to centrifugal force is no more than a few tenths of a percent under the conditions of interest to most meteorologists. Nevertheless, there are times when it is important to take into account these differences when performing sensitive calculations.

Geopotential height

One way of doing this is to change one's frame of reference slightly. If you are interested in transformations of energy, as most meteorologists are, a useful measure of how far you are above sea level is how much gravitational potential energy you have. If you give up

[1]Conventionally, meteorologists use ϕ to denote latitude. Here we use θ_{lat} instead to avoid conflict with the use of ϕ for geopotential in the next subsection.

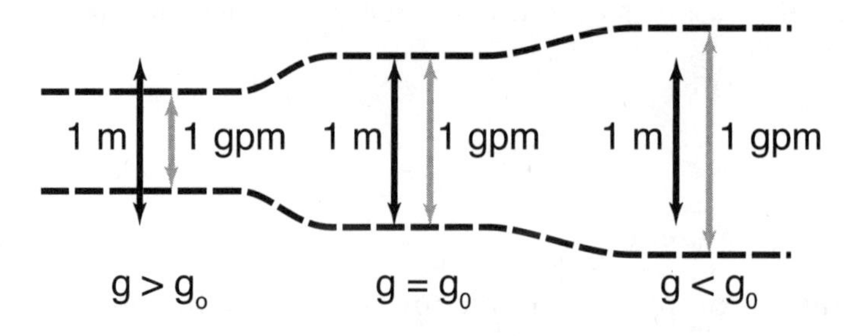

Fig. 4.2: Illustration of the relationship between conventional meters and geopotential meters. While conventional meters (black arrows) represent a fixed geometric distance, geopotential meters (gray arrows) represent a fixed change of gravitational potential energy per unit mass. The dashed lines represent surfaces of constant geopotential.

some or all of that potential energy (e.g., by jumping out of a plane), you will gain an equal amount of some other type of energy, such as kinetic.[2] The same principle applies to moving air parcels.

The intensive version of potential energy is *potential energy per unit mass*, more conveniently known as **geopotential** ϕ. The surface of any fluid at rest, such as an ocean without tides or currents, corresponds to a surface of constant ϕ. There is no "right" choice for where we set $\phi = 0$; it is only *changes* in ϕ that are physically meaningful. Therefore, we usually choose mean sea level as our convenient reference point.

Now for the math: A mass M lifted a small distance dz against the local force of gravity gains potential energy in the amount

$$d\Phi = Mg'dz \quad . \tag{4.21}$$

Dividing through by M, we have

$$\frac{d\Phi}{M} \equiv d\phi = g'dz \quad . \tag{4.22}$$

We now define a new vertical coordinate Z, called **geopotential height**, such that

$$d\phi = g'dz \equiv g_0\, dZ \quad . \tag{4.23}$$

[2]The job of your parachute, if you remembered to pack one, is to transfer most of your acquired kinetic energy to the atmosphere *before* you reach the ground.

where $g_0 = 9.80665$ m sec^{-2} is the *standard* value of the acceleration due to gravity. Thus,

$$dZ = \frac{g'}{g_0} dz \quad . \tag{4.24}$$

The units of Z are **geopotential meters**. Thus, when $g' < g_0$, a geopotential meter is proportionally larger than a "real" meter; when $g' = g_0$, the two units correspond to the same physical distance (Fig. 4.2).

Integrating (4.23) upward from mean sea level, we have

$$\phi(z) = \int_0^z g'(z')\, dz' \equiv \int_0^Z g_0\, dz' = g_0 Z \quad , \tag{4.25}$$

or

$$\boxed{Z = \frac{\phi(z)}{g_0} \quad .} \tag{4.26}$$

The advantage to using geopotential height Z (in geopotential meters) to describe altitude rather than the actual altitude z (in conventional meters) is that one may usually disregard the variability in the apparent gravity g' and just use the constant value of g_0 everywhere. You will encounter geopotential height whenever you deal not only with atmospheric soundings but also standard upper-air (constant pressure) weather maps, such as the 500 hPa maps used routinely by forecasters.

Key fact: Henceforth, whenever meteorologists (including this author) refer to a height z, it should be understood (unless otherwise indicated) that they really mean *geopotential* height. All references to the acceleration due to gravity g then automatically translate to the standard value $g_0 = 9.80665$ m/sec^2.

4.1.3 The hypsometric equation

Having dispensed with that minor complication, let us now continue examining how changes in pressure p are related to changes in (geopotential) height z. In particular, we may ask the question: Given two pressure levels p_1 and p_2, where $p_2 < p_1$, what is the difference in altitude $\Delta z = z_2 - z_1$ between those levels? This difference is conventionally known as the **thickness** of the atmospheric layer bounded by those pressure levels.

We integrate the hydrostatic equation (4.13) as follows:

$$\int_{z_1}^{z_2} dz = \frac{R_d}{g} \int_{p_2}^{p_1} T_v \, d \ln p \quad , \tag{4.27}$$

or

$$\Delta z = z_2 - z_1 = \frac{R_d}{g} \int_{p_2}^{p_1} T_v \, d \ln p \quad . \tag{4.28}$$

We can simplify this to

$$\Delta z = \frac{R_d \overline{T_v}}{g} \int_{p_2}^{p_1} d \ln p \quad , \tag{4.29}$$

or

$$\boxed{\Delta z = \frac{R_d \overline{T_v}}{g} \ln \left[\frac{p_1}{p_2} \right] \quad ,} \tag{4.30}$$

provided that we define the layer **mean virtual temperature** $\overline{T_v}$ as

$$\boxed{\overline{T_v} \equiv \frac{\int_{p_2}^{p_1} T_v \, d \ln p}{\int_{p_2}^{p_1} d \ln p} \quad .} \tag{4.31}$$

In words, given the bounding pressures p_1 and p_2, the layer thickness is directly proportional to $\overline{T_v}$ (Fig. 4.3) Equation (4.30) is known as the **hypsometric equation** and is routinely used to derive the heights of pressure levels from measured temperature and humidity profiles.

To be completely correct, the virtual temperature T_v must be used in the above relationships. However, we may often neglect

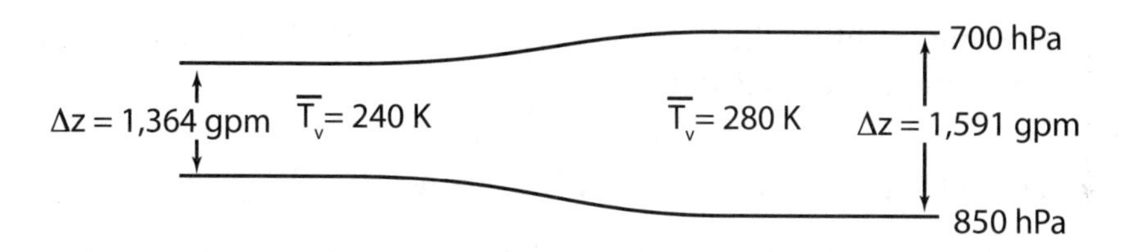

Fig. 4.3: Example of the application of the hypsometric equation. Solid curves represent constant pressure surfaces at 850 and 700 hPa. The thickness Δz of the layer bounded by those pressure surfaces is proportional to the layer mean virtual temperature $\overline{T_v}$.

the minor difference between T and T_v if the air is not too humid or if high accuracy is not required.

Problem 4.4: The lowest point on Earth, the Dead Sea, is 420 m below sea level.

a) If the lapse rate Γ in the lowest few hundred meters is 8°C/km, the surface pressure p_S at the Dead Sea is 1060 hPa, and the temperature T_S at the surface is 30°C, find a reasonable estimate for the mean temperature between the surface and sea level. Ignore the effects of humidity. (Hint: There are both crude and accurate methods for making this estimate, but all reasonable methods should yield similar results).

b) Find the pressure p_0 at sea level under the above conditions. *Answer: 1010.7 hPa*

c) By how many hectopascals would your answer to (b) be in error, if you made a one-degree error in the layer mean temperature?

4.2 Pressure Profiles For Idealized Atmospheres

We have discussed in general terms how temperature, pressure, and altitude are related in the atmosphere. We saw that if you prescribe any arbitrary temperature profile and surface pressure, one may in principle use the hypsometric equation to compute the height of any pressure level above the surface, or conversely, the pressure at any height.

Now we will examine some important special cases that allow particularly simple mathematical relationships to be derived as well as lending additional insight into the "real world" relationship between pressure and altitude.

4.2.1 The constant-density atmosphere

One of the simplest possible models of an atmosphere is one in which the density ρ is constant everywhere, irrespective of altitude. Within such an atmosphere, if it existed, pressure would decrease with altitude according to the hydrostatic law, but the density would remain constant until reaching the top of the atmosphere, at which point the density would abruptly go to zero. Actually, this model is a far better representation of an ocean than an atmosphere, because the density of seawater does not change much with pressure and because it has a sharply defined upper boundary. Nevertheless, let us consider a hypothetical atmosphere having these properties and see where it leads us.

If we integrate the hydrostatic equation from sea level, where the pressure is p_0 to an arbitrary height z, we have

$$\int_{p_0}^{p(z)} dp = -\rho g \int_0^z dz \quad , \tag{4.32}$$

or

$$\boxed{p(z) = p_0 - \rho g z \quad .} \tag{4.33}$$

That is, the pressure decreases linearly with altitude, and the greater the density, the more rapid the decrease. Of course, the pressure cannot become negative, so there is a finite altitude H where we *must* reach the top of the fluid, the pressure goes to zero, and that's the end of our "atmosphere." We find this altitude by setting the left hand side to zero and solving for $z = H$:

$$H = \frac{p_0}{\rho g} \quad , \tag{4.34}$$

or, solving instead for p_0,

$$p_0 = \rho g H \quad . \tag{4.35}$$

If we substitute typical values for p_0 and ρ into , namely 1013 hPa and 1.25 kg m^{-3}, respectively, we find that $H \simeq 8.3$ km. In other words, *if our atmosphere had the same mass that it has now but also had a constant density equal to its sea level density under standard conditions, it would only be 8.3 km deep!*[3]

An atmosphere could easily exhibit the above behavior if only air were completely incompressible, just as water is (well, almost). But this would mean throwing out the Ideal Gas Law and substituting a very different equation of state (i.e., $\rho \approx constant$ instead of $\rho = p/R_d T$), which we know is not correct for air. So let us consider whether it would *in principle* be possible for an atmosphere to exhibit constant density throughout its depth and still obey both the Ideal Gas Law and the hydrostatic law.

We substitute the Ideal Gas Law into the previous equation for H to get

$$H = \frac{p_0}{\rho g} = \frac{\rho R_d T_0}{\rho g} \quad , \tag{4.36}$$

or

$$H = \frac{R_d T_0}{g} \quad . \tag{4.37}$$

So we see that H can be written entirely in terms of the surface temperature T_0 and two physical constants, R_d and g. We don't know yet what the temperature is doing *above* the surface. But the pressure is decreasing with height, so we can infer that the temperature *must* also decrease with height for the density to stay constant.

To find the rate of decrease in temperature, let us write the Ideal Gas Law for dry air, $p = \rho R_d T$, and differentiate with respect to elevation, holding ρ constant. We get

$$\frac{\partial p}{\partial z} = \rho R_d \frac{\partial T}{\partial z} \quad . \tag{4.38}$$

Substitution into the hydrostatic equation leads to

$$\frac{\partial T}{\partial z} = -\frac{g}{R_d} = -34.1^\circ\mathrm{C\ km}^{-1} \quad . \tag{4.39}$$

So to have a constant-density atmosphere, you would need a lapse rate that is constant and very large —about six times as large as is typically observed in the free troposphere.

[3]Passenger airliners routinely fly at altitudes near 13 km and higher, so we *know* that this model is unrealistic!

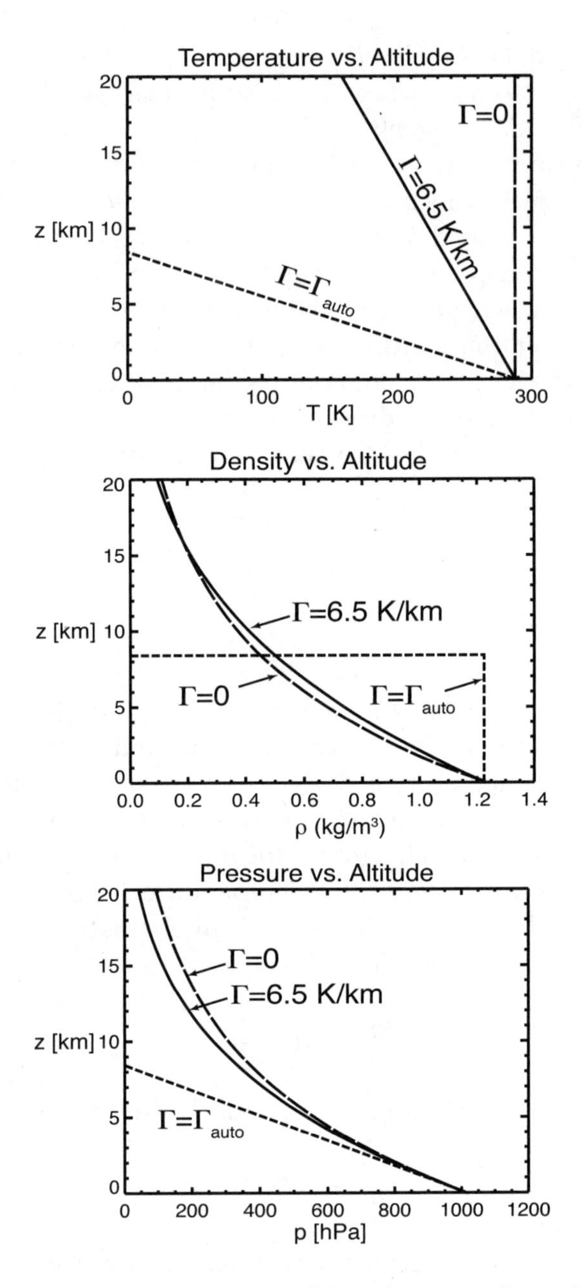

Fig. 4.4: Temperature (top), density (middle), and pressure (bottom) profiles corresponding to three simple model atmospheres: (1) constant density ($\Gamma = \Gamma_{\text{auto}} \equiv g/R_d$), (2) isothermal ($\Gamma = 0$), and (3) a constant lapse rate of $\Gamma = 6.5\,\text{K/km}$. For all three cases in this example, a surface pressure of 1013 hPa and surface temperature of 288 K is assumed.

Problem 4.5: If an atmosphere consisting of an ideal gas were indeed homogeneous (constant density) all the way to the top at $z = H$, find the temperature at that top. Could such an atmosphere actually exist, even in principle? Why or why not?

Autoconvective lapse rate

Notwithstanding the obvious lack of realism of a constant-density atmosphere, there is an important real-world lesson that can be gleaned from the above example. We just determined that an environmental lapse rate

$$\boxed{\Gamma_{\text{auto}} \equiv \frac{g}{R_d} = 34.1^{\circ}\text{C km}^{-1}} \tag{4.40}$$

leads to a density ρ that is constant with height. It follows that if the actual lapse rate Γ is *greater* than Γ_{auto}, then the density of the air must *increase* with height. Such an "upside-down" distribution of density—a *density inversion*—must inevitably result in the overturning of the affected layer: the warmer air below will spontaneously rise, and the cooler air aloft will spontaneously sink. You can no more prevent this overturning from taking place than you can keep the oil from rising to the top of your salad dressing! Because this convective overturning automatically takes place for any environmental lapse greater than Γ_{auto}, the latter is called the **autoconvective lapse rate.**

While an autoconvective lapse rate is *never* observed over deep layers of the atmosphere, it is quite common very close to the surface on a sunny day when surface heating is intense enough to sustain the sharp temperature gradient despite constant convective overturning. The density inversion leads to upward refraction of light rays approaching the surface at a grazing angle, giving rise to the illusion of reflective puddles of water—i.e., **mirages**. You have almost undoubtedly seen such mirages on the road surface some distance ahead of your car when driving on a summer day.

4.2.2 The isothermal atmosphere

Another simple model for the atmosphere is one in which not the density but rather the temperature is constant with height—that is, $\Gamma = 0$. Such an atmosphere is **isothermal**.

Again we start with hydrostatic equation and substitute the Ideal Gas Law:

$$\frac{dp}{dz} = -\rho g = -\frac{pg}{R_d T} \quad . \tag{4.41}$$

This can be rewritten

$$\frac{1}{p} dp = -\frac{g}{R_d T} \, dz \quad . \tag{4.42}$$

We can then integrate from sea level ($z = 0, \ p = p_0$) to some arbitrary level z where the pressure is p. Because T is a constant,

$$\int_{p_0}^{p} \frac{1}{p} dp = -\frac{g}{R_d T} \int_0^z dz \quad , \tag{4.43}$$

or

$$\ln\left(\frac{p}{p_0}\right) = -\frac{gz}{R_d T} \quad . \tag{4.44}$$

Once again using the definition $H = R_d T/g$, we get

$$\boxed{p(z) = p_0 \exp\left(-\frac{z}{H}\right) \quad ,} \tag{4.45}$$

where H in this case is interpreted as a **scale height**, i.e., the vertical distance over which the pressure decreases by a factor e^{-1} or to about 37% of its original value.

4.2.3 The constant lapse rate atmosphere

Let us assume that the temperature T varies linearly with height, i.e.,

$$T = T_0 - \Gamma z \quad . \tag{4.46}$$

In this case, the hydrostatic equation combined with the Ideal Gas Law becomes

$$\frac{dp}{dz} = -\frac{pg}{R_d T} = -\frac{pg}{R_d (T_0 - \Gamma z)} \quad , \tag{4.47}$$

or

$$\frac{1}{p}dp = -\frac{g}{R_d}\left(\frac{dz}{T_0 - \Gamma z}\right) \quad . \tag{4.48}$$

Once again this can be easily integrated. We shall again integrate between the limits $z = 0$, where $p = p_0$ and an arbitrary height z, where the pressure is p. The result is

$$\int_{p_0}^{p} \frac{1}{p}dp = -\frac{g}{R_d}\int_0^z \frac{dz}{T_0 - \Gamma z} \quad , \tag{4.49}$$

or

$$\ln\left(\frac{p}{p_0}\right) = \frac{g}{R_d\Gamma}\ln\left(\frac{T_0 - \Gamma z}{T_0}\right) \quad . \tag{4.50}$$

Taking the exponent of both sides, we get

$$\boxed{p(z) = p_0\left(\frac{T_0 - \Gamma z}{T_0}\right)^{\frac{g}{R_d\Gamma}} \quad ,} \tag{4.51}$$

or, alternatively,

$$\boxed{p(z) = p_0\left[\frac{T(z)}{T_0}\right]^{\frac{g}{R_d\Gamma}} \quad .} \tag{4.52}$$

In the usual case that T decreases with z (i.e., $\Gamma > 0$), this equation requires that pressure decrease with elevation, in agreement with the hydrostatic equation. In the less common case that T increases with elevation (an inversion), the ratio (T/T_0) is greater than unity (for levels above the surface) but the exponent of this ratio is negative; therefore, p still decreases with height, as required by the hydrostatic equation. In the special case of an isothermal layer ($\Gamma = 0$), the above formula cannot be used because Γ appears in the denominator of a fraction, and division by zero is undefined.

Key fact: In the U.S. Standard Atmosphere, the temperature profile in the troposphere ($z < 11$ km) is defined as $T(z) = T_0 - \Gamma z$, where $T_0 = 15°\mathrm{C}$, and $\Gamma = 6.5$ K/km. The surface pressure p_0 in the U.S. Standard Atmosphere is 1013.2 hPa. Thus, for altitudes below 11 km, (4.51) may be used with the above parameters to evaluate $p(z)$ in the Standard Atmosphere.

The exponent in (4.51) is simply the ratio of the autoconvective lapse rate $\Gamma_{\text{auto}} = g/R_d$, which we derived for the constant-density atmosphere, to the actual lapse rate Γ. If the two are equal, the exponent becomes unity, and pressure becomes a linear function of z again, as expected for constant density.

An atmosphere with a truly constant positive lapse rate (decrease of temperature with height) has only a finite vertical extent. Once the temperature reaches absolute zero, we have reached the top of our hypothetical atmosphere. Obviously this scenario is possible only for an atmosphere that behaves like an ideal gas all the way down to absolute zero, unlike any real gas. On the other hand, if the temperature *increased* steadily with altitude (i.e., $\Gamma < 0$), there is no upper limit!

Problem 4.6: a) Use the equation for $p(z)$ for a *constant density* atmosphere to calculate the *approximate* height of the 1000, 850, and 500 hPa levels, *assuming* that the density throughout the troposphere is the same as that at the surface (computed from T_0 and p_0).

b) Repeat your calculation using the somewhat more accurate expression for $p(z)$ in an *isothermal* atmosphere, *assuming* that the temperature of the entire atmosphere equals T_0 as given above.

c) Finally, repeat your calculation using the *most* accurate expression for $p(z)$, which in this case is the one for a *constant lapse rate* atmosphere. *Answer: 110 m, 1457 m, 5573 m*

d) For each of the pressure levels given, calculate the error (approximate minus true value) in meters that results from using the simpler constant density and isothermal approximations. Use a table having the following format to present your results: rows correspond to pressure levels; first three columns correspond to three model atmospheres; final two columns give errors (approximate value minus true) for the constant density and isothermal atmospheres. Record all values to a precision of 1 meter.

e) From your 1000 and 850 hPa heights, obtain the layer thicknesses for this pair of pressure levels. Then, invert the hypsometric equation to find the layer mean temperatures $\overline{T}$ for the three model atmospheres. *Answer: For constant density case,* $\overline{T}$ *= 262.3 K*

Problem 4.7: In earlier times, forecasts of 1000-500 hPa thickness were sometimes used by forecasters as a crude predictor of expected surface temperatures. Assuming a constant lapse rate of 6.5 K/km and a surface pressure near 1000 hPa, what thickness value should correspond to surface temperatures near freezing? *Answer: 5191 m*

4.2.4 The piecewise linear temperature profile

The ultimate approximation to a real atmosphere is a model based on a series of stacked layers, each of which exhibits a different constant lapse rate. We simply specify a series of levels z_i and corresponding temperatures T_i, and we assume that the temperature profile is linear (i.e., has constant lapse rate) between adjacent levels. In this manner, we can approximate any real profile $T(z)$ as accurately as we like, simply by choosing enough levels (Fig. 4.5).

The lapse rate between levels z_i and z_{i+1} is

$$\Gamma_i = -\frac{T_{i+1} - T_i}{z_{i+1} - z_i} \quad , \tag{4.53}$$

and within each layer, (4.51) can then be generalized to

$$p_{i+1} = p_i \left[\frac{T_{i+1}}{T_i}\right]^{\frac{g}{R_d \Gamma_i}} \quad . \tag{4.54}$$

Alternatively, if $T_{i+1} = T_i$, then the above equation cannot be evaluated, and you must use (4.45) to get

$$p_{i+1} = p_i \exp\left[\frac{g}{R_d T_i}(z_i - z_{i+1})\right] \quad . \tag{4.55}$$

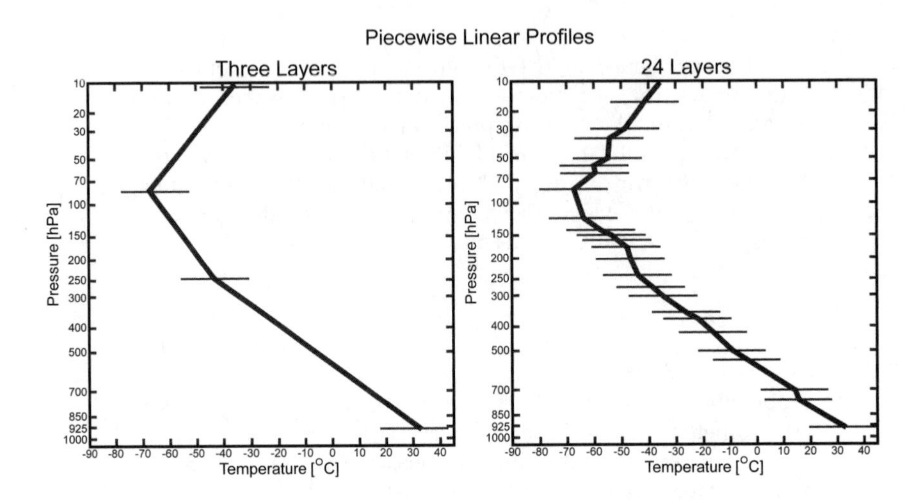

Fig. 4.5: An actual temperature profile approximated as a piecewise linear profile consisting of three layers (left) and much more accurately with the 24 layers (25 levels; right) included in the original radiosonde report.

Starting at the surface level z_0 with pressure p_0 and temperature T_0, you can use the above two equations to work your way upward, finding p_i for each successive level z_i.

4.2.5 Relationship to the hypsometric equation

We have looked at several different ways of relating changes of pressure p to changes in geopotential height z: first the hypsometric equation (4.30), then the expressions (4.33), (4.45), and (4.51) for $p(z)$ under various assumptions about density or lapse rate. While the latter three equations are valid only for specific cases, the hypsometric equation is *always* valid in a hydrostatic atmosphere. Therefore, you always have two ways of getting at the change of pressure with height:

1. If you happen to know (or can reasonably estimate) the mean virtual temperature $\overline{T_v}$ within the layer bounded by z_i and z_{i+1}, and if you know the pressure p_i at the base of the layer, then you can *always* use the hypsometric equation (4.30) to find p_{i+1}.

2. If, on the other hand, you know something specific about the (virtual) temperature profile $T(z)$, then you can use one of the appropriate model atmospheres to find $p(z)$.

Generally speaking, if a layer is thin enough that the density does not change drastically over its depth, then *all* of the above methods will give you about the same result. Over a deeper layer in which temperature and density vary significantly, the accuracy of various atmospheric models generally increases in the following order: (1) constant density, (2) isothermal, (3) constant lapse rate, (4) piecewise constant lapse rate.

Problem 4.8: On a certain day, the atmosphere has a temperature T_0 of 20°C and a pressure p_0 of 1000 hPa at the surface ($z_0 = 0$). The lapse rate is $\Gamma_0 = 6$ K/km from the surface to 3 km altitude; $\Gamma_1 = 3$ K/km from 3 km to 6 km altitude. Find the pressure p at an altitude of 5 km. *Answer: 542 hPa*

Problem 4.9: The hypsometric equation (4.30) gives the thickness Δz of a layer bounded by two pressure levels p_1 and p_2 in terms of the layer mean virtual temperature $\overline{T_v}$ (or just the layer mean temperature $\overline{T}$ if the air is assumed to be dry).

a) For the special case of a *constant lapse rate* layer with bottom and top temperatures T_1 and T_2, respectively, find an exact expression for the layer mean temperature $\overline{T}$ required by the hypsometric equation.

b) If $T_1 = 280$ K and $T_2 = 276$ K, find $\overline{T}$ to the nearest 0.1 K. Compare your result with a mean temperature derived from the much simpler arithmetic average of T_1 and T_2.

c) Repeat (b), but for $T_2 = 240$ K. *Answer: 259.5 K*

d) Based on your results for (b) and (c), speculate on when it is probably safe to use the simple arithmetic average of T_1 and T_2 as an approximation for the layer mean temperature.

4.3 In Practice

4.3.1 Measurement of pressure

Although pressure is the standard meteorological variable least apparent to someone going outside to fetch their morning newspaper (the others being temperature, humidity, wind, cloud cover, visibility, and precipitation), it is certainly one of the most important for understanding atmospheric processes. All modern weather forecasts, for example, begin with the best available analysis of pressure patterns over much of the Earth's surface. Measurements of pressure are therefore undertaken every hour at several thousand weather stations worldwide and then adjusted to yield an estimate of pressure at sea level. These estimates are then collected at a central location and analyzed to produce maps of sea level pressure.

Mercury barometers

An instrument used to measure pressure is called a **barometer.** Surprisingly, one of the most accurate ways to measure pressure is also the simplest (though not necessarily the most convenient): A mercury barometer (Fig. 4.6) consists of a simple vertical glass tube with the top end sealed and the open end immersed in a reservoir of mercury (Hg), a liquid metal whose density (13.54 g cm^{-3}) is even greater than that of lead (11.34 g cm^{-3}). Above the column of mercury in the tube is a near-vacuum.[4] Atmospheric pressure forces mercury up into the tube until the weight (per unit area) of the column of mercury exactly balances the pressure (weight per unit area) of the atmosphere. The higher the pressure, the higher the top of the column of mercury as measured from the top of the mercury in the reservoir. Small numerical corrections may be applied to account for the effect of temperature on the density of the mercury and for small regional variations in the acceleration due to gravity.

[4]It is not quite a perfect vacuum but rather corresponds to the vapor pressure of mercury, which is less than 0.0024 hPa at room temperature.

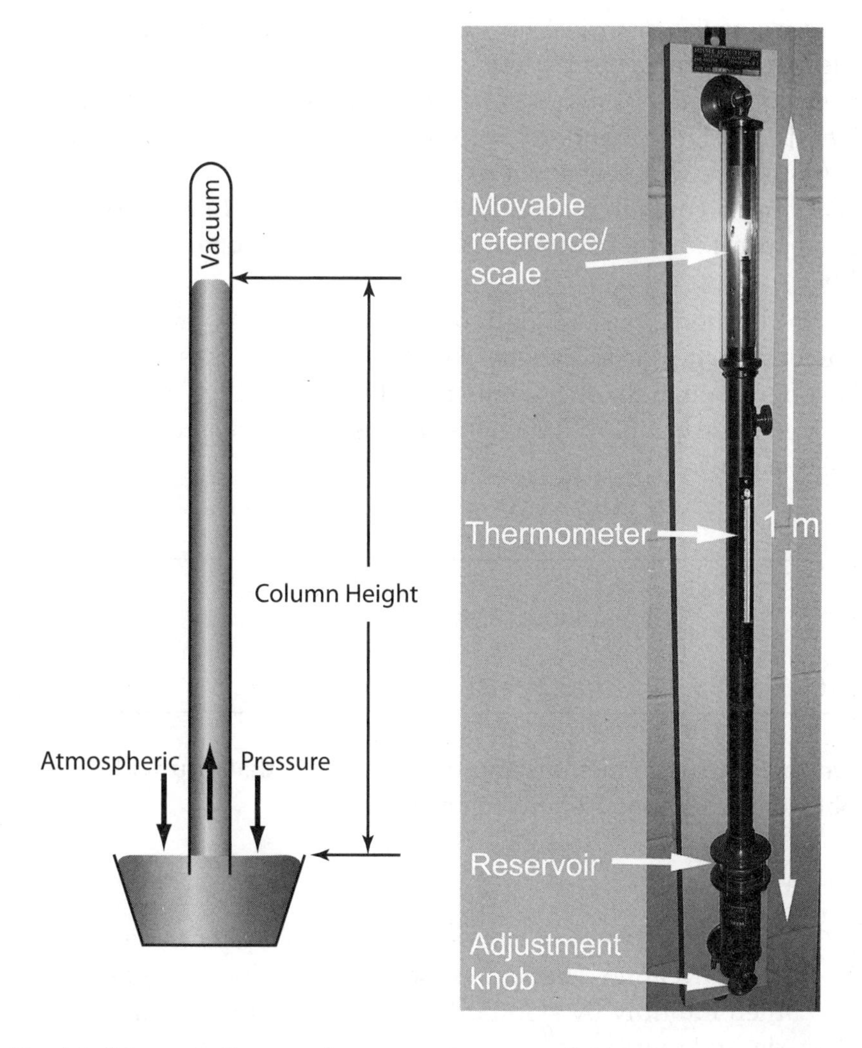

Fig. 4.6: Schematic diagram of a mercury barometer (left), and an example of an actual mercury barometer mounted on a wall (right). The adjustment knob is used to set the level of the top of the mercury in the reservoir to the zero point; the sliding vernier scale at the top then allows one to read the height of the column to the nearest 0.01 hPa. The temperature obtained from the thermometer is used to correct for variations in the density of the mercury; in addition, there may be a fixed correction for the local acceleration due to gravity.

Pressure units

Because of the historical importance of the mercury barometer in measuring atmospheric pressure, you will often hear pressures expressed in units of *inches of mercury* [in Hg] or *millimeters of mercury* [mm Hg][5]. **Standard sea level pressure** has been defined as 760 mm Hg, which is equal to 29.921 in Hg. In SI units of pascals [Pa], this is equivalent to 101.325 kPa, or 1013.25 hPa (recall that a hectopascal is synonymous with the more traditional unit of a millibar).

In this book, we will only occasionally refer to pressures measured in inches or millimeters of Hg. However, these units come up often enough in other contexts that you probably would do well to memorize standard atmospheric pressure expressed in *all* of the following ways:

Standard Atmospheric Pressure

101.325 kPa	=	1013.25 hPa	=	29.921 in Hg	=	760 mm Hg

One advantage to memorizing these values is that you will then be able to readily convert between pressure units:

> **Key fact:** To convert pressure units, simply divide by standard atmospheric pressure in the original units and then multiply by standard atmospheric pressure in the desired units.

[5]The pressure unit corresponding to one millimeter of mercury is also commonly known as the *torr*, after Evangelista Torricelli, an Italian physicist and mathematician who discovered the principle of the barometer in 1644.

Problem 4.10: The pressure measured by a mercury barometer on a certain day is 31.0 in Hg.

a) Express this pressure in hectopascals.

b) Find the corresponding column height in meters in a barometer that used water instead of mercury.

Problem 4.11: Many pilots learn the simple rule of thumb that atmospheric pressure decreases by roughly one inch of mercury per thousand feet of altitude. Use the Hydrostatic Law to evaluate the validity of this claim for the U.S. Standard Atmosphere (Appendix E.2) troposphere. For what range of altitudes (if any) is it accurate to plus or minus 10%? (Hint: Start by finding the range of *densities* for which the rule has the specified accuracy.)

Aneroid barometers

While mercury barometers are very simple and very accurate (if read carefully by a trained observer), they are fairly expensive (mercury is not cheap!), fragile, and difficult to safely transport (mercury is also very toxic!). Therefore, the most common and convenient way to measure pressure is with an **aneroid barometer**.[6] Basically, aneroid barometers rely on a disk-like metal can, or *aneroid cell* (Fig. 1.16), which is evacuated so that there is no internal pressure. An internal spring prevents it from collapsing. The corrugated sides of the aneroid cell thus compress and expand slightly in response to changes in atmospheric pressure. A sensitive mechanical linkage transfers this movement to a needle that can be read against a calibrated scale.

Aneroid barometers are small and can be very portable. Aircraft altimeters and even hiker's altimeters are usually small aneroid barometers. Aneroid cells may also be put to use in radiosondes and in mechanical recording devices such as the **microbarograph** depicted in Fig. 4.8.

[6] "Aneroid" is Greek for "not wet," as contrasted with a mercury barometer that relies on a liquid.

Fig. 4.7: A portable precision aneroid barometer designed for field use. This particular model requires the metal knob at the center to be turned until a small indicator needle (not visible) is exactly centered. The pressure is then obtained by reading the larger dial needle attached to the knob against one of three scales, depending on the expected pressure range. A small bubble level just to the right of the knob is used to ensure that the barometer is perfectly level, since the indicator needle may deflect in response to tilt.

Fig. 4.8: A recording microbarograph. An aneroid cell conceptually similar to that in Fig. 1.16 deflects the pen in response to changes in pressure. A mechanical spring-driven clockwork mechanism slowly rotates the chart drum. In recent years, mechanical recording devices such as this one have been largely supplanted by digital electronic devices. *(Photo: Alan Sim)*

Good-quality barometers used in weather stations are larger, are mounted on the wall, and have circular dials that resemble one-handed clocks. With training and a little practice, these can usually be read by eye to the nearest 0.1 hPa.

The main drawback to aneroid cells and the devices they serve is that, unlike mercury barometers, they are subject to mechanical variations and general wear and tear. They must therefore be compared with a mercury barometer from time to time (e.g., once every few months) in order to determine what small correction should be added to, or subtracted from, the aneroid barometer reading to make it agree with the mercury barometer reading at the same level. This is the standard procedure at any official weather station.

4.3.2 Correction of surface pressure to sea level

In addition to the constant pressure maps, one of the most important operational meteorological products used in forecasting is the surface pressure map. This is the type of map you most often see in the newspaper with the cold and warm fronts drawn in, as well as the position of lows and highs. The lows and highs refer to relative minima and maxima in the surface atmospheric pressure. Because altitude has a strong effect on the pressure actually measured at a meteorological station, the pressures on a surface map must again be referenced to a common altitude (sea level) to be meteorologically meaningful. Otherwise, you would always find a deep (but meaningless) pressure low over the Rocky Mountains and other regions of high terrain.

To calculate the sea level pressure p_0 from the observed station pressure, one need only set Δz in the hypsometric equation equal to the elevation h of the station above sea level and solve for the pressure at the bottom of the hypothetical layer of the atmosphere whose top is at the station pressure p_s:

$$h = \frac{R_d \overline{T_v}}{g} \ln \left[\frac{p_0}{p_s} \right] \quad , \tag{4.56}$$

or

$$p_0 = p_s \exp \left[\frac{g}{R_d \overline{T_v}} h \right] \quad . \tag{4.57}$$

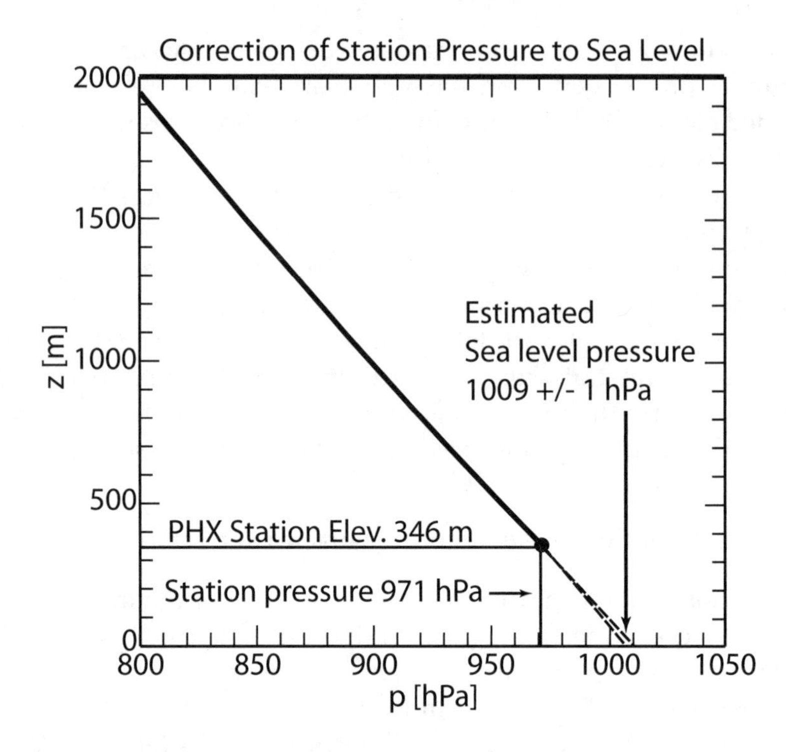

Fig. 4.9: Graphical illustration of the correction of station pressure to sea level, in this case for a hypothetical pressure observation of 971 hPa at Phoenix International Airport (elevation 346 m). The correction to sea level depends on what one assumes about the temperature of the hypothetical air column below ground level. The two dashed lines correspond to the daytime maximum temperature of 43°C (left) and nighttime minimum of 27°C (right), giving rise to a full 2 hPa spread in the computed sea level pressure. In practice, the temperature utilized is usually the average of the current temperature and the temperature from the observation 12 hours earlier.

But to perform this calculation requires an assumption about the layer mean virtual temperature $\overline{T_v}$. Since there is no actual atmosphere below ground, there is no unique basis for assigning a temperature to that hypothetical layer!

The exact assumption used varies from country to country and, sometimes, from station to station. It is important that whatever method is used, it should not lead to serious differences in the sea level pressure computed for a given higher altitude station as compared with that of a nearby low level station, as this would introduce spurious features into a surface pressure map.

One method is to simply assume the station temperature for the top of the hypothetical layer and then assume some standard lapse rate for the temperature profile down to sea level. The lapse rate assumed might reasonably be 6.5°C/km, which is the value used by the U.S. Standard Atmosphere; sometimes it is assumed to be 5.0°C/km, which is also fairly typical of the near-surface lapse rate at many locations. Finally, one might assume a representative lapse rate that has actually been determined individually for each station. At low altitudes, the correction is fairly insensitive to the exact assumptions used.

One disadvantage of using the current surface temperature alone is that this temperature at a high altitude station is often much warmer during the day (due to solar heating) and much colder at night (due to radiational cooling) than the atmosphere at the same altitude above sea level away from the high terrain. The result can be a serious underestimate of the "true" sea level pressure during the daytime and an overestimate during the night. One sometimes tries to get the two effects to cancel by instead using the average of the current surface temperature and that measured 12 hours earlier (Fig. 4.9).

At many inland stations, the terrain elevation is such that the station pressure is often, or even always, less than one or more of the mandatory pressure levels—1000 hPa, 925 hPa, even 850 hPa for stations like Denver. Thus, the (hypothetical) height of the mandatory pressure level is below the surface of the Earth at that location. In such cases, the determination of geopotential height of the pressure level is made in a manner analogous to the determination of sea level pressure.

4.3.3 The U.S. Standard Atmosphere

Definition

For operational meteorological or aeronautical calculations involving pressure, temperature, or density at various altitudes, it is rarely possible to predict in advance precisely what conditions will be encountered in any real-life situation. As we have seen, the vertical temperature structure of the atmosphere, and hence its density and pressure profiles, may vary markedly from day to day, season to season, and from location to location. Nevertheless, it is often necessary to assume *something* about the typical characteristics of the atmosphere, even if you know that, in any real situation, your assumptions may represent only crude approximations to reality.

For example, a pilot flying cross-country will be able to read the temperature at her altitude but usually won't have detailed or reliable knowledge of temperatures above or below the flight path. Likewise, an aeronautical engineer might need to evaluate an aircraft design based on a reasonable, if not necessarily exact, assumption concerning temperature, pressure, and density at a particular altitude.

It is for these and similar purposes that the **U.S. Standard Atmosphere** was created—to provide a standard basis for estimating *reasonable* values of operationally significant atmospheric variables. It is meant to be representative of *average* conditions in a midlatitude atmosphere.

The definition of the U.S. Standard Atmosphere is as follows:

- The temperature T_0 at the surface is 288.15 K (15°C).
- The atmosphere is subdivided into several layers, each having constant lapse rate as given in Table 4.1.

Table 4.1: Lapse rates in the layers defined for the U.S. Standard Atmosphere. Recall that positive values imply decreasing temperature with height.

Layer boundaries [km]	Lapse rate [°C km^{-1}]
0–11	+6.5
11–20	0
20–32	−1.0
32–47	−2.8
47–51	0
51–71	+2.8
71–84.852	+2.0

- The pressure p_0 at the surface is 1013.25 hPa.
- The air is assumed to be dry and to obey the Ideal Gas Law with a gas constant[7] $R_d = 287.05307$ J kg^{-1}K^{-1}.
- The acceleration of gravity is assumed to be constant and equal to 9.80665 m s^{-2}.

A graphical depiction of the U.S. Standard Atmosphere was already given in Fig. 1.7. Because the lapse rate is constant within each layer, the method developed in Section 4.2.4 may be used to evaluate the pressure as a function of altitude z. Appendix E.2 in the back of this book tabulates the temperatures, geopotential heights, and densities corresponding to various pressure levels in the U.S. Standard Atmosphere.

Pressure altitude

In view of the fixed temperature profile $T(z)$ and sea level pressure p_0 in the U.S. Standard Atmosphere, there is also a fixed relationship in the Standard Atmosphere between pressure p and altitude z.

Key fact: Given an arbitrary pressure p, the corresponding **pressure altitude** is the altitude at which you would find that pressure in the U.S. Standard Atmosphere.

For example, from the table in Appendix E.2, we find that a pressure of 925 hPa corresponds to a pressure altitude of 762 m above sea level, *regardless of the actual altitude.*

This means that even though the actual altitude of a particular airport is fixed, its pressure altitude will vary somewhat with fluctuations in the station barometric pressure. When the pressure drops, the pressure altitude rises, and vice versa.

[7]The above value for R_d differs slightly from that cited elsewhere in this book. The small discrepancy is due not only to a slightly different assumption about the composition of dry air but also to an outdated value for the Universal Gas Constant. For the sake of consistency, calculations involving the U.S. Standard Atmosphere continue to use the old value.

Problem 4.12: At a particular observation time, the station pressure at a certain airport is reported as 905 hPa. Using the temperature and pressure properties of the U.S. Standard Atmosphere, *compute* the pressure altitude of the airport to the nearest meter. Use Appendix E.2 to check whether your answer is reasonable. *Answer: 943 m*

Altimeters

An altimeter is a device used to estimate altitude above sea level. The simplest and most common altimeters, used by anyone from pilots to hikers, are essentially barometers calibrated in units of altitude instead of pressure (Fig. 4.10).

Because the pressure patterns along an airplane's flight path vary with the changing weather condition, there must be a way to adjust the altimeter to ensure a reasonable match between the altimeter's indicated altitude and the true altitude. The need for a good match is, of course, most critical near ground level, as an error in the altimeter indication could result in a pilot flying much closer to the terrain than is safe, or even flying into the terrain if visibility is obscured by darkness or fog (Fig. 4.11).

The above adjustment is accomplished by specifying a reference pressure nominally associated with sea level at the time and location in question. This reference pressure p_{alt} is called the **altimeter setting**. It is reported as a part of almost all standard hourly surface weather reports (e.g., METAR) around the world.

Temperature variations are not taken into account because they have only small effects on estimated altitude except at higher altitudes, where minor errors are tolerable. Instead, the U.S. Standard Atmosphere temperature and lapse rate are assumed so that, from (4.51), the assumed relationship between pressure and altitude is given by

$$p = p_{\mathrm{alt}} \left(\frac{T_0 - \Gamma_0 z}{T_0} \right)^{\frac{g}{R_d \Gamma_0}} , \qquad (4.58)$$

where $T_0 = 288.15$ K and $\Gamma_0 = 0.0065$ K/m. Solving (4.58) for z given a measured pressure p and substituting the above numerical

Fig. 4.10: An aircraft altimeter. The knob on the lower left is used to adjust the altimeter setting appearing in the small window between the '2' and the '3' *(Photo: Alan Sim).*

values gives the **barometer equation**

$$z\,[\mathrm{m}] \;=44330.8\left[1-\left(\frac{p}{p_{\mathrm{alt}}}\right)^{0.19026}\right] \quad . \tag{4.59}$$

Because they appear in a ratio, it does not matter what the units of p and p_{alt} are, as long as they are the same. In North America, p_{alt} is traditionally specified in inches of mercury, rounded *down* to a whole hundredth unit. Elsewhere, the altimeter setting may be specified either in inches of mercury or millibars.

Problem 4.13: A private pilot correctly sets her altimeter to reflect a reported altimeter setting of 1012 mb at her departure airport. She then climbs to an indicated cruising altitude of 1000 m above sea level. The highest terrain elevation between her and her destination is 850 m above sea level, which yields a fairly comfortable margin of 150 m. However, she does not realize that she is flying into an approaching low pressure system and that the correct altimeter setting will decrease to 992 mb well before she reaches her destination.

a) If she fails to update her altimeter, what will her actual altitude margin be in the worst case as she crosses the highest terrain? *Answer: −15 m*

b) Explain why you think that standard procedures require altimeter settings to always be rounded *down*.

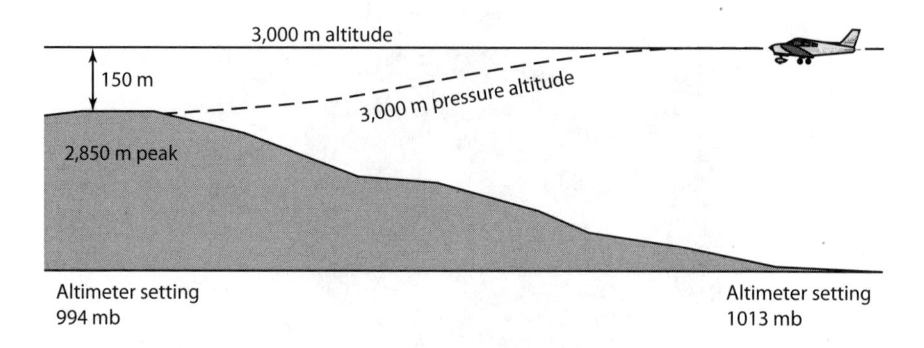

Fig. 4.11: The altimeter setting is used to compensate for variations in atmospheric pressure. If the altimeter setting is not changed en route, then a pilot flying at a constant indicated altitude is actually following a surface of constant pressure. When flying into a region of lower pressure, one might wind up with less than the intended clearance from the terrain below.

Density altitude

Just as there is a unique relationship between *pressure* and altitude in the U.S. Standard Atmosphere, there is also a unique relationship between atmospheric *density* and altitude. Any given density can therefore be expressed as a **density altitude** — i.e., the height above sea level at which that density is found in the Standard Atmosphere. The lower the density, the higher the density altitude.

Air density, and therefore density altitude, is of tremendous importance to airplane and helicopter pilots because it determines how much lift the wings or rotor blades can generate for a given air flow. In particular, the density altitude determines how long of a takeoff roll a particular airplane requires, all other factors being equal. It also determines how quickly the airplane can gain altitude to clear obstacles after takeoff (Fig. 4.12).

For any given pressure, density is inversely proportional to virtual temperature. Therefore, the density altitude at a particular airport will generally be much higher on a hot summer day than it will be on a cool day at the same airport. In marginal cases, such as a high-altitude airport with a relatively short runway, the density altitude may determine whether a particular aircraft can safely take off at all.

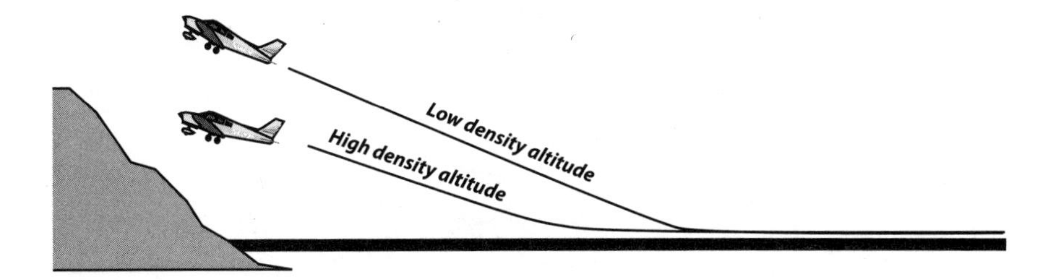

Fig. 4.12: Low density altitude (high air density) allows an airplane to lift the runway sooner and climb more steeply, making it easier to clear obstacles beyond the end of the runway. A pilot who fails to monitor density altitude and who attempts to take off from a high-altitude runway on a hot day may find himself in serious trouble.

Problem 4.14:

a) Using the definition of the U.S. Standard Atmosphere below 11 km altitude, derive a simple formula for the density altitude DA as a function of the local air density ρ.

b) The Big Bear City Airport, in the mountains of Southern California, has an elevation z of 2,057 m above sea level. The pilot of a fully loaded airplane contemplates taking off on a summer day when the air temperature T is 30°C, the humidity is very low, and the station pressure is 785 hPa. Given the length of the runway, he requires a density altitude less than 2,200 m in order to assure a safe takeoff and climbout. Determine whether he should proceed or wait for cooler weather.

4.3.4 Constant pressure maps

Recall that the hypsometric equation allows us to calculate the geometric thickness of an atmospheric layer bounded by any two pressure levels, provided only that we know the mean virtual temperature of the layer. Recall also that a radiosonde carried aloft on a balloon reports temperature and humidity at a series of fairly closely spaced pressure levels. It follows that, given a complete sounding, the hypsometric equation can be used to calculate thicknesses layer by layer and total them up, starting from the surface, to obtain the

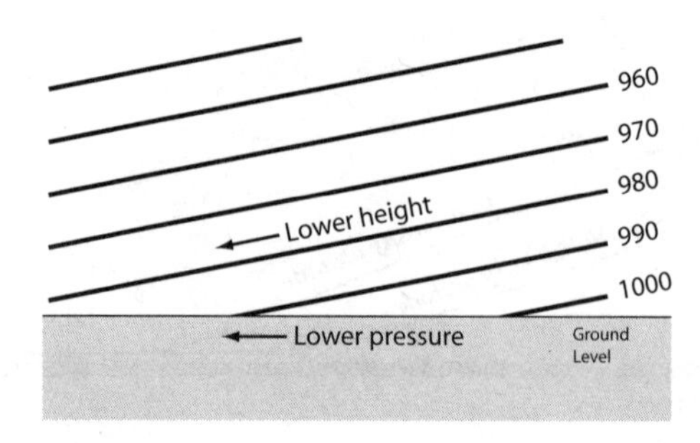

Fig. 4.13: Schematic depiction of the relationship between the height of constant pressure surfaces and the pressure at constant altitude.

geopotential height above sea level of every pressure level in the sounding.

Certain pressure levels are considered **mandatory levels** and must be included in any standard radiosonde report. These include 1000, 925, 850, 700, 500, 400, 300, 250, 200, 150, 100, 70, 50, 30, 20, and 10 hPa. The purpose of the mandatory levels is to ensure that geopotential heights are always available for those particular pressure values (barring premature sonde termination). For any observation time, one may then use all available soundings in a region to construct a **constant pressure map** (also known as **upper air chart**) depicting the pattern of geopotential heights associated with any particular mandatory pressure level.

The patterns of geopotential height are traditionally depicted using contours of constant height, or **isoheights**, completely analogous to altitude contours on a topographic map.

> **Key fact:** Maps of geopotential height at constant pressure have the same meteorological interpretation, as do maps of pressure at constant height (e.g., sea level) as suggested by Fig. 4.13. That is, low height at constant pressure is equivalent to low pressure at constant height, and so on.

As you continue your education in meteorology, you will undoubtedly become familiar with constant pressure maps for 850,

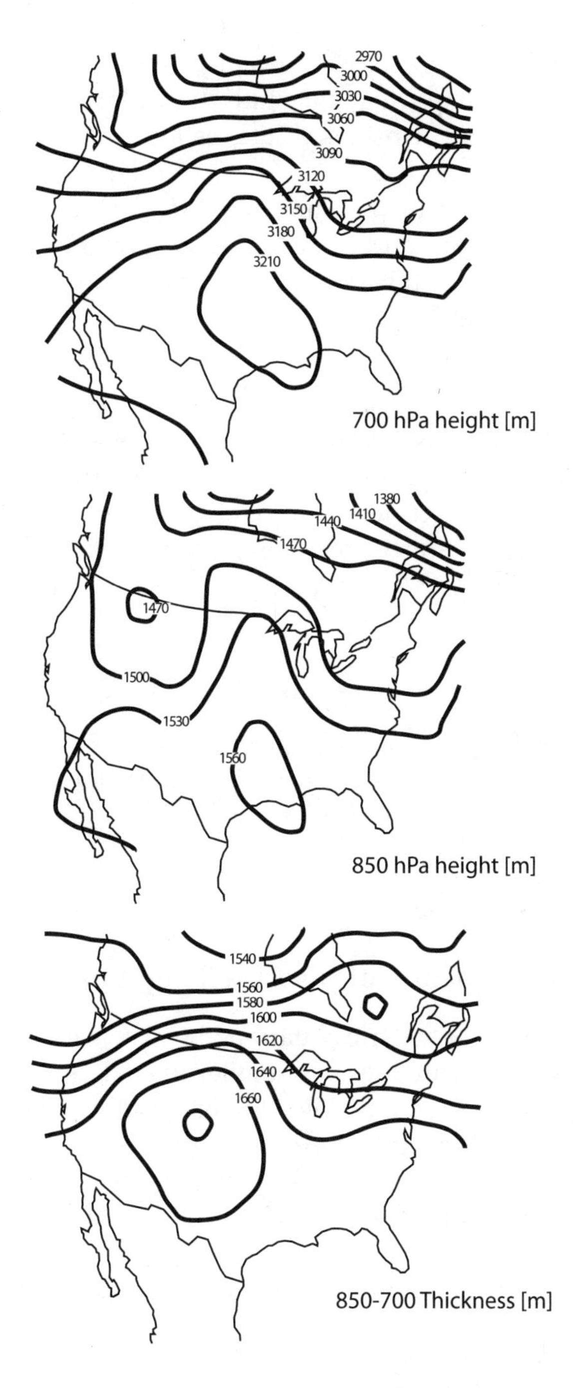

Fig. 4.14: Examples of constant pressure maps at 700 hPa (top) and 850 hPa (middle), as well as the corresponding 850-700 thickness map (bottom).

700, and 500 hPa, and possibly other standard pressures as well. For generations, these maps, together with the surface synoptic analysis, have been among the primary data resources utilized by human forecasters.

Examples of constant pressure maps for 700 and 850 hPa are shown in Fig. 4.14 (top and middle). Also shown is a map of the 850-700 thickness, which is obtained by subtracting the heights at 850 hPa from those at 700 hPa.

Key fact: Because of the hypsometric equation, differences in the *height* patterns at two different pressure levels are directly tied to the horizontal *temperature* structure in the atmosphere between those two levels.

Problem 4.15: Relabel the contours in the 850-700 thickness chart (Fig. 4.14, bottom) with the associated layer mean virtual temperatures expressed in degrees Celsius (nearest 0.1°C).

4.3.5 Vertical structure of pressure/height fields

According to the hypsometric equation, the distance (thickness) between standard pressure levels is smaller in cold air than in warm air. Pressure features such as lows, highs, troughs, and ridges are thus very closely related to the thermal structure of the atmosphere and may change shape and intensity, or even disappear altogether at higher or lower altitudes, depending on the horizontal distribution of temperature.

You can easily verify with simple sketches (see examples) that

- a surface warm-core *cyclone* (low pressure system) quickly weakens with height and may become an upper level *anticyclone* (high pressure system) (Fig. 4.15).

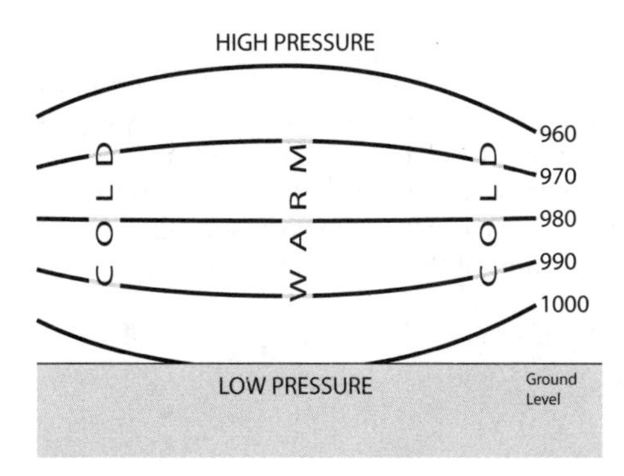

Fig. 4.15: Schematic cross-section of a warm core low.

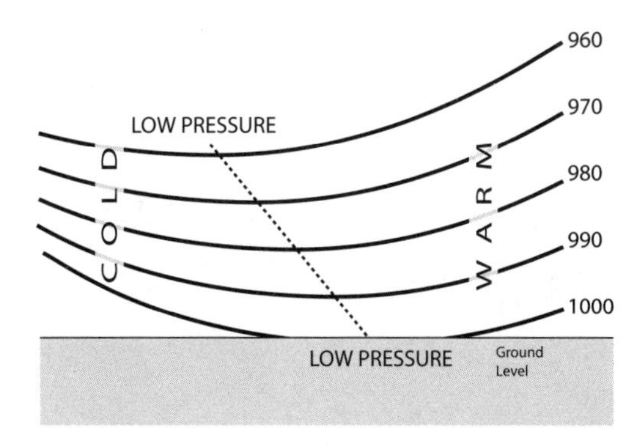

Fig. 4.16: Schematic depiction of the tilt of a pressure trough toward cold air.

- a surface warm-core anticyclone strengthens with height;
- a surface cold-core cyclone increases in intensity with height;
- a surface cold-core anticyclone at the surface quickly weakens with height and may become an upper level cyclone;
- Low pressure centers or troughs are tilted horizontally *toward colder air* with increasing height (Fig. 4.16).

Problem 4.16: On September 21, 2005, Hurricane Rita's central pressure at the ocean surface is believed to have fallen to 895 hPa. The surrounding region, away from the influence of the hurricane, had a mean sea level pressure of around 1010 hPa. The height depression associated with the center of the hurricane vanished relative to the surroundings at a pressure level of about 150 hPa. If the mean virtual temperature of the environment between the surface and the 150 hPa was $-10°C$, what was the corresponding mean virtual temperature in the center of the storm? *Answer: 7.8°C*

CHAPTER 5

The First Law and Its Consequences

Having outlined the basic physical properties of the atmosphere, we will now finally delve into topics truly worthy of the name *atmospheric thermodynamics*.

5.1 Pressure-Volume Work

As you probably remember from high school, mechanical **work** is one of the foundational concepts of physics. Work has dimensions of energy. If a certain amount W of mechanical work is performed *on* a system, that implies the addition of that much energy *to* the system. The law of conservation of energy tells us that the added energy cannot simply disappear; it *must* appear in the form of another form of energy.

Let us first consider how a parcel of air can do work or be the recipient of energy via mechanical work. Recall that mechanical work is defined as force times displacement; specifically, an infinitesimal increment of work is given by

$$\delta W = \vec{f} \cdot d\vec{x} \quad . \tag{5.1}$$

If the direction of the force vector $\vec{f}$ happens to be the same as the direction of the displacement $d\vec{x}$, then

$$\delta W = F\,ds \quad , \tag{5.2}$$

where $F = |\vec{f}|$ and $ds = |d\vec{x}|$. Pressure is just force per unit area, so we infer that *air does mechanical work whenever it expands against an external pressure; it is the recipient of work if it is compressed despite its own internal pressure.*

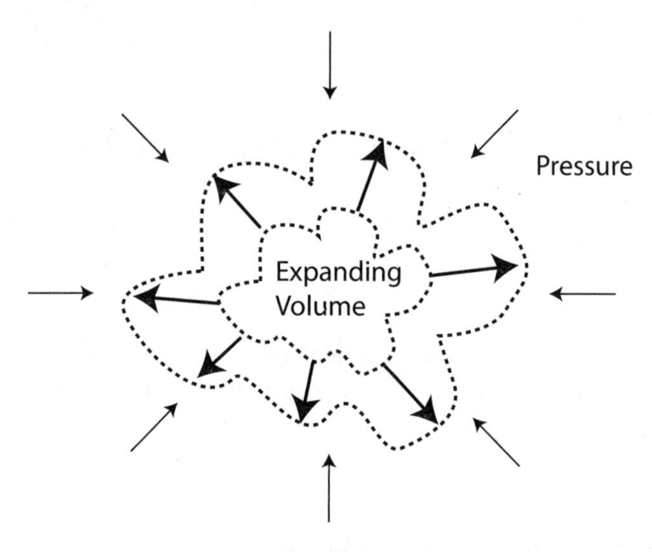

For example, consider a cylindrical piston of cross-sectional area A containing a volume V of air (or any substance, for that matter) with pressure p (Fig. 5.1). The total force F exerted on the face of the piston is equal to the product of A and p. If the piston is displaced outward by a small amount ds, then the air inside the cylinder will have done an increment of work equal to

$$\delta W = F\,ds = pA\,ds \tag{5.3}$$

The product $A\,ds$ in turn represents an incremental change in volume, which we can write as dV, so that

$$\delta W = p\,dV \tag{5.4}$$

Mechanical work associated with changes of volume is known as **pressure-volume work.**

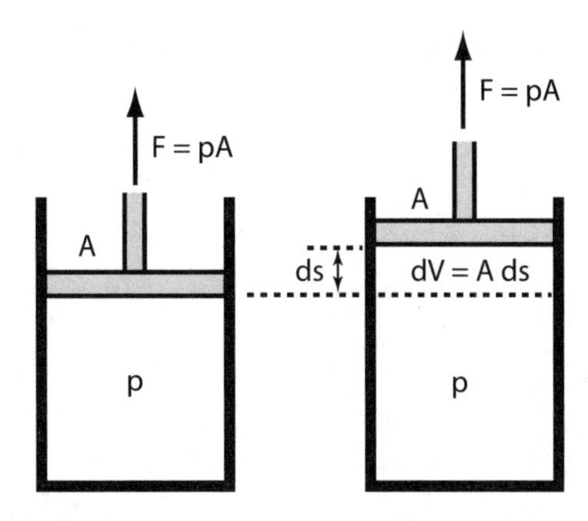

Fig. 5.1: Illustration of pressure-volume work for a movable piston with area A acted on by pressure p. The total force acting on the piston is given by $F = pA$. If the piston moves upward by an infinitesimal increment ds, then the mechanical work done on the piston is $\delta W = F\ ds = pA\ ds = p\ dV$, where dV is the incremental increase in volume.

Although we derived the above expression for a fluid expanding against a cylindrical piston, it is in fact valid irrespective of the geometry of the volume of air considered and regardless of how it expands. It is also valid for any fluid, regardless of whether it is an ideal gas.

The equation as given above is valid only for an *infinitesimal* change of volume dV leading to an *infinitesimal* amount of work δW. This is because if you make a larger change of volume in the cylinder by moving the piston a finite distance, the pressure within the cylinder is very likely to change, so that a simple product of p and the change in volume ΔV can no longer give the amount of work done. In such a case, we need to sum up the products $p\ dV$ over the entire path taken by the piston; in other words, we need to perform the integral

$$W = \int_{V_0}^{V_1} p\, dV \quad . \tag{5.5}$$

Recall that meteorologists prefer to use intensive units—i.e., work or energy *per unit mass*, rather than the total work or energy exchanged between a system and its environment. If M is the total mass of the parcel, then the work per unit mass is

$$w \equiv \frac{W}{M} \quad , \tag{5.6}$$

and we have

$$\delta w = p \, \frac{dV}{M} \quad , \tag{5.7}$$

or

$$\boxed{\delta w = p \, d\alpha \quad ,} \tag{5.8}$$

where α is, as usual, the specific volume. For a finite expansion or compression, we integrate to get

$$\boxed{w = \int \delta w = \int_{\alpha_0}^{\alpha_1} p \, d\alpha \quad .} \tag{5.9}$$

Path dependence

While the above expression for the total pressure-volume work w is universal, it is not self-contained and therefore cannot be evaluated "as is." In order to perform the above integral, we require knowledge of how the pressure changes (if it changes) as we go from volume α_0 to volume α_1. This is where the details of a specific problem come into play. In particular, the pressure in an ideal gas depends not only on α but also on its temperature T, which we have not yet constrained in any way.

In short, the *total work done by (or on) a parcel during a transition from one state to the next depends on how it gets there.* For this reason, work is not a state variable. One cannot look at a system in a particular state (i.e., having known pressure, volume, and temperature) and infer how much total accumulated mechanical work that state represents, just as one cannot guess the current odometer reading of a car based on where it is parked.

Let us consider a graphical representation of (5.9). One may plot the path a system takes from one state to another on a graph whose horizontal axis represents specific volume and whose vertical axis is pressure. Let us further assume that the system starts out in the

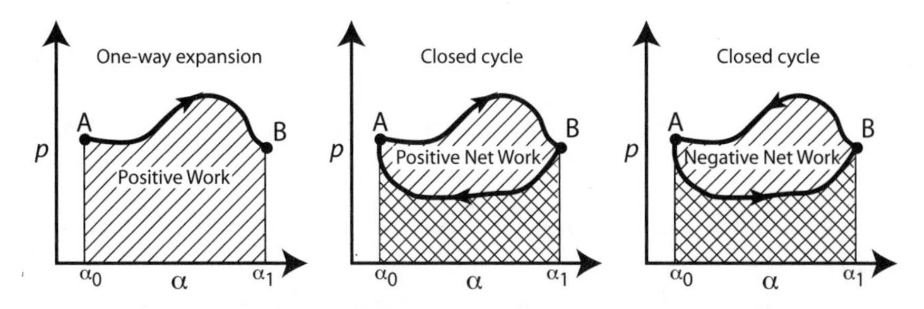

Fig. 5.2: Schematic depiction of pressure-volume work for an expansion/compression process or cycle.

state $A = (\alpha_0, p_0)$ and winds up in the state $B = (\alpha_1, p_1)$. The curve on the leftmost graph in Fig. 5.2 indicates *one* of many possible paths the system could have taken to get from the first state to the second state. The corresponding amount of work w done is given graphically by the area under that solid curve.

Problem 5.1: A sample of dry air has an initial pressure $p_1 =$ 1000 hPa and temperature $T_1 = 300$ K. It undergoes a process that takes it to a new pressure $p_2 = 500$ hPa with unchanged temperature $T_2 = T_1$. Compute the mechanical work per unit mass performed by the sample under the following scenarios:

a) Isochoric pressure reduction to p_2 followed by isobaric expansion to final state.

b) Isobaric expansion to final specific volume α_2 followed by isochoric pressure reduction to final state.

c) Isothermal expansion to final state.

Closed cycles

Now let us suppose that the system returns to its initial state, but this time via a different, lower curve (middle panel). Its final state is now the same as its initial state; that is, it has the same temperature, pressure, and specific volume that it started out with. The combination of the two paths thus represents a **closed cycle**. Mathematically, we represent the work done in a closed cycle as follows:

$$w = \oint p d\alpha \quad , \tag{5.10}$$

where in this case

$$\oint p d\alpha \equiv \int_{\alpha_1}^{\alpha_2} p_1(\alpha) d\alpha + \int_{\alpha_2}^{\alpha_1} p_2(\alpha) d\alpha \quad , \tag{5.11}$$

and $p_1(\alpha)$ and $p_2(\alpha)$ represent the two different paths between A and B.

As depicted here, the pressure-volume work performed during the second path (from B to A) corresponds to a smaller area. In other words, different amounts of work were performed in getting from A to B than from B to A. Moreover, because the limits of integration have been reversed, the work performed going from A to B has the opposite sign of that going from B to A. The **net work** involved in going from A to B and back to A again is the *difference* between the amount of work done in each direction separately and corresponds to the area enclosed by the two curves.

It is clear in this example that the closed cycle represents *net positive work* done by the system in going from A to B and back to A again. If the system had followed the exact same path but in reverse (i.e., counterclockwise), the magnitude of the work done would have stayed the same but it would now represent net negative work—i.e., work done on the system by the environment.

For now, we will leave unanswered the obvious (and important) question of *where the energy comes from* that gets converted to pressure-volume work in the above processes (open or closed); that will be the subject of Section 5.2.

Thermodynamic diagrams

A graph with pressure p and specific volume α as the two independent variables (as in the above example) represents one example of a **thermodynamic diagram**. Loosely defined, a thermodynamic diagram is any diagram for which the total work involved in an arbitrary cyclic process (one for which the starting and ending points are the same) is proportional to the area enclosed by the curve representing that process. For the α-p diagram we just used, the net work done by the system in a closed cycle is positive for a clockwise path, negative for a counterclockwise path.

Problem 5.2: A skew-T diagram is also a thermodynamic diagram. From what you know about its design and about the Ideal Gas Law, state whether a closed clockwise path on this diagram represents positive or negative work done *by* a parcel. Explain your reasoning, e.g., by pointing out how a specified cycle on an α–p diagram would appear on a skew-T diagram.

Problem 5.3: A typical scuba tank has a volume V of 10 liters. When fully charged, it contains compressed air at a pressure of 200 bars, or 2.0×10^7 Pa.

a) What is the uncompressed volume of the air if the ambient pressure is 1000 hPa and the temperature is 293 K for both the compressed and uncompressed air?

b) How much mechanical work in joules is required to fill the tank, if the process is isothermal? Hint: Recall that the pressure p will be a function of V, and consider the starting and ending volumes as your limits of integration. *Answer:* 1.1×10^6 *J*

c) If the compressor is able to deliver 1000 W of average power, how long does it take to fill the tank?

5.2 First Law of Thermodynamics

In the previous section, we saw that for a process in which a quantity of air changes volume at finite pressure, it is either performing pressure-volume work *on* the environment or is having work done on it *by* the environment. We also know by now that work implies a transfer of energy between the system and the environment. But energy must be conserved, so it is fair to ask: Where does the energy come from when a parcel does work, and what becomes of the energy that a parcel receives when work is done on it?

At the most basic level, there are only two possible sources for the energy an air parcel expends when it does mechanical work: either the energy is received from the environment (in a form other than mechanical work) and converted to mechanical work, or else some form of stored energy is expended, or a combination of both.

Likewise, when work is done on a parcel, the resulting energy must either somehow be stored in the parcel or else it must be transferred back into the environment in another form.

In atmospheric thermodynamics, the only energy transfer process we consider in addition to pressure-volume work is the addition or subtraction of heat, as discussed in Section 1.3.2 and elsewhere.

5.2.1 Internal energy

We define the energy stored by the parcel as its **internal energy**. A very simple statement of the Law of Conservation of Energy can then be written as follows:

- pressure-volume work done *by* the system = reduction in internal energy + heat supplied by the environment; or
- pressure-volume work done *on* the system = increase in internal energy + heat transferred to the environment

Mathematically, both statements can be written (in intensive form) as:

$$\delta w = -du + \delta q \quad , \tag{5.12}$$

where δw is, as usual, the increment of work (per unit mass) done *by* the system, du is the change in the internal energy (per unit mass) of the system, and δq represents an increment of heat energy (per unit mass) transferred *from* the environment *to* the system.[1]

Substituting $\delta w = p\, d\alpha$, we can write

$$\delta q = du + p\, d\alpha \quad . \tag{5.13}$$

This equality is called the **First Law of Thermodynamics**, which is really just a special case of the Law of Conservation of Energy.

[1] In atmospheric thermodynamics, we typically use a very narrow definition of "the system"— it is strictly the *gaseous* portion of the volume of the atmosphere being considered. By this definition, cloud droplets, raindrops, etc., within a volume of air are considered to be part of the environment, not the system, so that any energy absorbed or released by liquid water or other non-gaseous constituents is regarded has having been lost to or received from the environment. Likewise, chemical reactions and/or phase changes that involve conversion of energy count as external sources or sinks of energy from the perspective of the parcel of air.

In an ideal gas, which by definition consists of pointlike molecules exerting no attractive or repulsive forces on each other, the only possible reservoir of internal energy is the kinetic energy of those molecules. Thus, it is apparent from (1.5) that internal energy u is proportional to the temperature of the air parcel. This fact was demonstrated by James Prescott Joule[2] in 1848, when he showed that *if an ideal gas expands without doing external work* (for example, by expanding into a chamber which has been evacuated) *and without taking in or giving out heat* (i.e., the chamber is insulated), *then the temperature of the gas does not change.* This statement is known as **Joule's law** and is strictly true only for an ideal gas.

5.2.2 Heat capacity

Suppose a small quantity of heat δq is added to a unit mass of air and, as a consequence, its temperature increases from T to $T + dT$. The ratio $\delta q/dT$ is called the **heat capacity** of the material (also known as **specific heat**). It has SI units of joules per kilogram per Kelvin.

Now, we know from the Ideal Gas Law that a heated parcel of air will (a) increase in pressure (if the volume does not change—i.e., the *isochoric* case,[3]) (b) increase in volume (if the pressure does not change—the *isobaric* case), or (c) some combination of the two (if both volume and pressure are allowed to change). The value of the heat capacity for a particular sample of gas depends on which scenario applies.

The cases of greatest interest to us are the isochoric case (a) and the isobaric case (b). The first is relevant to air confined within a sealed, rigid container. The second is relevant to a free parcel of air in the atmosphere, as its pressure is always determined by the pressure of the surrounding environment.

---

[2]An English physicist, Joule (1818–1889) studied the nature of heat and discovered its relationship to mechanical work

[3]Strictly speaking, *isochoric* refers to a process in which *total* volume is preserved. A process in which *specific* volume is preserved is called *isosteric*, which is also *isopycnic* (constant density). Because we are usually dealing with a fixed mass of air, all three terms are effectively equivalent for the purposes of this text.

The **heat capacity at constant volume** is defined as

$$c_v \equiv \left(\frac{\delta q}{dT}\right)_{\alpha=\text{const}} \quad . \tag{5.14}$$

But if the α is constant, then $d\alpha = 0$, and (5.13) implies that $\delta q = du$. Therefore,

$$c_v = \left(\frac{du}{dT}\right)_{\alpha=\text{const}} \quad . \tag{5.15}$$

For an ideal gas Joule's law applies, so u depends upon temperature alone. We may therefore drop the requirement for constant volume, so that

$$c_v = \frac{du}{dT} \quad , \tag{5.16}$$

or

$$\boxed{du = c_v \, dT \quad .} \tag{5.17}$$

The techniques of statistical mechanics, which we won't try to summarize here, allow the heat capacity at constant volume for an ideal gas to be derived theoretically. For a monoatomic gas, it turns out that $c_v = (3/2)R$. For a diatomic gas, $c_v = (5/2)R$. Thus, for dry air, which consists almost entirely of diatomic constituents, $c_v = 718\ \text{J kg}^{-1}\ \text{K}^{-1}$.

With the help of (5.17), the First Law of Thermodynamics for an ideal gas can be written in the following extremely useful form:

$$\boxed{\delta q = c_v \, dT + p \, d\alpha \quad .} \tag{5.18}$$

The **heat capacity at constant pressure** is defined as

$$c_p \equiv \left(\frac{\delta q}{dT}\right)_{p=\text{const}} \quad . \tag{5.19}$$

In this instance, the gas is allowed to expand freely as the heat is added and its temperature rises while keeping its pressure constant. This is essentially what happens whenever an unconfined parcel of air in the free atmosphere is heated or cooled while remaining at the same pressure level.

A certain amount of the total heat added must be expended to account for the pressure-volume work as the gas expands against the constant pressure of the environment, while the remainder increases the gas's internal energy as in the constant volume case. We therefore anticipate that $c_p > c_v$.

The product rule for differentiation tells us that

$$d(p\alpha) = p\,d\alpha + \alpha\,dp \quad . \tag{5.20}$$

The Ideal Gas Law (3.15) allows us to substitute RT for $p\alpha$, so

$$d(RT) = p\,d\alpha + \alpha\,dp \quad . \tag{5.21}$$

R is constant, so we can write

$$R\,dT = p\,d\alpha + \alpha\,dp \quad , \tag{5.22}$$

or

$$p\,d\alpha = R\,dT - \alpha\,dp \quad , \tag{5.23}$$

Substituting the above into (5.18) yields

$$\delta q = (c_v + R)dT - \alpha\,dp \quad . \tag{5.24}$$

At constant pressure, $dp = 0$, so we have

$$\boxed{c_p = c_v + R \quad .} \tag{5.25}$$

For dry air, c_p equals 718 + 287 = 1005 J $K^{-1}kg^{-1}$.

The above two equations give us an extremely useful alternate form of the First Law of Thermodynamics valid for an ideal gas:

$$\boxed{\delta q = c_p\,dT - \alpha\,dp} \tag{5.26}$$

Key fact: The two special forms of the First Law given by (5.18) and (5.26) are applicable to ideal gases. They will be used over and over again in this book.

5.3 Special Cases of the First Law

Let us repeat for reference the two general forms of the First Law of Thermodynamics that we will be using most frequently:

$$\begin{aligned} \delta q &= c_v\, dT + p\, d\alpha \\ \delta q &= c_p\, dT - \alpha\, dp \end{aligned} \tag{5.27}$$

Starting with the above equations, we may now find simplifications relevant to each of our favorite special cases:

- An **isobaric process** is one in which the pressure does not change ($dp = 0$); therefore

$$\delta q = c_p\, dT = \left(\frac{c_p}{c_v}\right) c_v\, dT = \left(\frac{c_p}{c_v}\right) du \tag{5.28}$$

- An **isothermal process** is one in which the temperature does not change ($dT = 0$), so

$$\delta q = -\alpha\, dp = p\, d\alpha = \delta w \tag{5.29}$$

- An **isochoric process** is one in which the volume does not change ($d\alpha = 0$), so

$$\delta q = c_v\, dT = du \tag{5.30}$$

- An **adiabatic process** is one in which there is negligible exchange of heat between the system and its environment; that is, $\delta q = 0$:

$$c_v\, dT = -p\, d\alpha \tag{5.31}$$

$$c_p\, dT = \alpha\, dp \tag{5.32}$$

Key fact: The adiabatic process is of special significance in meteorology because many of the changes that affect a moving volume of air in the atmosphere can be approximated as adiabatic.

Problem 5.4: For each of the following conditions, compute (i) the mechanical work w done *by* a sample of dry air, and (ii) the heat q added *to* the sample.

a) Isothermal compression to one-fifth of its original volume at 15°C.
Answer: (i) -1.3×10^5 J kg^{-1} (ii) -1.3×10^5 J kg^{-1}

b) Isobaric heating from 0°C to 20°C.
Answer: (i) 5.7×10^3 J kg^{-1} (ii) 2.0×10^4 J kg^{-1}

c) Isochoric heating from 0°C to 20°C.
Answer: (i) 0 J kg^{-1} (ii) 1.4×10^4 J kg^{-1}

d) Adiabiatic expansion to five times its original volume, with initial temperature of 20°C.
Answer: (i) 1.0×10^5 J kg^{-1} (ii) 0 J kg^{-1}

Problem 5.5: A kitchen oven has an interior volume V of 0.12 m^3. The air in the oven is preheated from an initial temperature T_0 of 20°C to a baking temperature T_1 of 175°C. The initial pressure p_0 inside the oven equals the outside pressure of 1000 hPa.

a) If the oven is sealed (i.e., the process is isochoric), how much heat is added to the air in the oven? *Answer:* 1.6×10^4 *J*

b) If the oven is not sealed (the normal case), air will gradually leak out as the air expands from heating, so that the process is isobaric. Assume that the air leakage is one-way (no outside air enters the oven). How much total heat is added to the air? (Hint: You are heating not only the air that remains in the oven at the end of the heating process but also some of the air that escapes. You will have to set up and integrate a differential equation. Assume that the air temperature inside the oven is always uniform at any point in the

process and equals the temperature of any air that is leaking out.)
Answer: 1.8×10^4 J

5.4 Dry Adiabatic Processes

The assumption that many atmospheric processes are approximately adiabatic is an extremely important and useful one. When there is truly no diabatic heating or cooling of a parcel of air, we call the process **dry adiabatic.**

A related but distinct special case is a process that is not strictly adiabatic, but for which the *only* source for $\delta q \neq 0$ is the evaporation or condensation of moisture carried within the parcel. Such a process is called **moist adiabatic.** We will wait until Chapter 7 to discuss this case.

5.4.1 Poisson's equation

From the First Law for an adiabatic process and the Ideal Gas Law, we can write

$$c_p\, dT = \alpha\, dp = \frac{RT}{p} dp \tag{5.33}$$

By dividing through by c_p and T, we get

$$\frac{1}{T} dT = \frac{R}{c_p} \frac{1}{p} dp \tag{5.34}$$

Integrating from some initial temperature T_0 and pressure p_0 to an arbitrary temperature and pressure T and p

$$\int_{T_0}^{T} \frac{1}{T} dT = \frac{R}{c_p} \int_{p_0}^{p} \frac{1}{p} dp \tag{5.35}$$

we get **Poisson's equation,**

$$\boxed{\frac{T}{T_0} = \left(\frac{p}{p_0}\right)^{\kappa},} \tag{5.36}$$

where for dry air

$$\kappa \equiv R_d/c_p \approx 0.286 \quad . \tag{5.37}$$

Key fact: If you know the initial temperature and pressure of a parcel of air, and then you change its pressure adiabatically to some new known value, then Poisson's equation tells you what the new temperature will be.

5.4.2 Potential temperature

Poisson's equation may be used to define a new thermodynamics state variable, the **potential temperature** θ. The potential temperature is defined simply by setting T_0 equal to θ and p_0 equal to 1000 hPa:

$$\frac{T}{\theta} = \left(\frac{p}{1000\ \text{hPa}}\right)^{\kappa} \tag{5.38}$$

or

$$\boxed{\theta = T\left(\frac{1000\ \text{hPa}}{p}\right)^{\kappa}} \tag{5.39}$$

The potential temperature may be interpreted in a couple of ways: (1) if a parcel of air has a known potential temperature θ, then the above equation gives its pressure as function of temperature, or vice versa; (2) the potential temperature is equal to the final temperature of a parcel with known pressure and temperature p and T if it is compressed or expanded adiabatically to a final pressure of 1000 hPa.

In any dry adiabatic process, θ is constant—that is, no matter how you alter the pressure p, the temperature T will change in such a way that θ stays the same.

Key fact: Potential temperature θ is conserved in any dry adiabatic process.

Because θ is approximately conserved in the atmosphere when diabatic heating terms are small, it is sometimes used as a tracer of air masses. For example, if you plot contours of θ on two successive vertical cross sections of the atmosphere (oriented in the direction of motion of the air), the position of a contour having a certain value of θ will follow the parcels of air to which it was originally attached. If the contours of θ are found not to move much over, say, a 24 hour period, yet it is known that there is significant air flow, then one can often conclude that the motion of the air is parallel to (or along) the θ contours.

Problem 5.6: A transcontinental airliner cruises at an altitude of approximately 12 km, where the temperature may be $-55°$C and the pressure is approximately 200 hPa. (a) Compute the potential temperature of the air at this altitude. (b) Cabin pressure is typically maintained at about 750 hPa, corresponding to a pressure altitude of about 2,400 m. When the outside air is compressed adiabatically to the cabin pressure, compute the air temperature (in Celsius and Fahrenheit) that would result if no corrective action were taken.

5.4.3 Dry adiabats

Each point on a skew-T or similar thermodynamic diagram represents a particular combination of pressure p and temperature T. It is therefore also associated with a specific potential temperature θ according to (5.39). By setting θ to a constant value and then plotting the resulting function $T(p)$ on the diagram, we obtain a curve called a **dry adiabat**. By definition, the value of θ corresponding to any given dry adiabat is equal to the temperature at the point where the adiabat crosses the 1000 hPa level.

On the skew-T diagram, dry adiabats are slightly curved lines that slope from the lower right to the upper left of the chart (Fig. 5.3). If a parcel rises or sinks dry adiabatically, its potential temperature is conserved and it must remain on the same dry adiabat, as indicated by the arrow. Dry adiabats therefore provide a way to graphically determine the adiabatic change of temperature a parcel experiences as it moves vertically through the atmosphere.

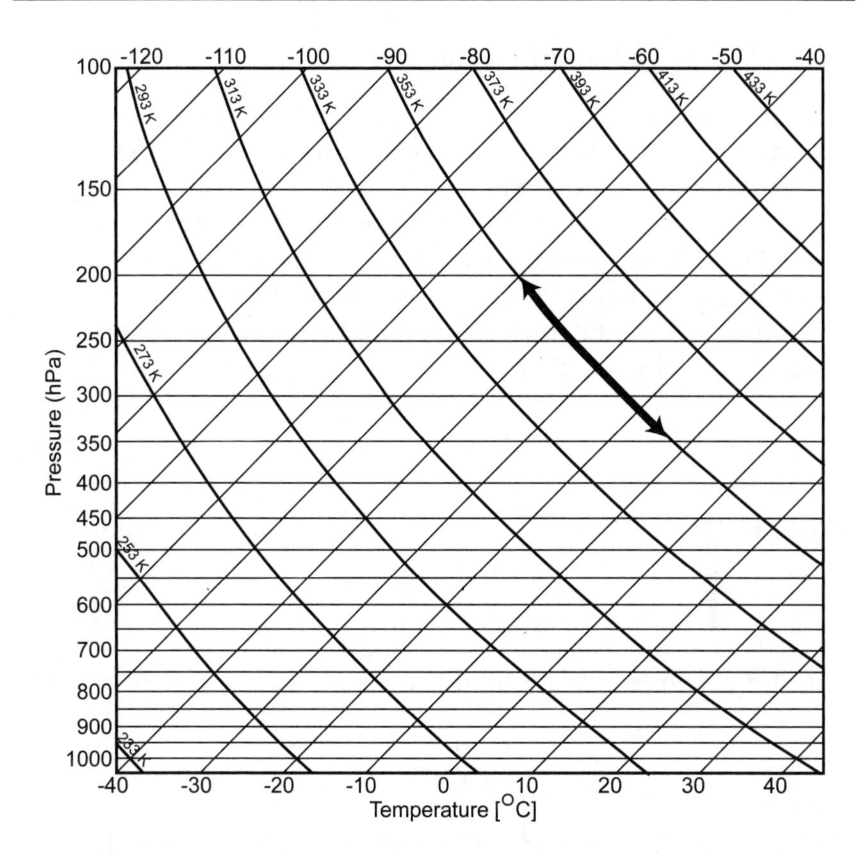

Fig. 5.3: Dry adiabats appear on a skew-T diagram as curves sloping toward the upper left. Labels give the associated potential temperature θ. The arrow illustrates how the temperature of a parcel that is changing pressure adiabatically is confined to a particular dry adiabat.

Problem 5.7: For a potential temperature of $\theta = 310$ K, compute the corresponding temperature T at 700 hPa, 300 hPa, and 100 hPa. Plot your results at the appropriate locations on a skew-T diagram and sketch in the corresponding dry adiabat. *Answer:* $T(100) = 160.6$ K

5.4.4 The dry adiabatic lapse rate

Poisson's equation gave us the means to determine how temperature changes with *pressure* for an adiabatic process. Now let us look at how the temperature of a moving parcel of air changes with *height* in the atmosphere. The answer to this question inevitably entails an approximation, as the relationship between Δp and Δz is not unique but varies somewhat with environmental conditions.

From the adiabatic form of the First Law (5.32) combined with the Ideal Gas Law, we have

$$c_p \, dT = \frac{R_d T}{p} dp \quad , \tag{5.40}$$

which can be rewritten

$$\frac{dT}{dp} = \frac{R_d T}{c_p p} \quad . \tag{5.41}$$

Thus, for a rising parcel of dry air

$$\frac{dT}{dz} = \frac{dT}{dp}\frac{dp}{dz} = \frac{R_d T}{c_p p}\frac{dp}{dz} \quad . \tag{5.42}$$

The pressure p in an unconfined parcel of air is the same as the pressure p' of the surrounding environment at the same level, so we use the hydrostatic equation to find the change of pressure with height:

$$\frac{dp}{dz} = \frac{\partial p'}{\partial z} = -\rho' g \quad , \tag{5.43}$$

where

$$\rho' = \frac{p'}{R_d T'} \tag{5.44}$$

is the density of the ambient air and T' is the ambient temperature.

Combining the above equations yields

$$\frac{dT}{dz} = \frac{R_d}{c_p}\frac{T}{p}\frac{p}{R_d T'} g = -\frac{g}{c_p}\frac{T}{T'} \quad . \tag{5.45}$$

Under most conditions, the temperature T of the parcel is different from ambient temperature T' by no more than a degree or two.

Therefore, $T/T' \simeq 1$, with the approximation almost always being accurate to better than 1%. The above result thus simplifies to

$$\frac{dT}{dz} = -\frac{g}{c_p} \equiv -\Gamma_d \quad , \tag{5.46}$$

where $\Gamma_d = g/c_p$ is the **dry adiabatic lapse rate**. With $c_p = 1005\ \mathrm{J/(kg\ K)}$ and $g = 9.81\ \mathrm{m/s^2}$, we have

$$\boxed{\Gamma_d \equiv \frac{g}{c_p} = 9.76 \times 10^{-3}\ \mathrm{K/m} \approx 9.8\ \mathrm{K/km} \quad .} \tag{5.47}$$

In summary, Γ_d gives the rate at which temperature decreases with height for a dry parcel that rises adiabatically. Strictly speaking, the value of Γ_d changes slightly if the air contains some water vapor or if the temperature of the parcel is much different from that of the environment, but these effects are usually small enough to be ignored.

The following schematic illustrates the effect of adiabatic ascent on a parcel's temperature.

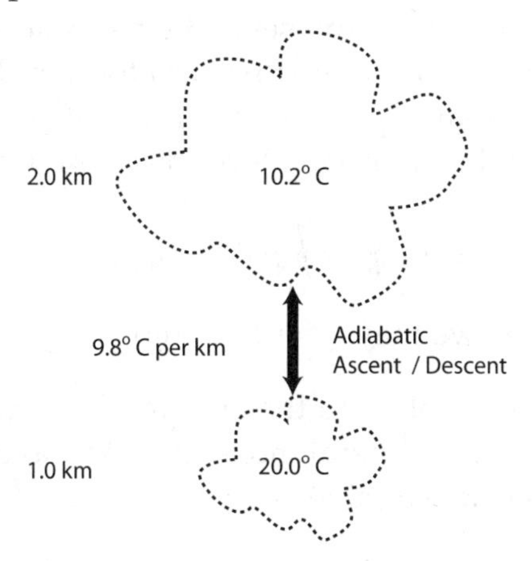

Let me reiterate that the dry adiabatic lapse rate is an *approximation* because it *assumes* a particular relationship between changes in pressure and changes in altitude. If you have information about the actual change of pressure between two atmospheric levels, Poisson's equation (5.36) gives a more direct and reliable path to the new temperature.

5.5 Heat Engines

In Section 5.1, we saw that it is possible to construct a closed cycle of compression and expansion that produces net pressure-volume work. Then, in Section 5.2, we found that the production of work by our system (e.g., air parcel), requires the expenditure of internal energy and/or heat supplied by the environment. We are now in the position to evaluate the detailed energy balance of such a cycle.

5.5.1 First Law applied to a cyclic process

Consider an arbitrary cyclic process involving an ideal gas. By definition, the final state is equal to the initial state, and the process may be depicted as a closed path on an α-p diagram (or other thermodynamic diagram, such as a skew-T).

We may evaluate the *net* outcome of the cycle by integrating the First Law of Thermodynamics (5.18) over the closed path:

$$\oint \delta q = \oint c_v \, dT + \oint p \, d\alpha \quad . \tag{5.48}$$

The first term on the right represents the net change in internal energy u, which by definition must be zero for a cyclic process. And already we know that $\oint p \; d\alpha$ is *non*-zero—it is equal to the net pressure-volume work w done along the closed path. So we are left with

$$q_{\text{net}} = \oint \delta q = \oint p \, d\alpha = w_{\text{net}} \neq 0 \quad . \tag{5.49}$$

From the above, we may infer two things:

1. The net heat supplied to the system by the environment in a closed cycle is, in general, non-zero. We have thus confirmed that q is not state variable.

2. The net heat supplied by the environment is converted to an equal amount of mechanical work.

Note further that because the above process returns the system to exactly its original state (no net change in any state variable), there is no reason why we can't repeat the cycle as many times as we want, each time converting a certain amount of heat supplied by the environment into mechanical work performed by the system. Such a cyclic process is called a **heat engine.**

A heat engine always entails the transfer of heat into a system at a comparatively warm temperature and then out of the system again at colder temperatures. In other words, the heat passes through the system in the direction it naturally "wants" to go—from warm to cold. In the course of this process, less heat leaves the system than is put in. The difference is converted to mechanical work.[4]

An automobile engine is one example of a heat engine. The atmosphere is also a heat engine—circulations are driven by heat added by the sun in the warm tropical belt and leaving again by way of infrared radiation from cooler parts of the atmosphere at high altitudes and more polar latitudes.

The **efficiency** of a heat engine is defined by the ratio of the work produced to the heat supplied:

$$\eta = \frac{w}{q_{in}} = \frac{q_{in} - q_{out}}{q_{in}} \quad , \tag{5.50}$$

where w is the mechanical work produced by one complete cycle, q_{in} is the heat supplied to the system, and q_{out} is the "waste" heat returned to the environment. In a non-ideal (i.e., real-world) engine, q_{out} includes energy losses due to internal friction, mechanical vibration, and/or sound.

5.5.2 The Carnot cycle

Definition

When it comes to the analysis of heat engines, the textbook prototype is the **Carnot cycle,**[5] an example of which is depicted on an α–p diagram in Fig. 5.4. The Carnot cycle consists of the following steps:

---

[4]A heat engine may also operate in reverse: by putting mechanical work *into* the system, heat may be drawn in at a relatively cold temperature and discharged again at a warmer temperature. This is the physical basis for refrigerators and air conditioners.

[5]Named after the scientist Nicolas Léonard Sadi Carnot (pronounced "Kar-*noh*"), who studied it in connection with the efficiency of steam engines in the 1820s.

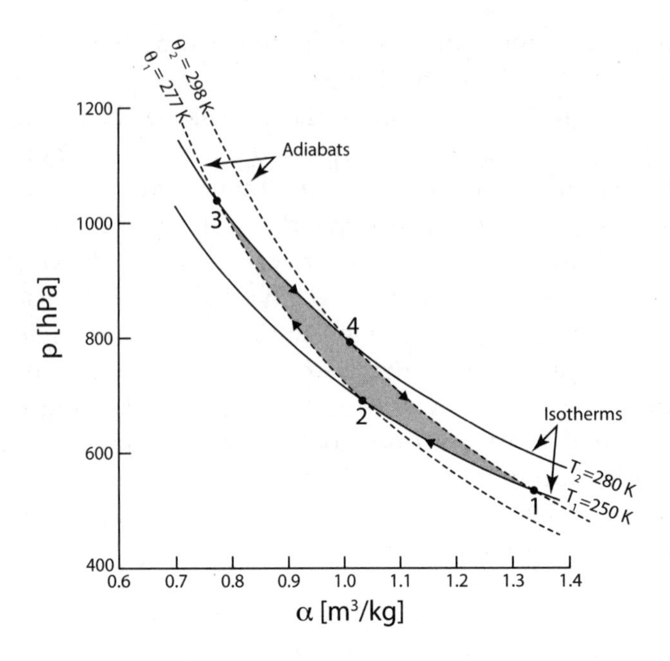

Fig. 5.4: Example of a Carnot cycle depicted on an α–p diagram. The shaded area enclosed by the cycle is proportional to the net mechanical work produced. The points marked 1–4 indicate the starting points for each of the four steps in the sequence described in the text.

1. Isothermal compression at a cooler temperature T_1,
2. Adiabatic compression to a warmer temperature T_2,
3. Isothermal expansion at T_2,
4. Adiabatic expansion back to temperature T_1.

At the end of the cycle, the gas is restored to its initial specific volume and pressure. The cycle can, of course, be started at any point in the sequence, and it may be repeated indefinitely.

A key characteristic of any heat engine is clearly evident here: during the isothermal legs of the cycle, heat is *extracted from the system at the cooler temperature* (otherwise the gas would warm during compression) and *transferred back into the system at the warmer temperature* (otherwise the gas would cool during expansion). Because heat can only spontaneously flow from hot to cold, this property requires that there be a high-temperature external reservoir supplying the heat during the warm phase of the cycle and a low temperature "sink" drawing off the heat during the cold phase. In the same way that a hydroelectric generator extracts mechanical energy from the tendency of water to flow downhill, a heat engine extracts mechanical energy from the tendency of heat to flow from a warm reservoir to a cold one.

The complete details of any particular Carnot cycle can be defined by specifying the temperatures T_1 and T_2 of the two isothermal steps and the potential temperatures θ_1 and θ_2 of the two adiabatic steps, where we take $\theta_2 > \theta_1$ in the analysis that follows.

Instead of the potential temperatures, we could specify the minimum pressure p_1 and maximum pressure p_3 encountered during the cycle (corresponding to points 1 and 3 in Fig. 5.4) because that is equivalent information when taken together with T_1 and T_2. The potential temperatures θ_1 and θ_2 are then

$$\theta_1 = T_2 \left(\frac{1000\ \text{hPa}}{p_3} \right)^{R/c_p} , \tag{5.51}$$

$$\theta_2 = T_1 \left(\frac{1000\ \text{hPa}}{p_1} \right)^{R/c_p} . \tag{5.52}$$

The pressures p_2 and p_4 at the start of the adiabatic steps need not be specified but follow from Poisson's equation in combination with the other information given.

Let us now evaluate the contributions of each leg in the cycle to (a) the mechanical work done and (b) the heat supplied by the environment.

Isothermal compression

For the isothermal legs of the process, we use (5.29):

$$\delta q = p\ d\alpha = \delta w \quad , \tag{5.53}$$

which shows that the work w_1 done is equal to the heat supplied q_1, and that both may be obtained as

$$q_1 = w_1 = \int_{\alpha_1}^{\alpha_2} p(\alpha)\ d\alpha \quad . \tag{5.54}$$

To evaluate this integral, we need suitable expressions for $p(\alpha)$ and for α_1 and α_2. Because the process is isothermal at temperature T_1, the first is given by the Ideal Gas Law

$$p(\alpha) = \frac{RT_1}{\alpha} \quad , \tag{5.55}$$

and the starting and ending specific volumes are

$$\alpha_1 = \frac{RT_1}{p_1} \quad , \tag{5.56}$$

$$\alpha_2 = \frac{RT_1}{p_2} \quad . \tag{5.57}$$

In order to evaluate α_2, we need to find the pressure p_2 at the end of the leg, which occurs when the potential temperature reaches θ_1:

$$\theta_1 = T_2 \left(\frac{1000 \text{ hPa}}{p_3} \right)^{R/c_p} = T_1 \left(\frac{1000 \text{ hPa}}{p_2} \right)^{R/c_p} \quad . \tag{5.58}$$

Solving for p_2, we have

$$p_2 = p_3 \left(\frac{T_1}{T_2} \right)^{c_p/R} \quad , \tag{5.59}$$

and

$$\alpha_2 = \frac{RT_1}{p_3} \left(\frac{T_2}{T_1} \right)^{c_p/R} \quad . \tag{5.60}$$

We now have what we need to evaluate (5.54):

$$\begin{aligned} q_1 = w_1 &= RT_1 \int_{\alpha_1}^{\alpha_2} \frac{1}{\alpha} \, d\alpha \\ &= RT_1 \log \left(\frac{\alpha_2}{\alpha_1} \right) \end{aligned} \quad . \tag{5.61}$$

Substituting (5.56) and (5.60),

$$q_1 = w_1 = -RT_1 \log \left[\frac{p_3}{p_1} \left(\frac{T_1}{T_2} \right)^{c_p/R} \right] \quad , \tag{5.62}$$

where we have deliberately arranged the argument of the logarithm to bring a minus sign out front, indicating that w_1 is a negative work term (work is performed *on* the parcel during compression).

Equation (5.62) gives the work and heat exchange in terms of the minimum and maximum temperatures and minimum and maximum pressures of the cycle. But you can easily verify with the help of (5.51) and (5.52) that (5.62) can be written much more simply as

$$q_1 = w_1 = -c_p T_1 \log\left(\frac{\theta_2}{\theta_1}\right) \quad . \tag{5.63}$$

Adiabatic compression

For the adiabatic compression step, the following information is known: the initial temperature is T_1, the initial pressure is p_2, and the final temperature is T_2.

We already know that the heat supplied, q_2, is zero by definition for an adiabatic process. The mechanical work contribution w_2 is obtained from the First Law (5.31):

$$\delta w \equiv p \, d\alpha = -c_v \, dT \quad . \tag{5.64}$$

We therefore have

$$q_2 = 0 \quad , \tag{5.65}$$

$$w_2 = -c_v(T_2 - T_1) \quad . \tag{5.66}$$

Because we used Poisson's equation to find the starting pressure p_2 for this leg, we already ensured that the final pressure will be p_3 once the temperature T_2 is reached. This pressure is therefore the starting point for the next leg.

Isothermal expansion

By analogy to the isothermal compression leg, we have

$$p(\alpha) = \frac{RT_2}{\alpha} \quad , \tag{5.67}$$

and the starting and ending specific volumes are

$$\alpha_3 = \frac{RT_2}{p_3} \quad , \tag{5.68}$$

$$\alpha_4 = \frac{RT_2}{p_4} = \frac{RT_2}{p_1}\left(\frac{T_1}{T_2}\right)^{c_p/R} \quad . \tag{5.69}$$

We then have

$$q_3 = w_3 = RT_2 \log\left[\frac{p_3}{p_1}\left(\frac{T_1}{T_2}\right)^{c_p/R}\right] \quad . \tag{5.70}$$

As before, we can write the above more simply in terms of potential temperature as follows:

$$q_3 = w_3 = c_p T_2 \log\left(\frac{\theta_2}{\theta_1}\right) \quad . \tag{5.71}$$

Adiabatic expansion

For the second adiabatic leg, we use the same reasoning as before to get

$$q_4 = 0 \quad , \tag{5.72}$$

$$w_4 = c_v(T_2 - T_1) \quad . \tag{5.73}$$

Total energy

We can now put the results from the four steps together to obtain the total mechanical work produced by the Carnot cycle, which we know must equal the total heat supplied by the environment:

$$\begin{aligned} q = w = \oint \delta w &= w_1 + w_2 + w_3 + w_4 \\ = \oint \delta q &= q_1 + q_2 + q_3 + q_4 \quad . \end{aligned} \tag{5.74}$$

We see that $q_2 = q_4 = 0$ and $w_2 = -w_4$, so we conclude that the adiabatic legs contribute neither net heat or nor net work to the cycle. We are left with

$$w = q = w_1 + w_3 \quad , \tag{5.75}$$

or

$$w = q = R(T_2 - T_1) \log\left[\frac{p_3}{p_1}\left(\frac{T_1}{T_2}\right)^{c_p/R}\right] \quad , \tag{5.76}$$

or, equivalently,

$$w = q = c_p(T_2 - T_1) \log\left(\frac{\theta_2}{\theta_1}\right) \quad . \tag{5.77}$$

Efficiency

Last but not least, we can evaluate the efficiency of the Carnot cycle according to the definition (5.50) and noting that $q_{in} = q_3$:

$$\eta = \frac{w}{q_3} = \frac{T_2 - T_1}{T_2} \quad . \tag{5.78}$$

For the Carnot cycle to produce net positive work, T_2 must be greater than T_1; therefore, for any T_1 greater than absolute zero,

$$\eta < 1 \quad . \tag{5.79}$$

It can be shown theoretically that (5.78) gives the maximum possible efficiency for *any* ideal heat engine operating between the two temperature limits T_1 and T_2. While the Carnot cycle is just one of several possible cycles that achieve this maximum efficiency in the ideal case, there are other possible cycles that do not. Also, as we shall see in the following section, maximum efficiency is only achieved for a heat engine that is *reversible*.

Problem 5.8: A dry air parcel undergoes a complete Carnot cycle consisting of the steps indicated in (a)–(d). For each individual step, calculate the mechanical work w (per unit mass) done by the air parcel and the heat q added to the parcel.

a) Adiabatic compression from $p_1 = 600$ hPa and $T_1 = 0$°C to a temperature T_2 of 25°C;
Answer: $w = -1.8 \times 10^4$ J kg^{-1}

b) isothermal expansion to a pressure p_3 of 700 hPa;
Answer: $q = 1.3 \times 10^4$ J kg^{-1}

c) adiabatic expansion to a temperature T_4 of 0°C;

d) isothermal compression back to the original pressure p_1.

Also, compute

e) the total work done and heat added for the complete cycle, and

f) the efficiency of the cycle.

Hint: You will need to keep track of the state of the parcel at the end of one step to use as the starting point for the next step.

5.6 Reversible and Irreversible Processes

For maximum efficiency to be realized by any heat engine, all steps associated with the closed cycle (e.g., the Carnot cycle described above) must occur as idealized **reversible** processes, meaning that the system is always in a state that is extremely close to equilibrium. This in turn implies that the processes must be undertaken extremely gradually relative to the speed with which the system re-equilibrates in response to those changes.

Consider, for example, the adiabatic expansion of a parcel of air that rises very slowly through the atmosphere without mixing (this is, of course, impossible in the real world unless the parcel is loosely enclosed in a thin plastic bag). The change of pressure is very gradual, and at all times the pressure of parcel is effectively the same as that of the ambient environment. The parcel expends pressure-volume work on the environment and thereby gives up internal energy. But this exchange is reversible: if the parcel's ascent is reversed and it returns to its original level, closing the cycle, the final states of *both the parcel and the environment* may be effectively indistinguishable from their initial states. No energy is "wasted" by effecting a permanent change on the environment, and all internal energy expended by the parcel during its ascent can be recovered by the parcel during its subsequent descent. The net work in this particular cycle, and the net input of heat, is zero.

Now consider the expansion of the air in a party balloon that bursts. The initial pressure inside the balloon is significantly greater than that of the environment, so when the air almost instantaneously escapes its confinement, it is far from being at equilibrium with the environment. This is therefore an example of an **irreversible** process. The sudden expansion results in a sound wave that carries energy some distance from the balloon, where it ultimately dissipates by being converted to heat. The rush of air escaping the balloon also generates turbulent motions that again ultimately dissipate through viscosity (friction) and lead to a warming of the environment. Finally, the balloon itself is irreversibly altered—part of the internal energy of the air inside the balloon is expended on the destruction of the balloon; there is no way to reverse this process in such a way that the balloon is reassembled and the energy restored to air trapped inside it.

Key fact: A fundamental characteristic of an irreversible process is that the *environment* is permanently altered in some way, even if the *system* returns to exactly its initial state.

The above is an informal statement of the **Second Law of Thermodynamics**, which we will revisit in the next chapter. One important implication of the Second Law is that any heat engine based on real-world (irreversible) processes will always be less efficient than the ideal Carnot cycle because some of the supplied energy is wasted on irreversible alterations (e.g., heating and/or mixing) of the environment itself.

Nevertheless, the concept of a reversible process is extremely useful because it establishes an *upper bound* on the realizable efficiency of any real-world process. In addition, many atmospheric processes are indeed *well approximated* as reversible.

5.7 Enthalpy

5.7.1 Definition

Another state variable that is used extensively in atmospheric thermodynamics is **enthalpy**. For dry air, its definition (in intensive units — i.e., **specific enthalpy**) is

$$\boxed{h \equiv u + p\alpha \quad ,} \tag{5.80}$$

where u is the internal energy of a system, and p and α have the usual meanings. The second term may be thought of as the work required to "make room" for the parcel by displacing the surrounding atmosphere. If you were to somehow annihilate the parcel and completely remove it from the atmosphere, you could theoretically extract both the internal energy u and also the mechanical work

$w = p\alpha$ done by the surrounding atmosphere as it collapses to fill the space previously occupied by the parcel.

Differentiating the above equation term by term

$$dh = du + d(p\alpha) = du + \alpha\, dp + p\, d\alpha \quad . \tag{5.81}$$

We may substitute the First Law of Thermodynamics written as

$$\delta q = du + p\, d\alpha \quad , \tag{5.82}$$

so that

$$dh = \delta q + \alpha\, dp \quad . \tag{5.83}$$

Rearranging terms gives us

$$\delta q = dh - \alpha\, dp \quad . \tag{5.84}$$

Comparing this equation with the following form of the First Law

$$\delta q = c_p\, dT - \alpha\, dp \quad , \tag{5.85}$$

it dawns on us that

$$\boxed{dh \equiv c_p\, dT \quad .} \tag{5.86}$$

In other words, we have already seen the quantity we are now calling enthalpy; now we just have a convenient name for it! For a dry parcel of air, the physical interpretation is straightforward: If we add Q units of heat to a parcel of air held at constant pressure, the air gains the same Q units of enthalpy. It thus accounts for both the gain in internal energy of the parcel and the mechanical work done in displacing the surrounding air as it expands.

Key fact: When a parcel of air in contact with warmer or colder ground is heated or cooled (isobarically) by conduction, the heat energy exchanged between the two reservoirs is equal to the change of enthalpy of the air parcel. In this context, enthalpy is often known by meteorologists as **sensible heat.**

5.7.2 Conservation property

If we assume that the environmental temperature is not too different from the temperature of a parcel (just as we did in deriving the dry adiabatic lapse rate), then we can use the hydrostatic relation

$$dp = -\rho g\, dz \tag{5.87}$$

to write

$$\delta q = dh - \alpha\, dp = dh - \alpha(-\rho g\, dz) \quad , \tag{5.88}$$

or

$$\boxed{\delta q = dh + d\phi = d(h + \phi) \quad ,} \tag{5.89}$$

where ϕ is just the geopotential (gravitational potential energy per unit mass). In other words, for an air parcel moving about adiabatically and reversibly in a hydrostatic atmosphere of comparable temperature, the quantity $s_d \equiv h + \phi$, sometimes known as the **dry static energy**, is conserved.

5.7.3 Generalization to an irreversible process

It is fair to ask, "What happens when the environmental temperature T is *not* equal to the parcel temperature T'?" In that case, the process is no longer reversible because the parcel is not at equilibrium with its environment but rather has significant positive or negative buoyancy. This example gives us an opportunity to see whether we can successfully generalize the above conservation property from the reversible to the irreversible case.

Let us consider the sequence of events as the parcel ascends or descends through the surrounding air:

1. As noted above, the difference in temperature implies that the parcel has positive or negative buoyancy relative to its environment.

2. Due to the vertical force acting on the parcel as it is vertically displaced, work is done on/by the parcel as it ascends or descends. The immediate result is that it gains/loses kinetic energy; i.e., it accelerates.

3. The parcel eventually reaches a speed for which the kinetic energy of the parcel is dissipated by turbulence/viscosity as rapidly as it is gained, which means that the vertical speed of the parcel becomes constant, and for any given short time interval, $de_k = 0$.

4. The dissipated kinetic energy contributes to a heating of the parcel and/or the environment. Unfortunately, we have no basis for saying how much heat goes into each reservoir. Some of it undoubtedly adds to the enthalpy h of the parcel, but how much?

At step 2, above, we can still write a conservation equation as follows:

$$\delta q = d(h + \phi + e_k) \quad , \tag{5.90}$$

where e_K is the kinetic energy per unit mass of the parcel. In other words, the sum of the enthalpy, geopotential, and kinetic energy is conserved for an adiabatic, frictionless process. By step 4, however, we are stuck—the best we can do is write

$$\delta q \geq d(h + \phi) \quad , \tag{5.91}$$

because we don't know how much of the dissipated kinetic energy feeds back into the parcel's enthalpy, as opposed to being lost to the environment.

5.8 In Practice

As usual, we conclude the theoretical portion of this chapter with a couple of specific real-world applications.

5.8.1 Subsidence inversion

Under the influence of high pressure systems, it is common for entire layers of the atmosphere to sink, or *subside*, adiabatically, experiencing a substantial change of pressure in the process. The result of this process is often a *subsidence inversion* at lower levels.

The process by which subsidence inversions form is illustrated graphically in Fig. 5.5. In this example, a layer that is 100 hPa thick

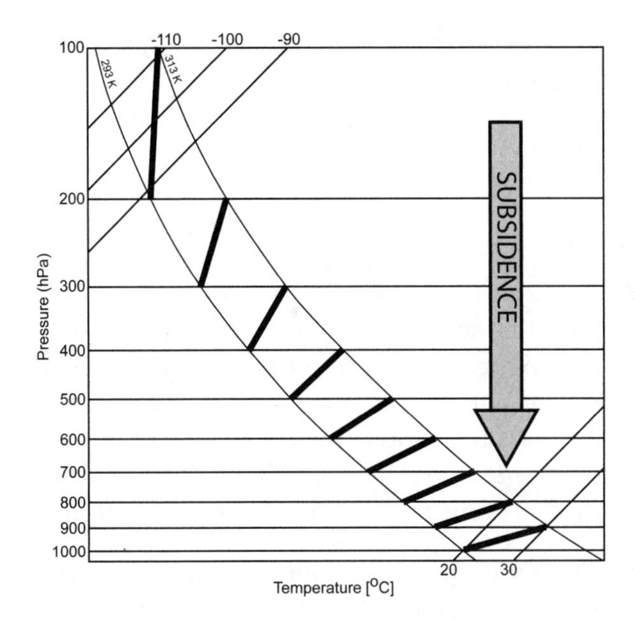

Fig. 5.5: The evolution of the lapse rate in an atmospheric layer that descends adiabatically, as depicted on a skew-T diagram. At all times, the pressure difference between the top and the bottom of the layer is 100 hPa, implying constant mass within the layer (no horizontal divergence). For clarity, only selected isobars, isotherms and dry adiabats are depicted.

starts out bounded by the 100 hPa and 200 hPa levels. The potential temperature θ is 313 K at the top of the layer, 293 K at the bottom. The actual temperature difference between top and bottom is initially 21°C with the lapse rate positive; i.e., the temperature within the layer decreases with height.

When this layer subsides adiabatically while preserving the total mass within the layer and thus also the pressure difference of 100 hPa, the potential temperatures are conserved. Thus, the top and bottom temperatures each follow dry adiabats downward.

As the layer descends, we see that the lapse rate steadily decreases, becoming isothermal near 500 hPa. Below this level, we have an ever-strengthening inversion. By the time the layer is found between the 1000 hPa and 900 hPa pressure levels, the temperature is *greater* at the top than at the bottom by 10°C.

A subsidence inversion can be further intensified if there is also lateral loss of air mass from within the layer, as *must* occur near the surface in order for air at higher levels to sink. In this case, the top of the layer experiences a greater change of pressure than the bottom and therefore also experiences a relatively greater degree of adiabatic warming.

5.8.2 Diabatic processes

While we idealize many atmospheric processes as adiabatic, we must not forget that an atmosphere in which there were truly no sources or sinks of heat would be a boring atmosphere indeed. We must therefore recognize the circumstances under which heating and cooling terms cannot safely be swept under the rug.

Any atmospheric process in which $\delta q \neq 0$ is called a **diabatic** process. Examples of diabatic heating processes include

Radiation: Energy in the form of electromagnetic radiation is continuously exchanged within the atmosphere and between the atmosphere and space. For example, energy from the sun heats the Earth and atmosphere via this process. We often ignore radiative heating/cooling in the free atmosphere over short time scales (hours or less), even though it is almost never completely negligible, especially at the boundaries of clouds or at the surface.

Molecular conduction: Heat flows by conduction when there is a temperature gradient. Air is a poor conductor of heat, so the temperature gradient must be very strong for significant heat transfer to take place. Typically, sufficiently strong gradients are found only within a few cm of the surface. Air in contact with the ground heats or cools by conduction; thereafter, atmospheric fluid motions are responsible for transferring the warmer or cooler air to other parts of the atmosphere.

Evaporation/condensation (latent heat release): Whenever water evaporates or condenses, freezes or melts, latent heat is taken up or released. Latent heating is an important form of diabatic heating in the atmosphere, especially in growing clouds.

Frictional dissipation of kinetic energy: Organized circulations in the atmosphere often become turbulent as the result of interactions with obstacles or because of other fluid instabilities. Kinetic energy of the mean flow is converted to turbulent kinetic energy, which in turn cascades down to smaller and smaller eddies until eventually friction dissipates the kinetic energy entirely, converting it to thermal energy. While frictional dissipation is an important mechanism for *removing* kinetic energy from the atmosphere, it is not terribly significant as a *source* of atmospheric heating.

Problem 5.9: A 20 m/sec (approximately 40 knot) surface wind flowing over open ground encounters a forest that converts 3/4 of the kinetic energy of the flow into heat via frictional dissipation. What is the maximum possible air temperature rise as a result of this isobaric process? *Answer:* 0.15 K

Problem 5.10: On a clear night, the loss of infrared radiation to space causes the lowest 10 m of the atmosphere to cool by 5 K over 10 hr. Assuming a density of 1.25 kg m^{-3} for the air, what is the net rate of heat loss by radiational cooling, in W m^{-2}? *Answer:* 1.74 W m^{-2}

Problem 5.11: A steady rain of 1 mm/hr falls from a cloud base at 1.5 km (about 700 hPa pressure) altitude into much drier air below, with the result that only 0.5 mm/hr reaches the surface (about 1000 hPa pressure) before evaporating. By interpreting the above information in terms of a mass of water evaporated per unit time, per unit mass of air, find the average rate (in degrees per hour) at which the air below the cloud is cooled by the evaporation. Take the density of water ρ_l to be 1000 kg m^{-3} and the latent heat of vaporization of water L to be 2.5×10^6 J kg^{-1}. *Answer:* 0.4 K hr^{-1}

Problem 5.12: Assume that the layer of the atmosphere between 800 hPa and 700 hPa absorbs 1.0×10^6 J m^{-2} of solar radiation. Calculate the resulting increase in the mean temperature and in the thickness of the layer. (Hint: What type of process is this, if the layer remains bounded by the same two pressure levels?) *Answer:* 3.8 m

5.8.3 Work and energy on a skew-T diagram

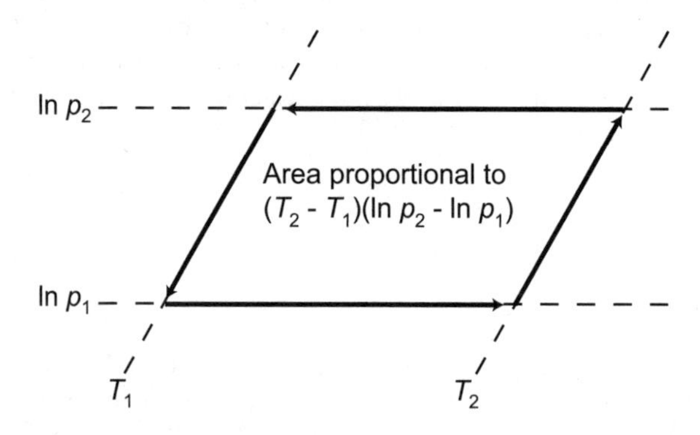

Fig. 5.6: Schematic skew-T depiction of a closed cycle entailing isothermal and isobaric processes

On a skew-T diagram, both isotherms and isobars appear as straight lines. Moreover, isotherms are equally spaced so that a unit horizontal distance on the diagram always corresponds to the same change of temperature ΔT. The vertical spacing of isobars is not proportional to changes in pressure p, however, but rather to changes in $\ln p$.

Consider a cyclic process consisting of isobaric warming/cooling between temperatures T_1 and T_2 and isothermal expansion or compression between pressures p_1 and p_2 (Fig. 5.6). This cycle appears as a parallelogram on the skew-T diagram, and the area A enclosed by the parallelogram is proportional to the product of the base and the height:

$$A \propto (T_2 - T_1)(\ln p_2 - \ln p_1) = (T_2 - T_1) \ln \left(\frac{p_2}{p_1} \right) \quad . \tag{5.92}$$

Let us now compute the mechanical work done in the above cycle. For the isobaric legs of the cycle, we have

$$w = \pm \int_{\alpha_1}^{\alpha_2} p \, d\alpha = \pm R_d (T_2 - T_1) \quad , \tag{5.93}$$

and for the isothermal legs

$$w = \pm \int_{\alpha_1}^{\alpha_2} p \, d\alpha = \pm R_d T \int_{\alpha_1}^{\alpha_2} \frac{1}{\alpha} \, d\alpha = \pm R_d T \ln \left(\frac{p_1}{p_2} \right) \quad , \tag{5.94}$$

where T is either T_1 or T_2.

The net mechanical work yielded in the complete cycle is contributed only by the isothermal legs (the isobaric contributions cancel), and we have

$$w_{\text{net}} = R_d (T_2 - T_1) \ln \left(\frac{p_1}{p_2} \right) \quad , \tag{5.95}$$

which is greater than zero (net positive work is done *by* the parcel) when $T_2 > T_1$ and $p_1 > p_2$; that is, for a counterclockwise cycle as depicted on the skew-T. Comparing this result with (5.92), we see that

$$\boxed{w_{\text{net}} \propto A \quad .} \tag{5.96}$$

In words, *the mechanical work produced by the cyclic process is exactly proportional to the area enclosed by the process depicted graphically on a skew-T diagram.* This also true, of course, of the net heating q_{net} required to supply the energy for the net work.

The above result is true for the area enclosed by *any* cyclic process, regardless of the "shape" of the cycle—that is, it need not consist only of isobaric and isothermal legs. The direct relationship between energy and area on a skew-T diagram even extends beyond just cyclic processes, and this fact turns out to be very useful for the visual interpretation of plotted soundings.

Problem 5.13: For the cycle depicted in Fig. 5.7, *compute* the work done. Then, with the help of your answer, graphically *estimate* the work done by another cycle defined by isobaric processes at 500 and 400 hPa and isothermal processes at −20 and −30°C.

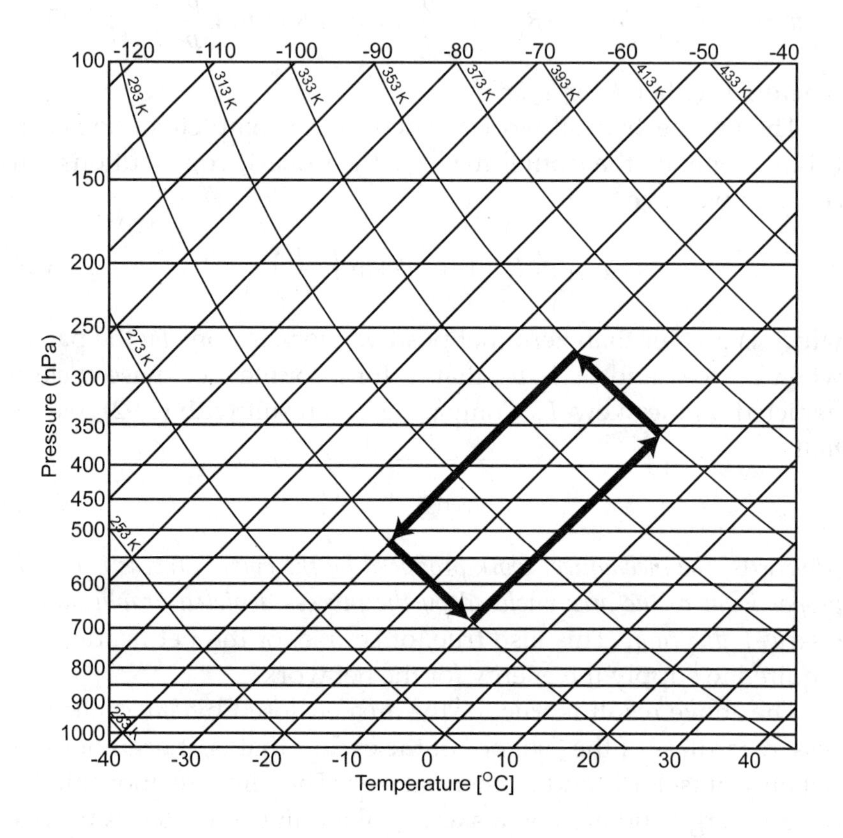

Fig. 5.7: Skew-T depiction of a Carnot cycle producing positive work.

CHAPTER 6

The Second Law and Its Consequences

6.1 Entropy—A New State Variable

With equation (5.48), we saw that net work w_{net} and net heating q_{net} over a closed cycle (a) is generally non-zero and (b) depends on the path taken. Thus, neither work nor heat is a state variable. Interestingly, we can introduce a minor modification that allows *all* of the terms in the equation to vanish when integrated over a closed cycle. Specifically, we divide the entire equation through by the absolute temperature T, so that we are now evaluating

$$\oint \frac{1}{T}\,\delta q = \oint c_v \frac{1}{T}\,dT + \oint \frac{p}{T}\,d\alpha \quad . \tag{6.1}$$

From the Ideal Gas Law, we can replace p/T with R/α. Also, c_v and R are constants. So we have

$$\oint \frac{1}{T}\,\delta q = c_v \oint \frac{1}{T}\,dT + R \oint \frac{1}{\alpha}\,d\alpha \quad . \tag{6.2}$$

Both integrals on the right now evaluate to zero, because both T and α are state variables. *We therefore infer that the integral on the left-hand side must also evaluate to zero:*

$$\oint \frac{1}{T}\,\delta q = 0 \quad . \tag{6.3}$$

It follows that

$$\boxed{ds \equiv \frac{\delta q}{T}} \tag{6.4}$$

represents an exact differential (hence the use of ds instead of δs), and the new variable s, known as the specific **entropy**, is therefore a state variable. In words, ds is the increase in specific entropy accompanying the addition of a small amount of heat δq at temperature T.

From (6.4), it follows that for an adiabatic, reversible process, $ds = 0$. In other words, entropy is conserved in such a process. For this reason, dry adiabats on a thermodynamic diagram are also known as **isentropes**, or lines of constant entropy.

For our ideal gas, the First Law of Thermodynamics gives us the following relationships between s and our more familiar state variables:

$$ds = c_v \, d \ln T + R \, d \ln \alpha \quad . \tag{6.5}$$

$$ds = c_p \, d \ln T - R \, d \ln p \quad . \tag{6.6}$$

In practical terms, then, increases in the specific entropy of a gas are generally associated with (a) increases in temperature, (b) increases in volume, and/or (c) decreases in pressure.

Countless students (and instructors) have struggled with the question of what, exactly, entropy *is*. Most explanations invoke some concept of "randomness" or "disorder." A more precise definition invokes the degree to which the positions and velocities of the constituent molecules are constrained by the state of the system—the looser the constraints, the higher the entropy. Such technical definitions are not intuitively helpful for most students considering the bulk behavior of gases for the first time. In the next section, we will simply highlight an important practical property of entropy and ask the reader to trust that it has been well-verified by both theoreticians and experimentalists.

6.2 Thermodynamic Equilibrium

The First Law of Thermodynamics, which we have already used extensively, is simply a statement of energy conservation. It tells you that the energy budget for an isolated system must balance—if energy appears in one form, an equal amount of it must disappear in another form.

For example, assume that we have two identical bodies, each with mass M, specific heat capacity c_p and different temperatures T_1 and T_2. If we bring the two masses together but insulate them from the rest of the universe, then they collectively represent an isolated system, and they can exchange energy only with each other. If we further assume that the masses are effectively incompressible, so that we can neglect pressure-volume work, the only energy exchanges occur in the form of heat conduction across the point of contact. The First Law then tells us that the heat transferred from mass two to mass one is related to their respective changes of temperature as follows:

$$Mc_p \, dT_1 = M\delta q = -Mc_p \, dT_2 \quad , \tag{6.7}$$

or, integrating, followed by elimination of the common factor Mc_p,

$$T_{1,f} + T_{2,f} = T_{1,i} + T_{2,i} \quad , \tag{6.8}$$

where the subscripts i and f denote the initial and final temperatures, respectively. Given the initial temperatures $T_{1,i}$ and $T_{2,i}$, we have an equation that the final temperatures, $T_{1,f}$ and $T_{2,f}$, must satisfy in order for the First Law to hold. In words, the increase in T_1 must equal the decrease in T_2 because both bodies have the same thermal mass Mc_p.

We have two unknowns but only one equation! This means that there is no *unique* solution—we could choose any value we want for $T_{1,f}$, and our equation would only tell us what $T_{2,f}$ must then be in order to conserve the total energy of the system. The First Law alone cannot tell us what $T_{1,f}$ and $T_{2,f}$ *will* be when our system reaches equilibrium!

Now let us consider the role of entropy in the above example. If an increment of heat δq is transferred *from* the first mass *to* the second mass, entropy change (extensive units) for the first mass is

$$M \, ds_1 = -M\frac{\delta q}{T_1} = Mc_p \, d\ln T_1 \quad , \tag{6.9}$$

while that for the second mass is

$$M \, ds_2 = M\frac{\delta q}{T_2} = Mc_p \, d\ln T_2 \quad . \tag{6.10}$$

The incremental entropy change of the *entire system* is thus

$$dS = M(ds_1 + ds_2) = Mc_p(d\ln T_1 + d\ln T_2) \quad . \tag{6.11}$$

Integrating from the initial state to the (as-yet-unknown) final state, we have the *total entropy of the final state*

$$S = Mc_p\left[\ln\left(\frac{T_{1,f}}{T_{1,i}}\right) + \ln\left(\frac{T_{2,f}}{T_{2,i}}\right)\right] + \text{constant} \quad , \tag{6.12}$$

or, equivalently,

$$S = Mc_p \ln\left(T_{1,f}T_{2,f}\right) + \text{constant} \quad , \tag{6.13}$$

where the unspecified constant on the right hand side now encompasses the logarithms of the initial temperatures as well.

Recall that the final temperatures, $T_{1,f}$ and $T_{2,f}$, are not independent of one another; they are firmly tied to one another by (6.8). We may use the latter equation to eliminate $T_{2,f}$, yielding

$$S = Mc_p \ln\left[T_{1,f}(T_{1,i} + T_{2,i} - T_{1,f})\right] + \text{constant} \quad . \tag{6.14}$$

We now have an expression for the total entropy S of our system in terms of the final (equilibrium) temperature of *one* of the masses $T_{1,f}$, but we still don't know what that temperature is.

Here's where we now invoke the remarkably powerful thermodynamic principle known as the **Second Law of Thermodynamics**. The following is one statement[1] of the Second Law:

Key fact: Within any isolated system that is not at equilibrium, the net effect of any active process is always to *increase* the total entropy of the system. A state of equilibrium is therefore reached when the total entropy of the system has achieved its maximum possible value. At this point, no further evolution of system state variables is possible.

[1]"There are almost as many formulations of the second law as there have been discussions of it."—P.W. Bridgman (1941).

An interesting compilation of different formulations may be found at `http://www.humanthermodynamics.com/2nd-Law-Variations.html`.

Assuming that this claim is true (and it is!), we may find the equilibrium temperature of our two-body system simply by finding the value of $T_{1,f}$ that maximizes S in (6.14).

We do this in the usual way: by (1) taking the derivative of S with respect to $T_{1,f}$, (2) setting the resulting expression equal to zero, and (3) solving for $T_{1,f}$. Thus,

$$\frac{d}{dT_{1,f}}\left\{Mc_p \ln\left[T_{1,f}(T_{1,i}+T_{2,i}-T_{1,f})\right] + \text{constant}\right\} = 0 \quad , \tag{6.15}$$

$$\frac{1}{T_{1,f}(T_{1,i}+T_{2,i}-T_{1,f})}\cdot\frac{d}{dT_{1,f}}\left[T_{1,f}(T_{1,i}+T_{2,i}-T_{1,f})\right] = 0 \quad , \tag{6.16}$$

$$\frac{1}{T_{1,f}(T_{1,i}+T_{2,i}-T_{1,f})}\cdot\left[T_{1,i}+T_{2,i}-2T_{1,f})\right] = 0 \quad . \tag{6.17}$$

Solving for $T_{1,i}$ and invoking (6.8), we find that

$$T_{1,f} = T_{2,f} = \frac{1}{2}(T_{1,i}+T_{2,i}) \quad . \tag{6.18}$$

What the First Law of Thermodynamics could not tell us, the Second Law does: *thermal equilibrium in our two-body system is reached when both bodies have the same temperature.*

This result is not unexpected—in fact, I already pointed out in Section 1.3.1 that heat always flows in such a way as to eliminate temperature differences. The purpose of the above exercise was not to prove the obvious but rather to illustrate how the Second Law indeed supplies us with a crucial constraint on the behavior of physical systems in cases where conservation of energy alone is insufficient to reach meaningful conclusions.

It is impossible to exaggerate the fundamental importance of the Second Law of Thermodynamics with respect to the workings of the atmosphere and, for that matter, the universe. It not only predicts that heat will always flow from a warm body to a cold body, it also explains why gases will spontaneously expand into a vacuum, why heat engines can never be 100% efficient, and why it is easier to scramble an egg than to unscramble one. Many eminent physicists, including Albert Einstein, have asserted that the Second Law is the single law of nature that is least likely to be overturned or modified in light of new theories or experimental evidence.

Despite its profound implications for everything from heat flow to chemical reactions to even the evolution of hurricanes, we will not need to explicitly refer to the Second Law of Thermodynamics again for the remainder of this introductory text. We will, however, invoke the definition of *entropy* one more time when we study phase changes in the next chapter.

CHAPTER 7

Moist Processes

7.1 Water Vapor Saturation

The moisture variables we introduced in Chapter 3 do not require any assumptions concerning the range of water vapor content that can actually occur—all we know so far is that if you have a mixture consisting of this much water vapor and that much dry air, then we can express the ratio as either the mixing ratio w or the specific humidity q. Moreover, these are easily related to two other humidity variables, the water vapor density (or absolute humidity) ρ_v and the vapor pressure e, via the Ideal Gas Law and Dalton's Law of Partial pressures.

Of course, the reality is that if you try to pack too much water vapor into a particular volume, the excess will almost inevitably condense to form liquid water or ice. The point at which this occurs is called **saturation**. In general, the saturation point is different with respect to ice than it is with respect to liquid at the same temperature.

A volume that contains less water vapor than that found at saturation is called **subsaturated** or **undersaturated**. Any liquid water or ice present may evaporate into this volume until saturation is reached. If there is more, then it is **supersaturated,** and usually enough condensation will quickly occur to reduce the vapor content back to saturation. If the latter occurs in the free atmosphere, the result is fog or cloud and, possibly, precipitation. If it occurs instead on a surface, then we have dew or frost.

The condensation and evaporation of water substance are exceedingly important processes in the atmosphere. We will not only spend considerable time examining processes that lead to saturation but also introduce several useful humidity variables that are explicitly defined in terms of the saturation point.

7.1.1 The molecular nature of saturation

Imagine a sealed container from which all gases have been evacuated — the initial pressure p in this container is therefore zero. Now add some water to the container without letting any air in and watch what happens (Fig. 7.1a).

Because the liquid water is not at absolute zero, its molecules vibrate with an average kinetic energy that is related to the temperature. Even though the *average* kinetic energy is fixed at any given temperature, not all molecules individually have the same energy. In particular, some fraction of the molecules at the surface of the water have enough energy to break free from the attractive forces that hold them in the liquid state. Thus, molecules begin to escape from the surface of the water into the vacuum. In short, the water begins to **evaporate**.

Initially, there are no molecules in the space above the water that can go the other way; therefore, the flux of water molecules is one way. There is therefore a net loss of liquid water and a net increase in the number of water molecules occupying what used to be the vacuum.

As the number of molecules in the vapor phase increases, however, they inevitably impinge on the surface of the liquid water again and a fraction of these are recaptured and return to the liquid phase. This process is what we call **condensation**. But as long as more molecules leave than return, *net* evaporation is still occurring, and the vapor in the space above the water surface is still, by definition, subsaturated (Fig. 7.1b).

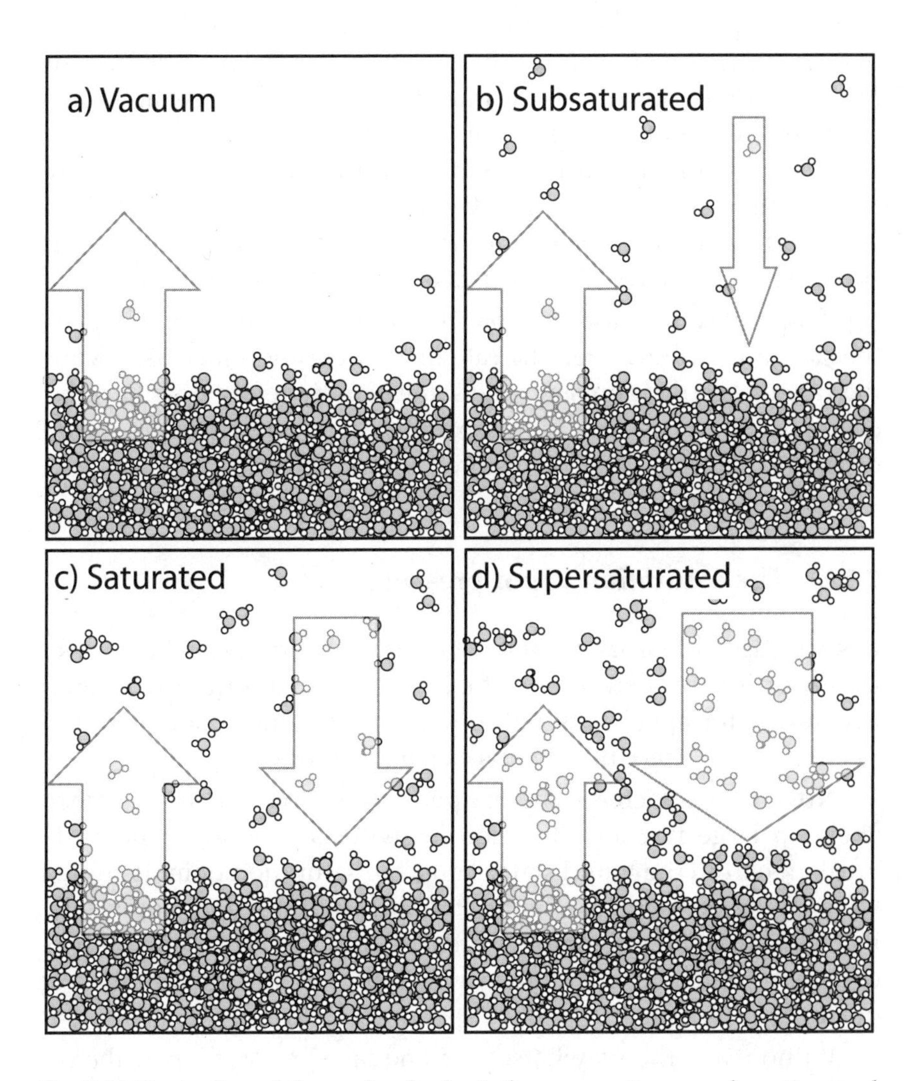

Fig. 7.1: Illustration of the molecular basis for evaporation, condensation, and saturation. At any given temperature, the rate at which molecules leave the liquid phase and enter the gas phase is fixed (upward arrow). The rate at which molecules return to the liquid phase (downward arrow) is proportional to the concentration of molecules in the vapor phase and thus to the vapor pressure. Equilibrium (saturation) exists when the two fluxes are equal (c); otherwise, there is either net evaporation (b) or net condensation (d).

As long as the rate of evaporation exceeds the rate of condensation, the vapor pressure continues to increase. Eventually, however, the concentration of water vapor molecules is great enough that the rate of condensation equals the rate of evaporation. Once this occurs (and assuming both vapor and liquid have the same temperature), the system is in **equilibrium**, and the water vapor is exactly saturated with respect to the liquid water (Fig. 7.1c). At this point, there is neither *net* condensation nor *net* evaporation; however, there is still a steady *exchange* of molecules between the two phases).

If you now increase the concentration of water vapor beyond the saturation point, then the rate of condensation increases while the rate of evaporation stays the same. We therefore now have *net* condensation (Fig. 7.1d). In this example, the vapor pressure would decrease until the system is restored to equilibrium.

7.1.2 The saturation vapor pressure

It is the vapor pressure e that most directly determines whether water vapor is saturated or not: if e is less than the **saturation vapor pressure** e_s for the given set of conditions, then the vapor is unsaturated; if $e = e_s$, then the vapor is exactly saturated.

Now, if you increase the temperature of the system described above, a large fraction of molecules will have enough energy to break free from the liquid state. Thus, the saturation point is shifted toward a higher vapor pressure. It follows that e_s is a monotonically increasing function of temperature. Less obviously, e_s depends *only* on temperature and is *not* in any way influenced by the presence of other gases like air.

Without any theory whatsoever, one can simply measure the vapor pressure of water (and ice) in the laboratory as a function of temperature and tabulate the results. A graph of measured $e_s(T)$ is shown in Fig. 7.2.

How can it be that the addition of air to the space in our chamber does not alter the saturation vapor pressure? But consider that even at sea level pressure, molecules of air only occupy around 0.1% of a given volume, the rest being empty space. Any introduced air molecules merely coexist passively with the water molecules—they

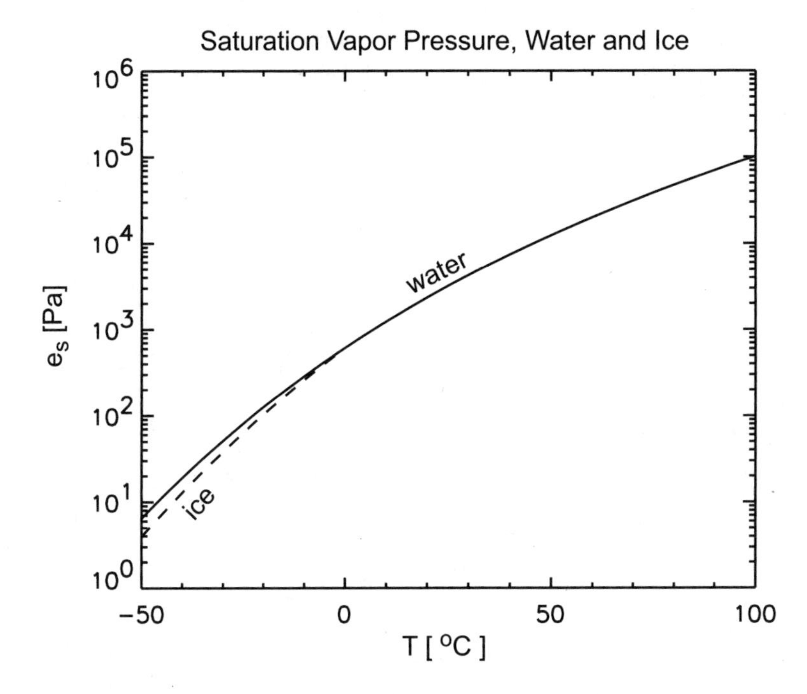

Fig. 7.2: The saturation vapor pressure of liquid water over the range −50°C to 100°C. Also shown is the saturation vapor pressure with respect to ice for temperatures below freezing.

neither hinder the leaving of molecules from the liquid phase nor influence the rate at which they return.[1]

One claim you might have heard many times is that "warm air can hold more water vapor than cold air." In view of the above molecular explanation, it should now be clear that this assertion is erroneous, or at least sloppily formulated, as the *air* present has no bearing on the amount of water vapor that can occupy a given volume of space. Moreover, the saturation point has nothing whatsoever to do with filling up the *space* between any air molecules present. *Air is not a sponge.*

[1]The presence of air in the mixture *does* influence the rate at which water vapor can diffuse from one part of the chamber to another. When air is present, the saturation vapor pressure is achieved very quickly in the thin film of air immediately in contact with the water surface, but it can take considerably longer for a uniform vapor pressure to be established throughout the chamber, especially if other processes are at work to upset the equilibrium.

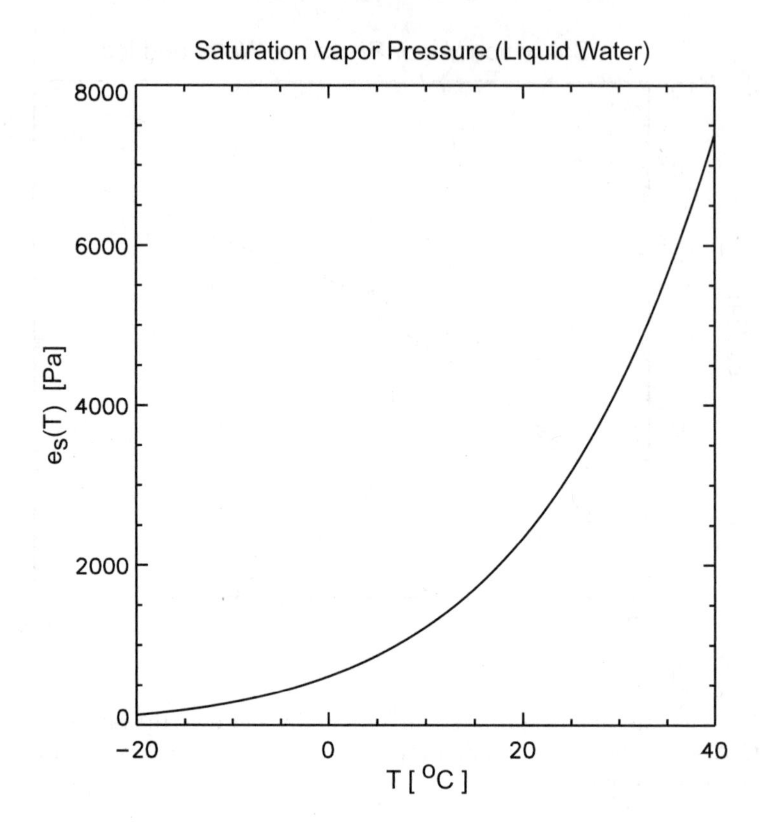

Fig. 7.3: The saturation vapor pressure of liquid water over the temperature range most commonly of interest to meteorologists.

Relationship to boiling

Although meteorologists seldom have to be concerned with temperatures near the boiling point of water, it is worth noting that there is a direct connection between the saturation vapor pressure of water and its boiling point. Specifically, the boiling point is the temperature at which e_s equals the ambient atmospheric pressure.

Water at sea level boils at 100°C, so we can infer that $e_s(T)$ evaluated at this temperature equals standard sea level pressure of 1013 hPa. At higher altitudes, atmospheric pressure is lower and therefore the boiling point of water occurs at a significantly lower temperature as well. At sufficiently low pressure, water boils at room temperature!

Problem 7.1: By consulting Fig. 7.2 and Fig. 1.7, estimate the altitude at which the boiling point of water drops to room temperature (20°C).

Summary

If you know or can calculate the actual vapor pressure e in a parcel of air with temperature T, then you can compare this value with the saturation vapor pressure $e_s(T)$ to determine whether or not the parcel is saturated. If $e < e_s(T)$, then any liquid water present can evaporate until $e = e_s(T)$. Conversely, if $e > e_s(T)$ then water will tend to condense out as liquid water until e has again been reduced to the saturation vapor pressure e_s.

Later, we will derive the mathematical dependence of e_s on T.

7.1.3 Relative humidity

The fundamental importance of the saturation point led meteorologists to define the **relative humidity** RH as the *actual* vapor pressure e expressed as a fraction of the *saturation* vapor pressure e_s. That is,

$$\boxed{RH = \frac{e}{e_s(T)}} \quad . \tag{7.1}$$

Often, this ratio is expressed as a percentage, though that convention is not an essential part of the definition. Occasionally, you will see the term **saturation ratio** used to describe the same thing as relative humidity.

Occasionally, situations develop in which $e > e_s(T)$—that is, the water vapor is **supersaturated**. This case may either be expressed as a relative humidity greater than 100% or by a **supersaturation** defined as

$$s \equiv RH - 100\% \quad . \tag{7.2}$$

Significant supersaturation with respect to liquid water generally exists in the atmosphere only when the air temperature drops very rapidly—more rapidly than excess water can condense out to maintain a state of saturation. The typical maximum supersaturation observed in convective updrafts is of the order of 1–2%. Outside such updrafts, we can safely assume that environmental air is *never* significantly supersaturated with respect to liquid water.[2]

It is because the relative humidity is a fairly direct measure of the rate at which evaporation can occur (or whether it can occur at all) that RH plays such an important role in our perception of temperature. If the RH is high on a warm day, then the perspiration that is supposed to cool our bodies by evaporation simply accumulates and turns our shirts soggy instead.

Note, however, that the relative humidity is *not* a very useful measure of the *absolute* moisture content of the air because as the temperature changes, so does e_s and therefore the RH, even if the actual vapor pressure e (or mixing ratio or vapor density) remains constant.

7.1.4 The dewpoint

I have already pointed out that e_s always increases with increasing temperature. The physical reasons for this are clear: the higher the temperature of the liquid phase, the more molecules have sufficient energy at any given time to overcome the attraction to their fellow molecules and enter the gas phase.

It follows that if $e < e_s(T)$ (or equivalently, $RH < 100\%$), then we can always reduce e_s to equal e—and thus achieve saturation—simply by reducing the temperature T while keeping the vapor pressure e constant. The temperature at which saturation occurs for fixed e is called the **dewpoint**. Mathematically,

$$\boxed{e_s(T_d) = e \quad .} \tag{7.3}$$

In words, the dewpoint T_d is the temperature you would have to plug into the function $e_s(T)$ in order to get a saturation vapor pressure equal to the actual vapor pressure.

[2]We shall see later that the same assurance cannot be made concerning saturation with respect to ice.

Key fact: The vapor pressure e cannot normally exceed the saturation vapor pressure e_s in the free atmosphere without rapid condensation occurring, which reduces e. For virtually all practical purposes, therefore, $T_d \leq T$.

Key fact: Unlike the relative humidity, which depends both on the vapor pressure *and* the temperature of the air, the dewpoint depends only on the vapor pressure. Therefore, most meteorologists prefer to use the dewpoint to characterize humidity.

Fig. 7.4: A tanker passing out of a fog bank off the coast of southeast Alaska. This is an example of *advection fog*, which occurs when warm, humid air moves over cold water, chilling the air to its dewpoint. The fog that famously affects San Francisco is also advection fog. For millennia, advection fog at sea has posed one of the greatest hazards to shipping, though the hazard has been greatly reduced in recent decades by the advent of radar. *(Courtesy of the NOAA Photo Library. Photo by Lt. (j.g.) Steve Snow, NOAA Corps.)*

Among other things, the dewpoint determines the temperature at which inanimate surfaces will "sweat"—that is, become damp with condensation. For example, if you put out a glass of water with plenty of crushed ice in it, the surface of the glass will have a temperature close to 0°C. If the outside of the glass does *not* become wet, that's an indication that the dewpoint is colder than 0°C and that the air is rather dry.

Of greater interest to meteorologists, of course, is the occurrence of saturation and condensation within the atmosphere. The result is either fog, if it occurs at ground level, or cloud, if it occurs above ground level. Fog can occur any time surface air is chilled to its dewpoint by any of several possible processes, including contact with a colder underlying surface (Fig. 7.4). Clouds are most often the result of cooling by adiabatic ascent, which we will discuss in Section 7.6.

7.2 Latent Heat of Condensation/Vaporization

When liquid water evaporates to form water vapor, individual molecules must break free of the attractive forces exerted by other water molecules. In the same way that a spacecraft requires a certain minimum energy to escape the gravitational pull of Earth, molecules require a certain minimum of energy to escape those attractive forces. It is the most energetic molecules that are able to escape and take their energy with them (converting part of it from kinetic energy to chemical potential energy); the average kinetic energy, and therefore the temperature, of the remaining liquid is reduced. Thus, evaporation is associated with cooling. Conversely, molecules that leave the gas phase and return to the liquid phase convert their chemical potential energy back to kinetic energy; hence, condensation is associated with heating.

The total energy required to convert a unit mass of a substance from one phase to another while keeping the pressure and temperature constant is called the *specific enthalpy* of the phase change. In the case of a phase change from liquid to vapor, it is more commonly called the **latent heat of vaporization**. In this book, it is given the symbol L.

For the reverse process (i.e., gas to liquid) L may be called the **latent heat of condensation**, but it then refers to the amount of energy released rather than taken up. But it is the same quantity, regardless—indeed, it *must* be the same, otherwise it would be possible to create or destroy energy via a closed cycle of evaporation and condensation!

Due to thermal motions, water molecules in the liquid phase already possess part of the energy required to overcome their attraction to neighboring molecules. The higher the temperature, the less additional energy they require. Hence L decreases slightly with increasing temperature. Here are some representative values:

T [°C]	L [J kg^{-1}]
−40	2.60×10^6
0	2.50×10^6
40	2.40×10^6
100	2.26×10^6

The range −40°C to 40°C covers the range of greatest interest to most meteorologists. Within this range, it is not a bad approximation to use the value of $L = 2.5 \times 10^6$ J kg^{-1} at 0°C for most calculations unless the problem specifically calls for a more accurate value.

Of course, there is also latent heat associated with the phase change from solid to liquid (e.g., from ice to water). This latent heat is called the **latent heat of fusion**, which we denote with L_f. If we allow ice to sublimate directly to the vapor phase (or vice versa) without the intermediate stage of melting, there is a **latent heat of sublimation** L_s. Energy conservation requires that

$$\boxed{L_s = L_f + L \quad .} \tag{7.4}$$

At 0°C, $L_f \approx 3.3 \times 10^5$ J kg^{-1}. Thus, $L_s > L$ and is approximately 2.83×10^6 joules/kg.

Problem 7.2: On a winter day, the outside air has a temperature of $-15°C$ and a relative humidity of 70%.

a) If outside air is brought inside and heated to room temperature of 20°C without adding moisture, what is the new relative humidity? *Answer:* 6%

b) If the room volume is 60 m^3, what mass of water must be added to the air by a humidifier to raise the relative humidity to 40%? *Answer:* 0.36 kg

c) How much heating energy is needed in order accomplish (a) and (b), and what fraction of the total heating energy is represented by (b)? *Answer:* 9.0×10^6 J, 26%

Problem 7.3: A pot contains one kg of ice at 0°C and is placed on a stove with a burner that provides 900 W of power to the pot. Ignoring the heat capacity of the pot itself as well as other heat losses, compute the following, using a specific heat capacity $C_{\text{water}} = 4186\ \text{J}/(\text{kg K})$ for water.

a) The time required to melt the ice;
b) the time required to raise the water temperature to boiling;
c) the time required to boil the water away.

Problem 7.4: A container of pure water is set outside on a cold night and supercools to a temperature T [°C] without freezing. Once it is disturbed, however, ice crystals form and rapidly spread throughout the container until all that remains is a fairly uniform ice-water slush with temperature of 0°C.

(a) Derive an expression for the fraction of ice in the resulting mixture as a function of the initial temperature T.

(b) It is impossible to supercool pure water to less than about $-40°C$ without it spontaneous freezing. Therefore, what is the maximum fraction of ice that can be achieved from supercooled water without additional cooling? *Answer:* 51%

7.3 The Clausius-Clapeyron Equation

Having previously introduced the new state variable **specific entropy** s in Chapter 6 and now the latent heat of vaporization L, we have what we need to derive the dependence of the saturation vapor pressure e_s on temperature T.

If L denotes the latent heat associated with a phase change from liquid (or solid) to vapor when pressure and temperature are held constant, we may write (using the First Law)

$$L = \int \delta q = \int_{u_1}^{u_2} du + \int_{\alpha_1}^{\alpha_2} p d\alpha \quad . \tag{7.5}$$

The pressure in the final integral is just the saturation vapor pressure e_s, which stays constant, so we can solve all the integrals and write

$$L = (u_2 - u_1) + e_s(\alpha_2 - \alpha_1) \quad . \tag{7.6}$$

Because the temperature is also constant, we can also write

$$L = T \int \frac{\delta q}{T} = T \int_{s_1}^{s_2} ds = T(s_2 - s_1) \quad . \tag{7.7}$$

So we now have two independent expressions for L that we may equate and rearrange so that terms involving the initial state and the final state are on opposite sides of the equal sign:

$$u_1 + e_s\alpha_1 - Ts_1 = u_2 + e_s\alpha_2 - Ts_2 \quad . \tag{7.8}$$

In other words, the quantity $G \equiv u + e_s\alpha - Ts$ remains constant during an isothermal, isobaric change of phase. This quantity G is called the **Gibbs energy** of the system, and the above equation can therefore be rewritten

$$G_1 = G_2 \quad . \tag{7.9}$$

The Gibbs energy is *not* constant with respect to pressure and temperature, so we may differentiate G as follows:

$$dG = du + e_s d\alpha + \alpha\, de_s - T\, ds - s\, dT \quad . \tag{7.10}$$

But $du + e_s d\alpha = \delta q = T\, ds$, so the last equation reduces to

$$dG = \alpha\, de_s - s\, dT \quad . \tag{7.11}$$

Because G is the same for both the liquid and vapor phases when the two are at equilibrium (i.e., same pressure and temperature), $dG_1 = dG_2$, or

$$\alpha_1 \, de_s - s_1 \, dT = \alpha_2 \, de_s - s_2 \, dT \quad , \tag{7.12}$$

$$\alpha_1 \frac{de_s}{dT} - s_1 = \alpha_2 \frac{de_s}{dT} - s_2 \quad , \tag{7.13}$$

$$\frac{de_s}{dT} = \frac{s_2 - s_1}{\alpha_2 - \alpha_1} = \frac{L}{T(\alpha_2 - \alpha_1)} \quad . \tag{7.14}$$

We have thus obtained an expression for the rate of change of saturation vapor pressure with respect to temperature. This equation is called the **Clausius-Clapeyron equation**. We will now introduce some convenient approximations that allow us to integrate this equation to get a simple closed-form (though approximate) expression for $e_s(T)$.

Under typical atmospheric conditions, the specific volume of water vapor α_2 is vastly greater than that of liquid water α_1. We can further assume that water vapor behaves as an ideal gas. With both facts in mind, we can write

$$\frac{de_s}{dT} \approx \frac{L}{T\alpha_2} = \frac{Le_s}{R_v T^2} \quad . \tag{7.15}$$

This form of the Clausius-Clapeyron equation may be integrated by assuming that L is a constant (as we saw earlier, this is not quite correct but it is close enough).

$$\int_{e_{s0}}^{e_s} \frac{de_s}{e_s} = \frac{L}{R_v} \int_{T_0}^{T} T^{-2} \, dT \quad , \tag{7.16}$$

or

$$\boxed{e_s(T) = e_{s0} \exp\left[\frac{L}{R_v}\left(\frac{1}{T_0} - \frac{1}{T}\right)\right] \quad ,} \tag{7.17}$$

where e_{s0} is the *measured* value of the saturation vapor pressure at temperature T_0. Although the Clausius-Clapeyron equation gives us the *rate of change* of e_s with respect to changes in T, it tells us nothing about the actual value of e_s at any particular temperature.

Hence, e_{s0} can be regarded as a (mathematically) arbitrary constant of integration whose actual value must be determined experimentally.

The above expression is simple and reasonably accurate as long as the temperature T does not deviate too far from the reference temperature T_0 (which in turn determines e_{s0} as well as the correct value of L). The approximations employed introduce errors that become larger the further away you get from T_0 (Fig. 7.5).

7.3.1 Vapor pressure with respect to water

If we choose $T_0 = 273$ K, then e_{s0} for water is found experimentally to be 6.11 hPa or 611 Pa. Substituting these values into the expression for e_s, along with $L = 2.50 \times 10^6$ J/kg and $R_v = 461.5$ J/(kg K),

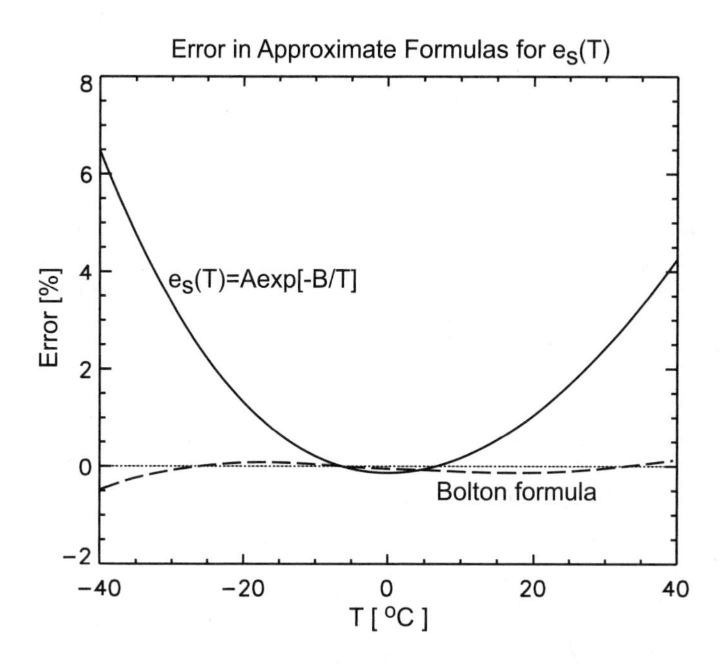

Fig. 7.5: The error associated with the two approximate expressions (7.18) and (7.19) of the saturation vapor pressure of water, as compared with laboratory measurements.

we get the simplified expression

$$e_s(T) \approx Ae^{-B/T} \qquad A = 2.53 \times 10^{11}\ \text{Pa},\ B = 5420\ \text{K}. \tag{7.18}$$

You may use the above simple form for solving problems in this book unless otherwise indicated.

Problem 7.5: A chemist working in a laboratory requires a version of (7.18) that is valid in the vicinity of the boiling point of water. Rederive the coefficients A and B using $T_0 = 373$ K, noting that e_{s0} at this temperature is equal to one standard atmosphere, and $L = 2.26 \times 10^6$ J/kg.

Problem 7.6: Use (7.18) to find the dewpoint temperature T_d corresponding to a mixing ratio w of 20 g/kg at a pressure p of 1000 hPa and a temperature of 35°C.

Problem 7.7: On a humid day in the central or southeastern United States, one sometimes hears the casual comment that "it is 90 degrees (Fahrenheit) and 90% humidity." What dewpoint (in °F) would this combination represent? Note: Even in Houston, one of the muggiest cities in North America, dewpoints rarely exceed 82°F.

If in your future meteorological work you require a more accurate formula for e_s, you should be aware of the following empirical[3] formula[4] which is accurate to within 0.1% over the temperature

[3]The term *empirical* means that the formula was not derived theoretically but rather by fitting a simple curve to a series of known values of the desired function. Empirical formulas are often employed when an exact one either cannot be derived in closed form or else is too complicated for routine use.

[4]From D. Bolton (1980): The computation of equivalent potential temperature. *Mon. Wea. Rev.*, **108,** 1046–1053.

range $-30°\text{C} \leq T \leq 35°\text{C}$ (Fig. 7.5):

$$e_s(T) \approx 611.2 \exp\left(\frac{17.67\, T_c}{T_c + 243.5}\right) \tag{7.19}$$

where e_s is in Pa and T_c is the temperature in degrees C (*not* K!).

Key fact: To a rough approximation, the saturation vapor pressure of liquid water doubles for every 10°C increase in temperature.

7.3.2 Vapor pressure with respect to ice

We just derived an expression for the saturation vapor pressure e_s with respect to liquid water. In some situations, we also need to know the vapor pressure of ice. The Clausius-Clapeyron equation is just as valid for solid to vapor phase changes as it is for liquid to vapor changes. All we have to do is substitute the latent heat of sublimation L_s for L in the above equation and supply an appropriate laboratory-measured value for e_{s0} at some reference temperature T_0.

Making these substitutions, we have an expression for the saturation vapor pressure with respect to ice:

$$e_i(T) \approx e_{i0} \exp\left[\frac{L_s}{R_v}\left(\frac{1}{T_0} - \frac{1}{T}\right)\right]. \tag{7.20}$$

Conveniently, at 273 K, the saturation vapor pressure is nearly identical for both ice and water.[5] Thus, if we again take T_0 to be 273 K, then $e_{i0} = e_{s0} = 611$ Pa.

As before, we may substitute values for the various constants and simplify the above equation down to the following convenient form:

$$\boxed{e_i(T) \approx A_i e^{-B_i/T} \quad A_i = 3.41 \times 10^{12}\ \text{Pa},\ B_i = 6130\ \text{K}.} \tag{7.21}$$

It is easy to verify that for temperatures T *below* freezing, $e_i(T) < e_s(T)$, consistent with the laboratory measurements depicted in Fig. 7.2. We are therefore led to the following extremely important conclusion:

> **Key fact:** At subfreezing temperatures, an environment that is *saturated* with respect to liquid water will be *supersaturated* with respect to ice. Conversely, an environment that is *saturated* with respect to ice will be *subsaturated* with respect to supercooled liquid water at the same temperature.

[5]This is because 273 K is very close to the *triple-point* of water, namely 273.16 K, which is the temperature at which the three phases of water can coexist in equilibrium.

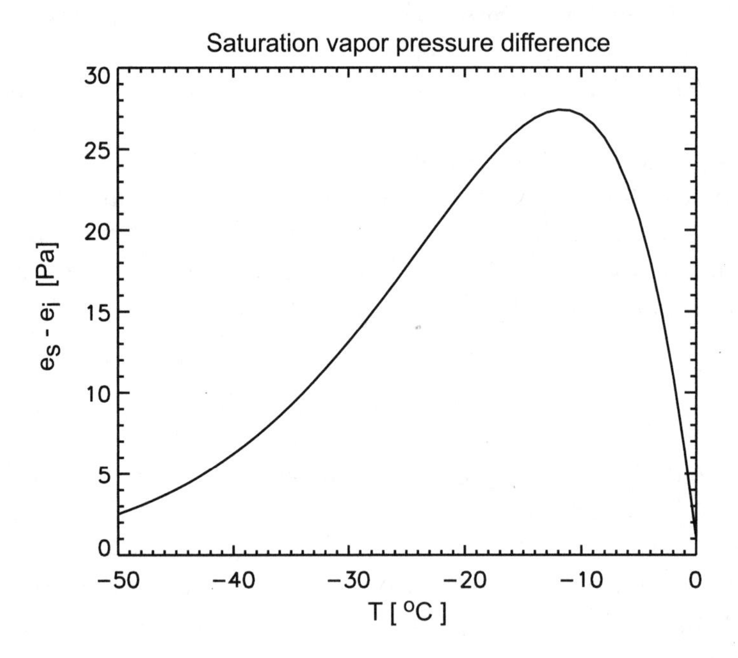

Fig. 7.6: The difference between the saturation vapor pressure of liquid water and that of ice for temperatures below freezing. This difference is closely related to the growth rate for snow crystals in a water-saturated environment; hence snowflakes grow most quickly in a supercooled cloud with temperatures near $-12°$C.

The difference between the two vapor pressures implies that, at any given temperature below freezing, ice simply cannot exist in equilibrium with supercooled liquid water. Whenever the two phases coexist (say, in a cloud that consists of both supercooled droplets and ice particles) the imbalance leads to the inexorable conversion of liquid to ice until no liquid is left (unless some other process continually replaces the liquid).

In particular, the difference between e_i and e_s is directly responsible for snow formation.[6] The magnitude of this difference is depicted in Fig. 7.6.

Problem 7.8: A certain cloud consists mostly of supercooled water droplets at $-10°C$ and maintains the ambient air at saturation with respect to liquid water at that temperature. Compute the supersaturation (in percent) with respect to a solitary ice particle that spontaneously forms in the cloud. *Answer:* 10%

7.4 Saturation Mixing Ratio

For almost every variable that can be used to describe the moisture content of a parcel of air, there is a counterpart that gives the value of that variable at saturation. An important example is the **saturation mixing ratio**, for which we use the symbol w_s.

w_s represents the mixing ratio w for which air at the specified temperature and pressure is saturated. One may easily compute w_s from e_s, and vice versa, using the same relationship we found earlier between w and e. That is,

$$w_s(T,p) = \frac{\varepsilon e_s(T)}{p - e_s(T)} \quad , \tag{7.22}$$

or

$$\boxed{w_s(T,p) \approx \frac{\varepsilon e_s(T)}{p} \quad .} \tag{7.23}$$

[6]The detailed mechanisms of snow production are normally left to a course in cloud and precipitation microphysics.

The saturation vapor pressure e_s is a function of T only, but the expression above shows that w_s is a function of both T and p. This implies that w_s is *not* conserved for most processes that entail changes in either pressure or temperature.

Problem 7.9: A sample of air has a temperature of 20°C, a relative humidity of 80%, and a pressure of 900 hPa.

a) Find its vapor pressure e.

b) Find its dewpoint T_d. (Continued next page.)

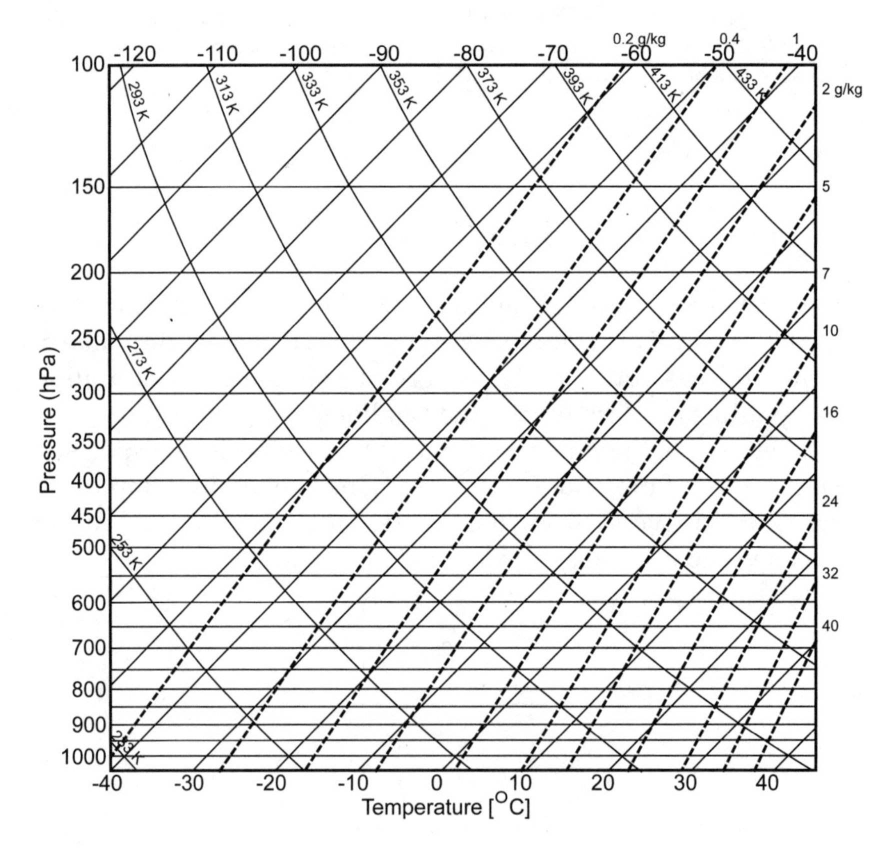

Fig. 7.7: Saturation mixing ratio lines (dashed) as they appear on a skew-T diagram. Labels (in g/kg) appear on the upper and right margins.

c) Find its mixing ratio w.

d) Find the saturation mixing ratio w_s.

e) If 1 m^3 of the air is compressed *isothermally* to a volume of only 0.2 m^3, find the mass of water that must condense out in order to eliminate any supersaturation. Hint: Determine the mass M_1 of vapor in the original volume and compare it with the mass M_2 of vapor at saturation after compression. *Answer:* 10.5 g

7.5 Moisture Variables on the Skew-T Diagram

7.5.1 Saturation mixing ratio lines

There is a unique value of w_s for any combination of T and p. Lines of constant w_s may therefore be drawn on any thermodynamic diagram such as a skew-T diagram, just as we have already done for temperature (isotherms), pressure (isobars), and potential temperature (isentropes). These lines are often informally known as **vapor lines** or **mixing ratio lines** (Fig. 7.7). Lines of constant saturation mixing ratio are usually labeled in units of g/kg.

7.5.2 Saturation vapor pressure

Recalling (7.23), we have

$$w_s(T,p) \approx \frac{\varepsilon e_s(T)}{p} \quad ,$$

where $\varepsilon \equiv R_d/R_v \approx 0.622$. If we choose the pressure p to be 622 hPa, then we have

$$w_s(T, p = 622\,\text{hPa}) \approx 0.001 e_s(T) \quad , \tag{7.24}$$

or

$$w_s(T, p = 622\,\text{hPa})\ [\text{g/kg}] \approx e_s(T)\ [\text{hPa}] \quad . \tag{7.25}$$

In other words, if we use a skew-T diagram to find the saturation mixing ratio in units of g/kg at a given temperature and at a fixed

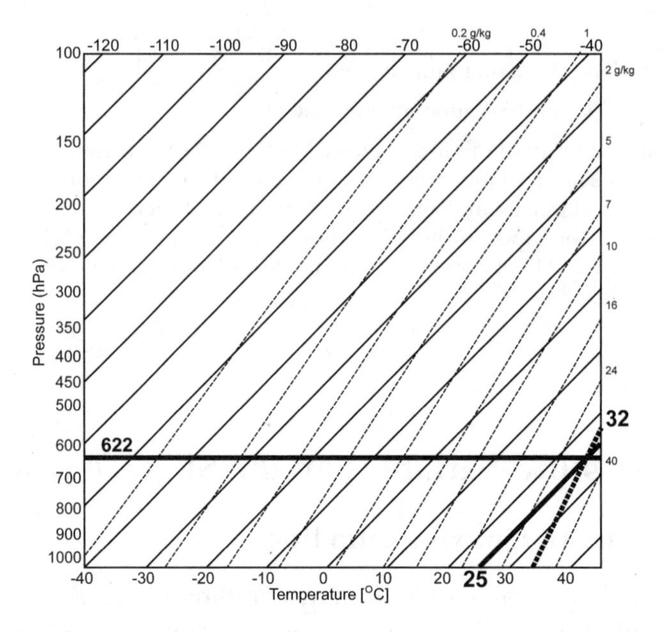

Fig. 7.8: Illustration of the use of a skew-T diagram to estimate saturation vapor pressure. In this example, a temperature of 25°C at 622 hPa is found to correspond to a saturation mixing ratio of 32 g/kg. The saturation vapor pressure at the same temperature is therefore approximately 32 hPa.

pressure of 622 hPa, the result is numerically equal to the saturation vapor pressure at the same temperature expressed in units of hectopascals.

Problem 7.10: Using the skew-T diagram at the back of the book, determine the saturation vapor pressure at a temperature of −20°C.

7.5.3 Dewpoint and mixing ratio

As we have seen, if you know the temperature T and pressure p of a parcel of air, you can plot a point on a thermodynamic diagram that uniquely identifies the values of those two state variables. Now you can also plot a point on the thermodynamic diagram corresponding to a parcel's pressure and *dewpoint*. What good is this? The line of

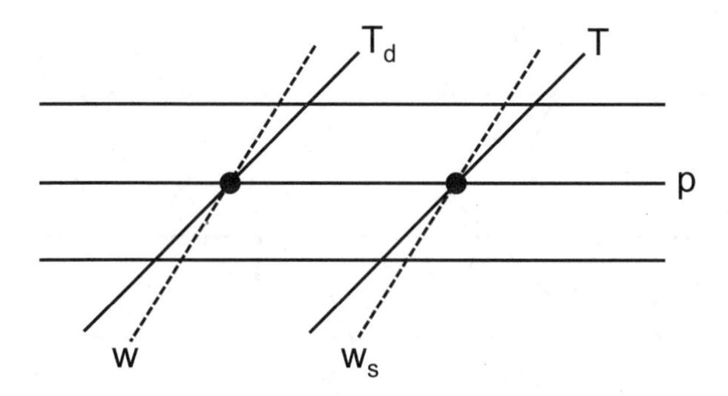

Fig. 7.9: Schematic depiction of the correspondence between the temperature and saturation mixing ratio of a parcel (right dot) and between the dewpoint and mixing ratio of the same parcel (left dot) on a skew-*T* diagram.

constant saturation mixing ratio w_s passing through this point tells you the *actual* mixing ratio w of the parcel, because if you were to cool the parcel isobarically to the dewpoint T_d, then w would equal w_s. Fig. 7.9 illustrates the relationships between the above variables for a specific parcel at pressure p on the skew-T diagram.

7.5.4 Relative humidity and dewpoint depression

By plotting the temperature and dewpoint of a parcel having a given pressure, one can immediately read off the values of w and w_s. The ratio w/w_s gives the relative humidity, so you can use the diagram to quickly and easily obtain the relative humidity of a volume of air, given T, T_d, and p.

The **dewpoint depression** ΔT_d is defined as the air temperature T minus the dewpoint T_d. The size of the dewpoint depression is indicated visually by the horizontal separation of the temperature and dewpoint on the skew-T. Where the separation is small, the relative humidity is large, and vice versa. If the two values coincide, the RH is 100%, and the air is saturated.

Problem 7.11: Using a skew-T diagram, determine the relative humidity of an air parcel having temperature 20°C, dewpoint 10°C, and pressure 900 hPa.

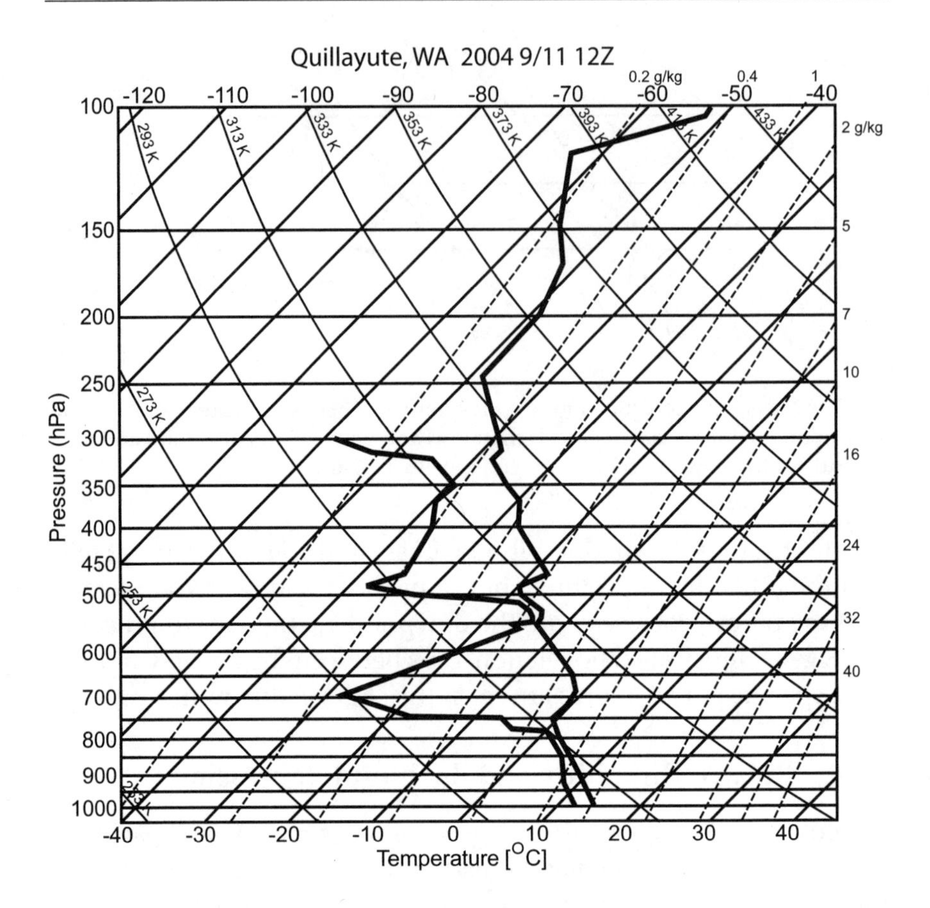

Fig. 7.10: Example of a skew-*T* depiction of both the temperature and dewpoint profiles for a sounding taken in Quillayute, Washington. Note that two layers are depicted as nearly saturated – between the surface and 800 hPa and again between 550 and 500 hPa. Both layers are likely associated with extensive cloudiness and possible precipitation. Although not depicted here as saturated with respect to liquid water, there is a layer of relatively high humidity near 350 hPa (approximately 8,000 m, or 25,000 ft.), which may be associated with cirrus (ice) cloudiness.

7.5.5 Dewpoint profiles

Fig. 7.10 shows a sounding with both the temperature and dewpoint profiles plotted on a skew-*T* diagram. The actual mixing ratio w at any level may be found from the intersections of the dewpoint profile with the mixing ratio lines.

Because air is never significantly supersaturated in real atmospheric soundings, you may see the dewpoint profile *touch* the temperature profile (at any level where the air is saturated), but you should never see it cross to the right of the temperature profile.

Many humidity sensors on weather balloons have trouble accurately reading humidity at temperatures below −40°C. It is therefore common for dewpoint profiles to terminate when the balloon reaches this temperature. Even when the dewpoint profile is reported at colder temperatures, the values should be viewed skeptically unless it is known that the instrument utilized performs well under those conditions.[7]

7.5.6 Unsaturated processes

In Section 5.4.3, we added lines of constant potential temperature θ, or dry adiabats, to our skew-T diagram. We further noted because that potential temperature is conserved in a dry adiabatic process, the (T, p) combination describing a parcel of air that undergoes only dry adiabatic lifting or sinking must remain on the same dry adiabat.

In the absence of condensation or evaporation, and therefore also for a dry adiabatic process, the water vapor mixing ratio w is conserved. Above we saw that when we plot the dewpoint-pressure combination of our parcel on the skew-T diagram, the corresponding saturation mixing ratio line is reinterpreted as the actual mixing ratio. It follows that the dewpoint of the parcel must remain on the same saturation mixing ratio line through changes in pressure and/or temperature, as depicted schematically in Fig. 7.11.

7.6 The Lifting Condensation Level (LCL)

Let us now consider in more detail what happens to an unsaturated parcel during adiabatic ascent. The adiabatic reduction in pressure

[7] In this book, I opt not to depict dewpoint profiles extending all the way to the top of the skew-T diagram even when data for those levels were included in the original report. Many upper air stations routinely report dewpoints that appear to be too moist for the lower stratosphere. Actual maximum mixing ratios there are typically less than 4 ppm, implying a dewpoint below −83°C at 100 hPa.

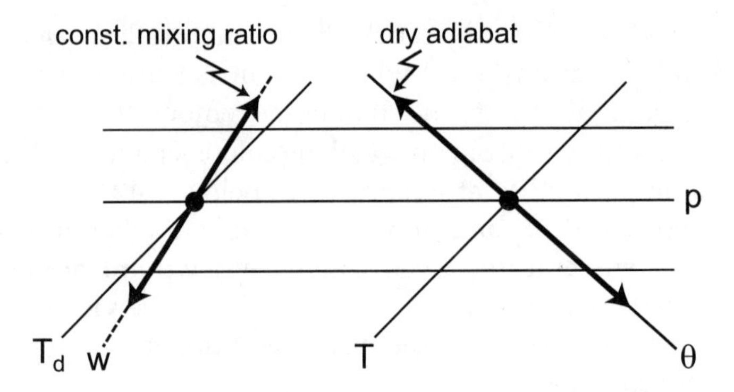

Fig. 7.11: During a dry adiabatic process, the temperature T of a parcel is constrained to remain on the same dry adiabat (line of constant θ) as pressure p changes, while the dewpoint T_d is constrained to remain on the same mixing ratio line.

also implies a reduction in temperature according to Poisson's equation, which in turn implies a reduction in the saturation vapor pressure e_s. Thus, according to (7.23), the reduction in pressure causes both the numerator and the denominator to decrease, but not necessarily at the same rates. Is the *net* result an increase or decrease in w_s? In other words, what is the *sign* of dw_s/dp for an adiabatic process? Let's find out:

$$\begin{aligned}
\frac{dw_s}{dp} &\approx \frac{d}{dp}\left[\frac{\varepsilon e_s}{p}\right] \\
&\approx \varepsilon\left[\frac{1}{p}\frac{de_s}{dp} - e_s\frac{1}{p^2}\right] \\
&\approx \varepsilon\left[\frac{1}{p}\frac{de_s}{dT}\frac{dT}{dp} - e_s\frac{1}{p^2}\right] \\
&\approx \frac{\varepsilon e_s}{p}\left[\frac{1}{e_s}\frac{de_s}{dT}\frac{dT}{dp} - \frac{1}{p}\right] \\
&\approx w_s\left[\frac{1}{e_s}\frac{de_s}{dT}\frac{dT}{dp} - \frac{1}{p}\right] \quad .
\end{aligned} \tag{7.26}$$

Substituting the Clausius-Clapeyron equation (7.15), the First Law for adiabatic processes (5.32), and the Ideal Gas Law $\alpha = R_d T/p$,

Fig. 7.12: Lens-shaped *altocumulus lenticularis* clouds occur when strong horizontal winds in a stable atmosphere move over elevated terrain, giving rise to standing waves, not unlike the quasi-stationary disturbance seen where a smooth-flowing river passes over a submerged boulder. The cloud appears where air ascends through its LCL in the upward phase of the wave. The cloud evaporates on the downwind side where the air descends below its LCL again. Although strong winds pass *through* the cloud, the cloud itself is usually quasi-stationary, being anchored to the terrain feature responsible for the wave. This photo was taken in the lee of the Rocky Mountains, near Fort Collins, Colorado. *(Courtesy of the NOAA Photo Library. Photo by Maxwell Parshall.)*

we have

$$\begin{aligned}\frac{dw_s}{dp} &\approx w_s\left[\frac{L}{R_vT^2}\frac{R_dT}{c_pp}-\frac{1}{p}\right]\\ &\approx \frac{w_s}{p}\left[\frac{\varepsilon L}{c_pT}-1\right] \quad .\end{aligned} \tag{7.27}$$

You can easily verify that for any reasonable atmospheric value of the temperature T, the above gives

$$\frac{dw_s}{dp} > 0 \quad , \tag{7.28}$$

so we see that w_s always decreases during an adiabatic decrease in pressure.

Although this is by no means an obvious result without going through the math as we just did, it is profoundly important. The actual mixing ratio w is conserved for dry adiabatic processes, so we can always reduce the pressure adiabatically until $w_s = w$, in which case we have achieved saturation. Any further reduction in pressure will lead to condensation in the form of a visible cloud (Fig. 7.12).

Key fact: The pressure at which saturation is achieved by a parcel during adiabatic ascent is called the **lifting condensation level**, or LCL. The LCL tells you the atmospheric pressure level at which to expect a cloud base to form when a parcel or layer is caused to rise adiabatically, either via free convection or by being mechanically lifted.

Key fact: On a thermodynamic diagram, the lifting condensation level (LCL) of a parcel is defined by the intersection of the dry adiabat corresponding to the parcel's temperature and the mixing ratio line corresponding to the parcel's dewpoint.

It is possible to derive an accurate mathematical relationship between T, p, and w of a parcel and the parcel's LCL, and this relationship may be easily solved numerically using a short computer program. However, the relationship does not lend itself to convenient solution using a hand calculator.

Problem 7.12: Derive an equation that relates T, p, and w of a parcel to the pressure p_{lcl} corresponding to the parcel's LCL. You may use the approximate relationships (7.18) and (7.23), as well as Poisson's equation (5.36). You do not need to solve it.

Fortunately, within the range of temperatures and pressures commonly of interest, the following *approximate* relationship is accurate enough for most routine purposes:

$$LCL \approx p \exp[-0.0144 \Delta T_d] \quad , \tag{7.29}$$

where the dewpoint depression $\Delta T_d = T - T_d$ is given in degrees Celsius.

Another common rule of thumb gives the approximate *altitude* of the LCL as

$$LCL \text{ [km]} \approx (T - T_d)/8 \quad . \tag{7.30}$$

Problem 7.13: During the summer, daytime temperatures are typically around 30°C both in the east central United States and over the high deserts in the west. In the first case, a typical relative humidity is 70%, while in the second, it may be as low as 10%.

a) Find the corresponding dewpoints. *Answer:* 297.2 K (eastern U.S.)

b) Find the expected altitude in meters of the base of any convective clouds that develop from surface heating. *Answer:* 741 m (eastern U.S.)

7.7 The Moist Adiabatic Lapse Rate

7.7.1 Terminology and physical basis

When air is lifted adiabatically to the pressure level given by the LCL, the vapor in the parcel reaches the saturation point. If the parcel is lifted further, it cools further, and excess water vapor condenses out rapidly so that the parcel spends very little time significantly supersaturated.

But when water condenses from the vapor phase to the liquid phase, it also releases latent heat of condensation to the air. It thus partially offsets the loss of internal energy due to the adiabatic expansion. It cannot, of course, *completely* offset it because there would then be no cooling and thus no condensation! The lapse rate Γ_s experienced by the rising saturated parcel is therefore greater than 0

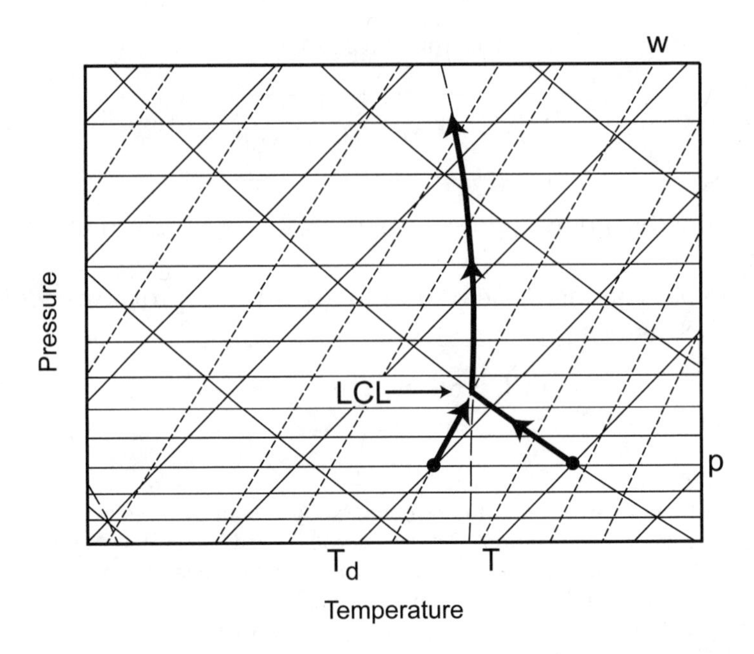

Fig. 7.13: Schematic depiction of the evolution of a parcel with initial temperature T, dewpoint T_d, and pressure p undergoing dry and then moist adiabatic ascent. The lifting condensation level (LCL) is defined as the pressure level where the parcel first achieves saturation. At all points above the LCL, the parcel remains saturated and $T = T_d$.

but less than Γ_d, the dry adiabatic lapse rate we derived in (5.46). This difference in cooling rate can be seen in Fig. 7.13—above the parcel's LCL, the temperature continues to decrease with decreasing pressure but no longer as rapidly as would be indicated by the original dry adiabat.

If we consider the water droplets that form within the rising parcel to be part of the thermodynamic system, and if we assume that the droplets do not fall out of the parcel, then the latent heat released simply represents a conversion of energy from one form to another within the parcel and does not involve the transfer of heat between the parcel and its surroundings. Seen in this way, the process is still adiabatic, though in a less "pure" sense than the dry adiabatic process we considered earlier. That is, although $\delta q \neq 0$ in the First Law equations we have been using, at least δq does not come from an external source.

A **saturated adiabatic process** (also commonly called a **moist adiabatic process**) is a process in which the only source of diabatic heating/cooling is condensation or evaporation at a rate that is sufficient to maintain exact saturation in parcel. A moist adiabatic process is reversible—if you were to lower a parcel which was previously ascending with condensation, the droplets that previously formed will simply evaporate again, taking latent heat with them, and the parcel will experience the same temperature evolution in reverse.

On the other hand, if we assume that all liquid water falls out of the parcel immediately after it is condensed (e.g., as rain), then it is no longer reversible. Not only is the parcel now an open rather than closed system (because it is exchanging mass with the environment), we also have to be concerned with the small amount of energy that is carried out of the parcel with the falling drops. For both reasons, such a process is often referred to **pseudoadiabatic.**

For calculating the change of temperature of a rising parcel of air with altitude, the difference between a moist adiabatic process and a pseudoadiabatic process is fairly small—usually less than one degree. Meteorologists therefore tend to use the terms *saturated adiabatic, moist adiabatic* and *pseudoadiabatic* more or less interchangeably when applied to *rising* air parcels.

The most important distinction between "moist adiabatic" and "pseudoadiabatic" arises for *sinking* parcels — is any condensed water still present in the parcel and therefore evaporating, or did it fall out, leaving the parcel permanently drier (and warmer) than it was before? We will compare these two cases again in Section 7.10.4.

7.7.2 Change of temperature with pressure

We can now proceed to derive an expression for the rate of change of temperature with a saturated adiabatic change in pressure. As we did for Poisson's equation, we start with the First Law of Thermodynamics:[8]

$$\delta q = c_p dT - \alpha dp \quad . \tag{7.31}$$

[8]Water vapor almost never makes up more than one or two percent of the total mass of a volume of air, so we may safely assume that the heat capacity c_p of saturated air is approximately that of dry air.

Unlike the case for dry adiabatic processes, δq is not zero but represents the latent heat released to the air by condensation. When rising air cools by expansion, the saturation mixing ratio w_s decreases. Moreover, in a saturated parcel, the actual mixing ratio is equal to the saturation mixing ratio; hence, a decrease in w_s implies an actual reduction in the vapor mixing ratio, and this reduction corresponds to the amount of water condensed to liquid form. The latent heating δq is therefore

$$\delta q = -L\, dw_s \quad . \tag{7.32}$$

Substituting this into the form of the First Law given just above, we have

$$-L\, dw_s = c_p dT - \alpha dp \quad . \tag{7.33}$$

We now express dw_s in terms of changes in temperature T and pressure p by differentiating as follows:

$$dw_s = \frac{\partial w_s}{\partial T} dT + \frac{\partial w_s}{\partial p} dp \quad . \tag{7.34}$$

Utilizing our approximate expression for w_s given by (7.23), we have

$$dw_s \approx -w_s \frac{1}{p} dp + w_s \frac{1}{e_s} \frac{de_s}{dT} dT \quad , \tag{7.35}$$

which we can further simplify using (7.15) to get

$$dw_s \approx -w_s \frac{1}{p} dp + w_s \frac{L}{R_v T^2} dT \quad . \tag{7.36}$$

The above can be combined with (7.33) and the Ideal Gas Law to get

$$\boxed{\frac{d \ln T}{d \ln p} \approx \left[\frac{1 + \frac{L w_s}{R_d T}}{1 + \frac{L^2 w_s}{R_v c_p T^2}} \right] \frac{R_d}{c_p}} \quad . \tag{7.37}$$

If $w_s \approx 0$, as is the case for very cold parcels, then the above reduces to the differential form of Poisson's equation and there is no distinction between dry and moist adiabatic ascent. At warmer temperatures, however, the rate of cooling is substantially smaller than that for dry ascent.

Unfortunately, the above result cannot be integrated in closed form to obtain a moist adiabatic counterpart to Poisson's equation (5.36). It can, however, be integrated *numerically* to obtain $T(p)$ for moist adiabatic changes in pressure, given the initial temperature T_0 and pressure p_0. When this function is plotted on a thermodynamic diagram, the corresponding curve is called a **moist adiabat**, a **saturation adiabat**, or a **pseudoadiabat**.[9]

Fig. 7.14 depicts a representative set of moist adiabats on a skew-T diagram. You can see that the difference in slope relative to dry adiabats is large in the warm lower right portion and vanishingly small in the cold (and therefore dry) upper left portion of the diagram.

Key fact: When a parcel moves through the atmosphere dry adiabatically, its temperature follows a dry adiabat and the dewpoint follows a saturation mixing ratio line. The lifting condensation level (LCL) of the parcel is defined by the pressure level where these two lines intersect. If the parcel reaches the LCL adiabatically, it will become saturated. If it continues to rise adiabatically, its temperature and dewpoint will be the same, both following a moist adiabat.

7.7.3 Change of temperature with altitude

Let us look again at moist adiabatic changes in temperature, but this time with respect to changes in height z. Once again, we start with the First Law of Thermodynamics:

$$\delta q = c_p dT - \alpha dp \quad , \tag{7.38}$$

[9]As mentioned earlier, there is a small difference between the rate of temperature change with pressure for a reversible moist adiabatic process and an irreversible pseudoadiabatic process. For technical reasons, the saturation adiabats appearing on thermodynamic diagrams like the skew-T are almost invariably based on the assumption of pseudoadiabatic ascent. The interested reader is referred to T07 for more thorough discussion of these and related topics.

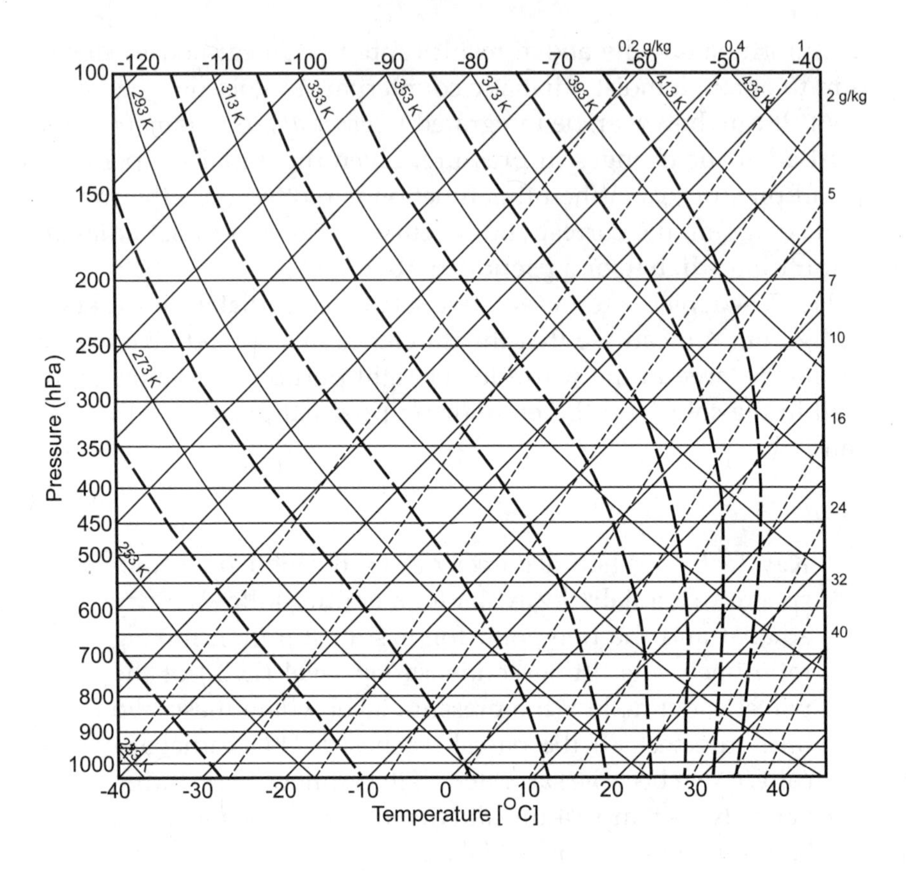

Fig. 7.14: Moist adiabats (long dashed curves) on a skew-T diagram.

or

$$-L\,dw_s = c_p dT - \alpha dp \quad . \tag{7.39}$$

We again utilize (7.36) to get

$$Lw_s \frac{1}{p} dp - w_s \frac{L^2}{R_v T^2} dT = c_p dT - \alpha dp \quad . \tag{7.40}$$

Again invoking the hydrostatic equation and the assumption that the parcel temperature is not too different from that of the environment, we may write

$$g dz \approx -\alpha dp \tag{7.41}$$

and divide each term in (7.40) by either the left or right of the above to get

$$-\frac{Lw_s}{p\alpha} - \frac{L^2 w_s}{R_v T^2 g}\frac{dT}{dz} = \frac{c_p}{g}\frac{dT}{dz} + 1 \quad . \tag{7.42}$$

We then recall the definition of the dry adiabatic lapse rate $\Gamma_d \equiv g/c_p$ and multiply through to get

$$-\frac{Lw_s}{R_d T}\Gamma_d - \frac{L^2 w_s}{R_v c_p T^2}\frac{dT}{dz} = \frac{dT}{dz} + \Gamma_d \quad . \tag{7.43}$$

Rearranging gives the **moist adiabatic lapse rate**

$$\Gamma_s \equiv -\frac{dT}{dz} = \left[\frac{1 + \frac{Lw_s}{R_d T}}{1 + \frac{L^2 w_s}{R_v c_p T^2}}\right]\Gamma_d \quad . \tag{7.44}$$

You will see many similarities between the above equation and (7.37), which looks at the change of temperature with pressure rather than with altitude. Because for any reasonable atmospheric temperature

$$\frac{LR_d}{R_v c_p T} > 1 \quad , \tag{7.45}$$

the term in brackets in (7.44) is always less than one, and

$$\boxed{\Gamma_s < \Gamma_d \quad ,} \tag{7.46}$$

as you would expect.

Actual values of Γ_s typically range from around 4 K/km near the ground in warm, humid air masses to around 6–7 K/km in the middle troposphere. At very high, cold altitudes (say, near the tropopause), Γ_s is only very slightly smaller than Γ_d because there is very little moisture left in the parcel to condense.

7.8 Equivalent Potential Temperature

7.8.1 Definition

Earlier we introduced the potential temperature θ, which is defined as the temperature a parcel would have if it were compressed (or expanded) dry-adiabatically to a pressure of exactly 1000 hPa. The potential temperature is conserved in a dry-adiabatic process; that is, if no condensation or evaporation occurs and no heat is added to or removed from a parcel of air, θ does not change as the parcel moves up and down in the atmosphere.

If condensation *does* take place—say, because the parcel is lifted dry adiabatically up to the LCL and moist adiabatically thereafter—the potential temperature no longer remains constant but increases due to the latent heat released by condensation. Therefore, whenever a process entails the possibility of condensation or evaporation, it is often useful to work with the **equivalent potential temperature** θ_e, which corresponds to the *maximum* potential temperature a parcel could achieve via condensation of all of its water vapor content.

Key fact: Whereas the potential temperature θ is conserved only for dry adiabatic processes, the equivalent potential temperature is conserved for both dry and moist adiabatic processes.

7.8.2 Isobaric equivalent potential temperature

There are actually different methods of computing θ_e, and they give slightly different results. The easiest version to derive mathematically is the **isobaric equivalent potential temperature**, which we will denote θ_e'. It is the temperature a parcel achieves when it is (1) warmed to its **equivalent temperature** T_e by condensing all of its water vapor isobarically, and (2) compressed dry adiabatically to 1000 hPa following the definition for potential temperature (5.39).

To execute the first step, we invoke the First Law for an isobaric process,

$$\delta q = c_p dT \quad , \tag{7.47}$$

to get

$$-L dw = c_p dT \quad , \tag{7.48}$$

where $-Ldw$ in this case is the increment of heating due to condensation of dw units of water vapor mass per unit mass of dry air. If we assume that L is independent of temperature (this is an approximation), we may integrate the above from the initial mixing ratio to a value of zero (all vapor removed by condensation):

$$-L \int_{w}^{0} dw = c_p \int_{T}^{T_e} dT \quad , \tag{7.49}$$

or

$$Lw = c_p(T_e - T) \quad , \tag{7.50}$$

which can be rearranged to get the equivalent temperature

$$T_e = \left(1 + \frac{Lw}{c_p T}\right) T \quad . \tag{7.51}$$

Substituting T_e for T in (5.39), we have

$$\theta'_e = T_e \left(\frac{1000\ \text{hPa}}{p}\right)^{\kappa} \quad , \tag{7.52}$$

$$\theta'_e = \left(1 + \frac{Lw}{c_p T}\right) T \left(\frac{1000\ \text{hPa}}{p}\right)^{\kappa} \quad , \tag{7.53}$$

$$\boxed{\theta'_e = \left(1 + \frac{Lw}{c_p T}\right) \theta \quad .} \tag{7.54}$$

7.8.3 Adiabatic equivalent potential temperature

Although the derivation of the isobaric equivalent temperature is mathematically straightforward, it also represents a physically impossible process: you can't *warm* a parcel isobarically by condensing water from it because you can't get isobaric condensation without (diabatic) *cooling*.

More realistic is the so-called **adiabatic equivalent potential temperature**, which is the temperature that an air parcel would have after undergoing a dry-adiabatic expansion until saturation is reached, a saturated adiabatic expansion up to some extremely cold temperature for which w essentially goes to zero, and then a dry adiabatic compression back to 1000 hPa. Graphically, this corresponds to taking the parcel along a dry adiabat up to the LCL, then following a moist adiabat[10] to a sufficiently cold temperature where $w_s \approx 0$, and then following a dry adiabat back down to the 1000 hPa level. This process is shown schematically in Fig. 7.15. The intermediate temperature T_e obtained as the parcel passes through its original pressure p is known as the **adiabatic equivalent temperature** and is analogous to the isobaric equivalent temperature given by (7.51).

Because of the different thermodynamic assumptions involved

[10] The curves representing saturated processes on most commonly used thermodynamic charts are actually *pseudoadiabats*, which are lines of constant *pseudoequivalent potential temperature*. We ignore the rather technical distinction between moist adiabats and pseudoadiabats in this introductory text.

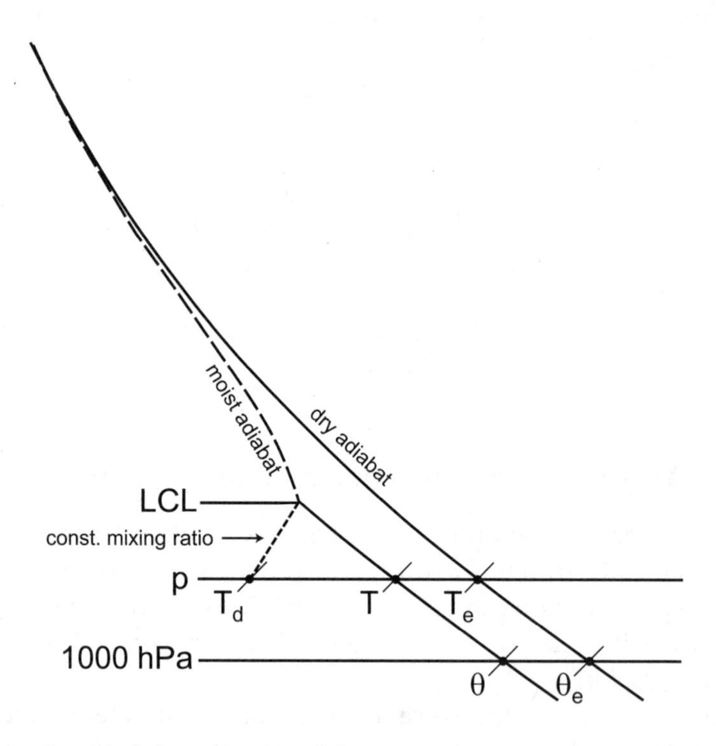

Fig. 7.15: Graphical determination of the potential temperature θ and (adiabatic) equivalent potential temperature θ_e for a parcel with initial pressure p, temperature T, and dewpoint T_d. Also shown is the (adiabatic) equivalent temperature T_e.

in moist adiabatic processes, the adiabatic equivalent potential temperature is given to reasonable accuracy by

$$\theta_e = \theta \exp \frac{Lw}{c_p T_{\mathrm{LCL}}} , \qquad (7.55)$$

where T_{LCL} is the temperature of the parcel at the LCL. The adiabatic equivalent potential is close to, but slightly larger than, isobaric equivalent potential temperature θ_e'.

Key fact: Because θ_e is conserved during a saturated adiabatic process, moist adiabats on a thermodynamic diagram may be regarded as lines of constant θ_e for any *saturated* parcel.

Problem 7.14: The definition (7.55) of equivalent potential temperature assumes that all condensation results in the appearance of liquid water, regardless of the temperature. If freezing occurs, additional latent heat is released, which further raises the temperature of the parcel. Assume that a parcel is at saturation at a temperature of freezing and a pressure of 900 hPa.

a) What is the equivalent potential temperature θ_e according to the traditional definition?

b) By how much would θ_e increase if all condensate were assumed to freeze? *Answer:* 1.5 K

7.9 Wet-bulb Temperature

7.9.1 Physical basis

If you take an ordinary dry thermometer and expose it to a volume of air, it will reach thermal equilibrium when it has the same temperature as the air. Therefore the temperature you read from the thermometer will simply be that of the air. Now imagine wrapping the bulb of the thermometer in a cotton wick or some other porous material and then moistening the wick with pure water. As long as the wick is kept moist and well-ventilated, and assuming the air is unsaturated, the water will evaporate at a steady rate. As it does so, heat must be continually supplied in an amount equal to the latent heat of vaporization of the water. This heat is taken from the air passing over the wick of the thermometer, resulting in a drop in temperature. The temperature measured in this way is called the **wet-bulb temperature** and is indicated by the symbol T_w.

Key fact: The wet-bulb temperature T_w is the temperature a volume of air attains when water is evaporated into the air exactly to the point of saturation and assuming that all of the latent heat of vaporization is supplied by the air.

Obviously, if the air is saturated, no evaporation takes place, in which case the wet-bulb temperature is the same as the ordinary (or dry-bulb) temperature T. If the air is very dry, on the other hand, the **wet-bulb depression**, which is the dry-bulb temperature minus the wet-bulb temperature, may be quite substantial.

It is tempting to think that the wet-bulb temperature should be the same as the dewpoint temperature—after all, evaporation leading to the absorption of latent heat should continue until the temperature of the wet bulb equals the dewpoint, right? This is not correct, however. The difference between the dewpoint and the wet-bulb temperature is best understood as follows: in the case of the dewpoint, we are speaking of the temperature we obtain if we simply cool a volume of air until saturation is reached *while keeping the moisture content constant*. By contrast, the wet-bulb temperature is the temperature we obtain if we cool the air to saturation *by evaporating water into it*. The latter provision implies that the moisture content has increased, and therefore saturation is reached at a higher temperature than the dewpoint. As a result, we have the following rule:

$$\boxed{T_d \leq T_w \leq T \quad .} \tag{7.56}$$

The equality between T_d, T_w, and T holds if and only if the air is saturated.

Not surprisingly, there is a well-defined relationship between the above three temperatures. If you know any two (at a given pressure), then the third can be accurately determined. As a result, one of the most accurate ways to measure atmospheric humidity is to use two thermometers—one with a ventilated moistened wick—to simultaneously measure T and T_w. Such an apparatus combining a wet-bulb and dry-bulb thermometer is called a **psychrometer**. Based on your measurement of T and T_w, you may compute the dewpoint T_d. From T and T_d, one may, of course, compute all other relevant moisture variables, such as specific humidity, vapor pressure, relative humidity, or mixing ratio.

Unfortunately, there is no simple mathematical formula for dewpoint as a function of the wet-bulb and dry-bulb temperatures. Meteorologists commonly use other means (tables, slide rules, or computer programs) to determine the dewpoint from the wet- and dry-bulb temperatures measured by a psychrometer. Some of these methods are discussed in Section 7.10.1. In the following section, we introduce a simple graphical method that can be utilized when a skew-T or similar thermodynamic diagram is available.

7.9.2 Normand's Rule

Key fact: **Normand's Rule** states that the wet-bulb temperature may be determined by lifting a parcel of air adiabatically to its LCL and then following a moist adiabat from that temperature back down to the parcel's actual pressure.

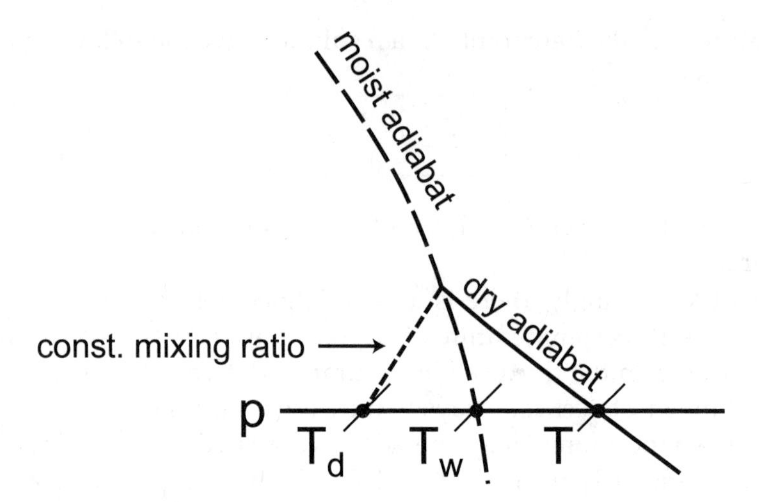

Fig. 7.16: The graphical relationship between temperature T, wet-bulb temperature T_w, and dewpoint T_d according to Normand's rule.

Normand's Rule actually yields what is called the **adiabatic wet-bulb temperature**, as contrasted with the **isobaric wet-bulb temperature** that is provided by a measurement using a wet-bulb thermometer. However, the difference between the two never exceeds a few tenths of a degree and is therefore usually ignored.

Often it is the wet-bulb temperature that is known from a psychrometer measurement and the dewpoint temperature that is to be determined. In this case, you simply find the intersection of the dry adiabat passing through T and the moist adiabat passing through T_w. You then follow a saturation mixing ratio line back to find the dewpoint.

Problem 7.15: With the help of a skew-T diagram, estimate the hottest possible air temperature for which the wet-bulb temperature is at or below freezing.

Problem 7.16: So-called "swamp coolers" are air-conditioning units that use evaporation of water to cool the air passing through the unit. Estimate the minimum temperature achievable by a swamp cooler operating in

a) extremely dry desert air having a temperature of 40°C (104°F), and

b) humid summer air in the southeastern U.S. having a temperature of 35°C (95°F) and a dewpoint of 25°C (77°F).

(The first of these cases describes a scenario in which you could easily feel hot enough to want to go swimming and yet feel uncomfortably chilly after you reemerge soaking wet from a heated pool, especially if there is a breeze blowing!)

7.9.3 Wet-bulb potential temperature

The **wet-bulb potential temperature** θ_w is defined as the wet-bulb temperature a parcel would have after adiabatic compression (or expansion) to the 1000 hPa pressure level. It is found graphically by first determining the wet-bulb temperature T_w using Normand's Rule and then following the same moist adiabat all the way to where it intersects the 1000 hPa level on the thermodynamic diagram. Note that θ_w is actually not a distinct variable from the equivalent potential temperature θ_e; there is a one-to-one correspondence between the two variables—any moist adiabat can be interpreted as a line of either constant θ_e or θ_w, though with different numerical values.

Problem 7.17: The equivalent potential temperature of a parcel is 310 K. (a) Graphically, estimate its wet-bulb potential temperature θ_w. (b) If its potential temperature θ is 300 K, graphically find its mixing ratio w.

7.10 In Practice

7.10.1 Measurement of humidity

Despite constituting only a minor fraction of air, water vapor plays an enormously important role in atmospheric energetics, clouds, precipitation and, indeed, weather of all kinds. It follows that frequent and reasonably accurate measurements of humidity (along with temperature, pressure, and wind) form the foundation upon which almost all practical meteorology is built. Interestingly, humidity is also the only *chemical* property of the atmosphere that is routinely measured. This section offers a concise overview of how routine humidity measurements are made.

Hygrometers

A **hygrometer** is any device that measures the water vapor content of air. There are several different physical principles on which hygrometers may be based. The most common of these include

Evaporative cooling: If a wet surface is exposed to a steady stream of subsaturated air, evaporation will occur. The evaporation lowers the temperature to the wet-bulb temperature. The lower the relative humidity, the larger the wet-bulb depression. As already discussed, a psychrometer (see also next subsection) is a device that exploits this effect to measure humidity.

Mechanical expansion: Some materials absorb moisture from the air and expand slightly as a result. Common examples include wood,[11] paper, and hair. The expansion and contraction of such materials in can be amplified mechanically to display or record changes in humidity (e.g., Fig. 7.17). A professional quality device based on this principle is the **hair hygrometer**, which relies on changes in the length of an array of strands of human hair to record humidity with an ink pen on a paper chart.[12] The external physical appearance is somewhat similar to that of the microbarograph depicted in Fig. 4.8, but with two pens: one for temperature and one for relative humidity.

[11] Guitars and other stringed instruments made of wood go very noticeably out of tune when the humidity changes.

[12] Invented in 1783 by Horace-Bénédict de Saussure, the hair hygrometer was one of the earliest successful devices for measuring humidity. For many years, hair hygrometers deployed by the U.S. military were required to use "fine natural blonde hair from a Norwegian female." The point of this rather picky specification was to ensure a high a degree of consistency in the calibration of the instrument.

Condensation: If a polished metal surface is cooled to the dewpoint, condensation occurs, and the surface fogs up. The condensation can be detected by an optical sensor and the temperature at which condensation occurred noted electronically. Such a device is called a **dewpoint hygrometer**. These devices are typically rather expensive but also quite accurate. They are often employed when high quality humidity measurements are required for research purposes.

Electrical properties: Some substances absorb moisture and exhibit measurable changes in certain properties such as electrical conductivity. Two such devices are the **dew cell** and the **carbon hygristor**. The first is commonly installed at automated weather stations; the second is often used as the lightweight, disposable humidity sensing element on radiosondes.

Of the above devices, the psychrometer is the one you are most likely to encounter in a meteorology lab course. It is also an important calibration standard for other instruments. For both reasons, it is worthwhile to devote some space to describing its correct use.

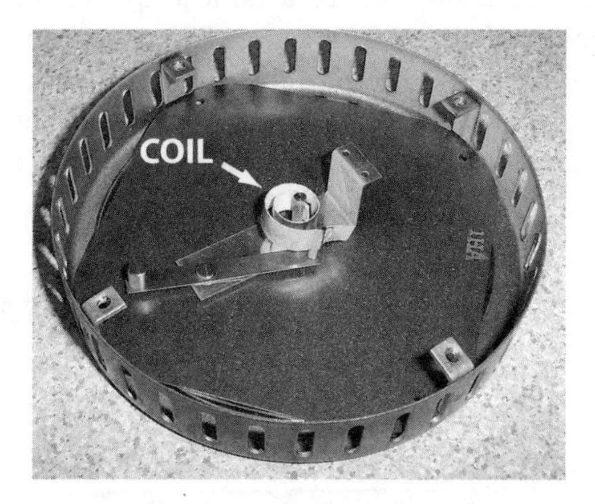

Fig. 7.17: The fairly inaccurate dial-type hygrometers that are sometimes displayed in people's homes to indicate indoor relative humidity are based on the internal mechanism shown here. A spring coil is layered on one side with a material that expands and contracts in response to changing humidity, causing the coil to loosen and tighten, moving the needle on the dial. *(Photo: Alan Sim)*

The psychrometer

Psychrometers exist in several forms, but all consist of two identical thermometers exposed side by side to the same ambient air. One is usually an ordinary liquid-in-glass thermometer intended to measure the actual air temperature and is called the **dry-bulb** thermometer. The other has its bulb covered with a sheath or wick of clean cotton mesh or muslin that is saturated with distilled water. It is called the **wet-bulb** thermometer, and its purpose is to measure the wet-bulb temperature described in Section 7.9.

Regardless of design, the main function of any particular psychrometer model is not only to supply the dry-bulb and wet-bulb thermometers themselves but also to incorporate a convenient means of **ventilating** both—that is, ensuring that they are exposed to a constant supply of fresh air. If they were not well-ventilated, then the air in contact with the wick would quickly be moistened by evaporation from the wet-bulb thermometer, and the resulting wet-bulb temperature would be in error. Here are the main types that you are likely to encounter:

Sling psychrometer: A psychrometer in which the wet- and dry-bulb thermometers are mounted side-by-side on a metal or plastic frame connected to a handle by a movable pivot or short length of chain (Fig. 7.18). The psychrometer is swung by hand in order to provide the necessary ventilation. This is the least expensive and therefore most common type of psychrometer. It is also the hardest to use *correctly* and by far

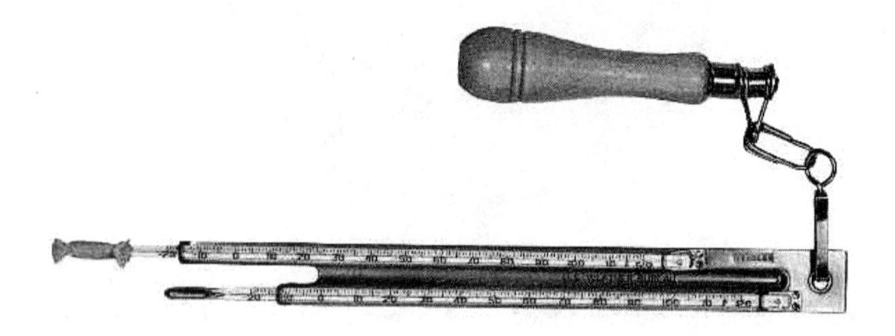

Fig. 7.18: A professional sling psychrometer. *(Photo: Greg Keefer)*

Fig. 7.19: An Assman aspirated psychrometer, the basic design of which has not changed significantly in over a century. A spring-wound fan provides the ventilation. The device is usually hung vertically from an eyelet on the end of the fan housing.

the easiest to break through inadvertent contact with nearby walls, tables, or fellow students.

Aspirated psychrometer: A psychrometer having both thermometers mounted inside a housing and ventilated by way of a built-in fan. All you have to do is moisten the wick, point it into the wind or hang it from a hook, turn on the fan, and monitor the wet-bulb temperature until it reaches its lowest value. An early model of aspirated psychrometer, still encountered in many university supply cabinets (including the author's), is the Assman[13] psychrometer (Fig. 7.19). To drive the fan, it relies on a mechanical spring that is wound up like an old-fashioned alarm clock or music box.

Using the sling psychrometer

Sling psychrometers are the traditional standard for manually measuring ambient temperature and humidity. Every meteorologist should know how to use one correctly.

[13]Named after the German meteorologist Adolph Richard Aßman (pronounced"ahss-mahn") (1845-1918).

1. Inspect the two thermometers for proper operation. When both bulbs are still dry and at equilibrium with the ambient air, the thermometers should read exactly the same temperature. If one reads significantly higher than the other, it might have a separated mercury or alcohol column. Your instructor can often cure this by carefully warming the thermometer until the column reunites. Otherwise, the affected thermometer might need to be replaced.

2. Inspect the muslin wick on the sling psychrometer, making sure that it is in good condition, securely attached, and firmly in contact with, and completely covering, the thermometer bulb. A psychrometer with a badly yellowed or frayed wick might not give an accurate reading, and the wick should be replaced. Do not touch the wick with your bare fingers any more than necessary (e.g., for installation of the wick), because contaminants will affect the accuracy.

3. Find a location outdoors that is as exposed as possible to the ambient environment. Sheltered or enclosed areas are usually bad locations.

4. Thoroughly saturate the wick with *distilled* water. If the water beads up and does not easily soak in, you may have to persist in applying the water until the wick is thoroughly wetted with no bubbles or dry spots. If you still have trouble, the wick should be replaced.

5. Face into the wind (if any) and begin swinging the psychrometer at a steady, *leisurely* pace—about 2 turns per second is ideal. There is no advantage to spinning the psychrometer more rapidly! *Be extremely careful that you don't strike the psychrometer on a nearby table, railing, or other obstruction!* Also, keep it far enough in front of your body that you don't pick up your own body heat.

6. After about 1 minute, stop and check the wet-bulb temperature, *quickly* reading it to the nearest tenth-degree (if you take too long, the temperature will start to change). Be careful not to let your hands, body heat, or breath affect the psychrometer bulbs while you are reading.

7. Continue swinging the psychrometer for another minute or so. Check the wet-bulb temperature again and see whether it has changed from your previous reading. If it has, continue swinging for yet another minute and check again. Repeat as necessary. Your goal is to get the *lowest possible reading* out of the wet-bulb thermometer. Once you have this, you can assume that the dry-bulb thermometer has equilibrated as well. *Important: ensure that the wick does not become too dry before you finish taking your reading. If it does, you will need to add another drop or two of distilled water and start over.*

8. *Carefully but quickly* read and record the final dry-bulb and wet-bulb temperatures to the nearest 0.1 degree, interpolating between tick marks as necessary. If the air temperature is

Fig. 7.20: The chief boatswain on a NOAA ship swings a psychrometer to obtain wet- and dry-bulb temperatures. *(Courtesy of the NOAA Photo Library. Photo by Cmdr. John Bortniak, NOAA Corps.)*

close to or below freezing, also note whether the wick is actually frozen — you will need this information for the next step.

9. Use whatever method your instructor specifies (see below) to compute the dewpoint and/or relative humidity from your recorded dry-bulb and wet-bulb temperatures.

Key fact: Most beginners do not get accurate psychrometer readings because of the following common mistakes: (1) not ventilating the psychrometer long enough to reach equilibrium, (2) not getting the wick wet enough or letting it dry out, (3) holding it too close to the body or taking too long to read the thermometers, (4) touching the bulb ends with the hands while reading, (5) not facing into the breeze. Each of these mistakes *usually* leads to a wet-bulb temperature reading that is too warm, which in turn means a humidity estimate that is too high.

Obtaining dewpoint and relative humidity

The **psychrometric formula** (also known as the **hygrometric formula**) is a semi-empirical relation giving the actual vapor pressure e in terms of the barometric pressure p, the psychrometer readings T and T_w, and the saturation vapor pressure e_s evaluated at T_w [using (7.19) for example]. When the two temperatures are given in degrees Celsius and the pressure is in the same units as e and e_s, the psychrometric formula is

$$e = e_s(T_w) - 6.60 \times 10^{-4}(1 + 0.00115T_w)(T - T_w)p \quad . \qquad (7.57)$$

If the wet-bulb is frozen, then 6.60×10^{-4} is replaced in the above by 5.82×10^{-4}.

Once e is determined, the relative humidity is of course

$$RH = \frac{e}{e_s(T)} \quad , \qquad (7.58)$$

and the dewpoint may be found by solving

$$e = e_s(T_d) \tag{7.59}$$

for T_d. While the above method is accurate and can be readily implemented in a short computer program, it is too cumbersome for routine use without the aid of a computer or programmable calculator. Traditionally, humidity and dewpoint have therefore been determined from psychrometer readings using any of a number of non-mathematical methods. The most common include the following:

Psychrometric computer: A specialized mechanical slide rule, this was long the standard method of evaluating psychrometer readings in operational weather offices. The most accurate psychrometric computer is a large-diameter (almost one foot) circular slide rule (Fig. 7.21). Simpler linear slide rules are often provided with commercial sling psychrometers intended for non-professional use; these generally provide relative humidity directly from the wet-bulb and dry-bulb temperatures. They are easy to use but less accurate.

Lookup table: The simplest but (usually) least accurate method uses a tabulation like that given in Table E.5. The low accuracy is due to the typically coarse intervals (e.g., whole degrees) used between table entries—a table accurate enough for research use could easily fill dozens of pages!

Normand's rule: When a thermodynamic diagram is available, Normand's rule may be used to find the dewpoint, as described in Section 7.9.2. The saturation mixing ratio w_s and mixing ratio w taken from the chart may then be used to compute the relative humidity.

It is apparent from Table E.5 that the maximum wet-bulb depression decreases sharply with decreasing temperature. This means that it becomes harder and harder to measure relative humidity accurately with a psychrometer when it is cold. In addition, when the wet-bulb temperature of the air is below freezing, you have to pay attention to whether the wick is actually frozen or not. If it is supercooled (below 0°C but still liquid), the usual psychrometric relationship (7.57) applies. If it is frozen, the temperature is known as the **frost-bulb temperature**, and (7.57) must be slightly modified, as described below that equation.

7.10.2 Heat index

For the human body to function properly, its core temperature must remain very close to 37°C. If the body loses heat faster than it can be regenerated by the body's metabolism, the temperature will fall and hypothermia will follow. If, on the other hand, internal heat is generated faster than it can be removed via conductive and evaporative cooling, then the body temperature will rise uncontrollably, and heat exhaustion or even heat stroke may eventually follow, sometimes with fatal consequences.

In semi-mathematical terms, the body will inevitably overheat if

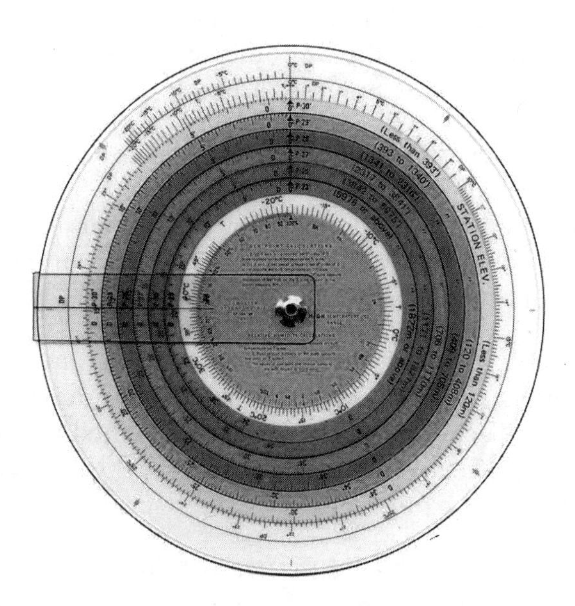

Fig. 7.21: A professional psychrometric computer used for decades by professional weather observers (including the author) to accurately compute dewpoint from manual dry-bulb and wet-bulb readings. In recent years, automated electronic measurements have become the norm at most weather stations. (*Image courtesy of the Dutch Circle of Slide Rule Collectors,* `http://www.rekeninstrumenten.nl`)

$$\text{Maximum achievable rate of heat loss due to conduction} + \text{Maximum achievable rate of heat loss due to evaporation} < \text{Rate of metabolic heat production}$$

The first term on the left describes *sensible heat exchange* and is roughly proportional to the difference between body temperature and the ambient air temperature. In fact, it is negative (becomes a heating term) for air temperatures greater than about 37°C. Thus, when the air temperature climbs above this level, you depend entirely on evaporative cooling (the second term on the left, or *latent heat exchange*) to keep your body at a safe temperature.

Of course, the effectiveness of evaporation as a cooling process depends strongly on both the humidity and the ability of the body to continually supply adequate moisture via a combination of perspiration and respiration.[14] Regardless of magnitude, latent heat exchange is always a positive (cooling) term in the above relationship *unless* the dewpoint exceeds body temperature, in which case moisture will condense *onto* your body rather than evaporating. Fortunately, such extreme dewpoints don't occur in the free atmosphere,[15] though you can personally experience this effect in a steam bath. Regardless of humidity, excess clothing and/or the lack of a breeze can greatly reduce the effectiveness of evaporative cooling.

The rate of metabolic heat production (the right-hand side of the equation) is a function of a person's body size, muscle mass, age, sex, and degree of activity. While a person at rest may typically burn only 200–400 kJ per hour (about 50–100W), someone engaged

[14]Dogs do not sweat and therefore rely entirely on panting to remain cool in hot weather.

[15]As of this writing, there is apparently no official world record high dewpoint. But the dewpoint of 35.0°C (95.0°F) reported from Dhahran, Saudi Arabia on July 8, 2003, and accompanied by an air temperature of 42.0°C (107.5°F), is currently seen as a strong candidate pending official validation of the quality of the measurement. Generally speaking, the world's highest dewpoints are found not in the Amazon rain forest, nor even in Houston, Texas, but rather in the vicinity of the very warm Red Sea and Persian Gulf, where dewpoints routinely exceed 30°C (86°F).

Table 7.1: Heat index for selected air temperatures and dewpoints in degrees Celsius. For other values and/or units, use the Heat Index Calculator at http://www.crh.noaa.gov/jkl/?n=heat_index_calculator.

T	T_d [°C]									
[°C]	16	18	20	22	24	26	28	30	32	34
26	27	27	27	28	28	28	.	.	.	.
28	28	29	30	31	32	34	36	.	.	.
30	30	31	32	33	35	37	40	44	.	.
32	32	33	34	36	38	41	44	49	54	.
34	34	35	37	38	41	44	47	52	58	66
36	36	37	39	41	43	46	50	55	61	68
38	39	40	41	43	46	49	53	58	64	71
40	41	42	44	46	48	51	56	60	66	74
42	43	45	46	48	51	54	58	63	69	75
44	46	47	48	51	53	56	61	65	71	78

Table 7.2: Hazards associated with high heat index.

27–32°C	Fatigue possible with prolonged exposure and physical activity.
32–41°C	Sunstroke, heat cramps, and heat exhaustion possible.
41–54°C	Sunstroke, heat cramps, and heat exhaustion likely, and heat stroke possible.
>54°C	Heat stroke highly likely with continued exposure.

in strenuous sports can easily burn four or more times that amount. Thus, the challenge of regulating one's temperature under hot, humid conditions becomes proportionally more difficult for a person who is active.

The purpose of the so-called **heat index** is to characterize with a single "effective temperature" the relative difficulty the human body will have shedding excess heat, taking into account both the air temperature and the humidity. The actual formula is rather ugly and won't be reproduced here. Instead, some representative values are given in Table 7.1 along with associated health hazards in Table 7.2.

Problem 7.18: Although the proverbial combination of "90°F and 90% relative humidity" is extremely rare in the United States, a value of the *heat index* corresponding to that nasty combination may occur more frequently.

a) Determine the heat index corresponding to the above combination.

b) For an air temperature of 40°C (104°F), estimate the dewpoint and relative humidity that would correspond to the same heat index.

Problem 7.19: An adult at rest breathes approximately 15 times per minute, and each breath takes in approximately 0.5 liters of air at the ambient temperature and humidity. It is then expelled with a near-constant temperature of 35°C and relative humidity of 95%. For each of the following ambient conditions, determine (i) the average cooling rate, in watts, due to the exchange of sensible heat (enthalpy) via respiration, (ii) the same, but due to latent heat exchange, (iii) the net cooling rate due to both effects, and (iv) the amount of water lost in a 24 hour period due to respiration alone. Put your results in tabular form, with the rows corresponding to (a)–(c) and columns corresponding to (i)–(iv).

a) Temperature 40°C, dewpoint 20°C.
Answer: −0.6 W, 6.8 W, 6.2 W, 0.24 kg/(24 hr)

b) Temperature 40°C, dewpoint 5°C.

c) Temperature −20°C, dewpoint −25°C.

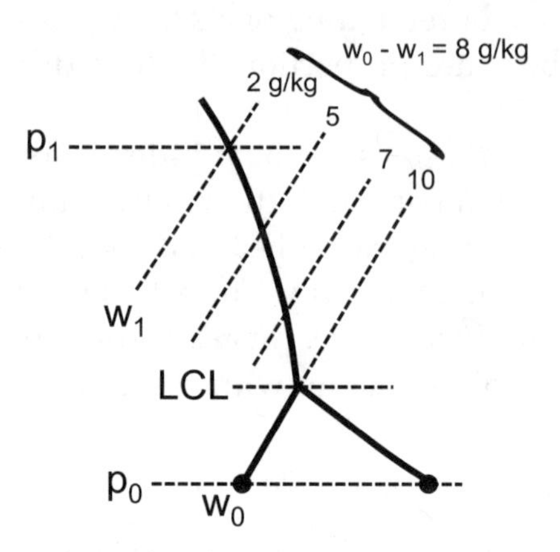

Fig. 7.22: Example of the determination of the adiabatic liquid water content from a skew-T diagram. At any given pressure level, the condensed water mixing ratio is equal to the original mixing ratio minus the saturation mixing ratio at that level.

7.10.3 Adiabatic cloud water content

In a parcel that rises above its LCL, its vapor mixing ratio w is no longer conserved but rather decreases as vapor condenses to liquid. What *is* conserved in the absence of either dilution by environmental air or fallout of condensate in the form of precipitation is the **total water mixing ratio** $w_{\text{tot}} \equiv w + w_l$, where w_l is the **cloud water mixing ratio**, commonly measured in grams of condensed water per kilogram of air.

Thus, the amount of liquid that condenses is equal to the difference between the parcel's initial and final vapor mixing ratios. This difference is called the **adiabatic cloud water mixing ratio** and may be easily determined from a thermodynamic diagram, as illustrated in Fig. 7.22. With the help of the Ideal Gas Law, it may also be converted to an adiabatic **cloud water density** having units of grams per cubic meter of air.

Adiabatic cloud water contents are only occasionally observed in real clouds because the moisture in the rising updraft is often diluted via mixing with the surrounding environmental air. In addition, rain-out of excess condensed water becomes almost inevitable once liquid water mixing ratios exceed a couple of grams per kilogram. Even at much lower cloud water concentrations, precipitation can easily occur under the right conditions, especially in deep clouds and/or when part or all of the cloud is significantly colder than 0°C.

Problem 7.20: Determine the adiabatic cloud water mixing ratio and density at 500 hPa for a parcel originating at the 850 hPa level in Sounding 1 (see Appendix F)

7.10.4 Flow over elevated terrain

Let us now consider one of the simplest practical applications of the concepts developed in this chapter: the adiabatic flow of air over a topographic barrier such as a mountain ridge. For the purposes of the present illustration, we will assume that air originates at a lower elevation (higher pressure) with an initial temperature T and water vapor mixing ratio w (or, equivalently, dewpoint T_d). It is then forced to ascend to a higher altitude (lower pressure) where it can pass over the top of the ridge. Finally, on the leeward side of the ridge, it descends back to its original pressure. The airflow is depicted schematically by the arrow in the left panels of Fig. 7.23.

As the air makes its initial ascent, its temperature cools dry adiabatically, and its mixing ratio remains constant. Assuming that the air is not *too* dry, it eventually reaches saturation and an **orographic cloud** forms with its base at the LCL of the rising air. Above that level, condensation occurs at a rate sufficient to maintain the air at saturation, and the temperature decreases at the moist adiabatic lapse rate.

Moist adiabatic case

We now have two alternative scenarios to consider. In the first (Fig. 7.23a), the condensed moisture remains with the rising air in the form of cloud water. The cloud water content increases steadily with distance above the LCL. In the absence of mixing with drier air aloft, the total water mixing ratio (vapor plus condensate) is conserved, and the condensed water mixing ratio has the adiabatic value defined in the previous subsection.

If absolutely no loss of condensate occurs, then the process is *reversible*: once the air begins descending on the lee side of the ridge, adiabatic warming is partially offset by the re-evaporation of cloud water, which takes up latent heat. The temperature of the air thus follows a moist adiabat for as long as condensate is present. Once the air reaches its original LCL, all condensate will have evaporated, and the original vapor mixing ratio is restored. The remainder of the descent is dry adiabatic. Finally, upon return to the parcel's original pressure level, it will be found to have the same temperature and mixing ratio (and dewpoint and relative humidity) as it had at the beginning.

On a skew-T diagram, the above process is illustrated in the right panel of Fig. 7.23a. The key point to note is that the parcel

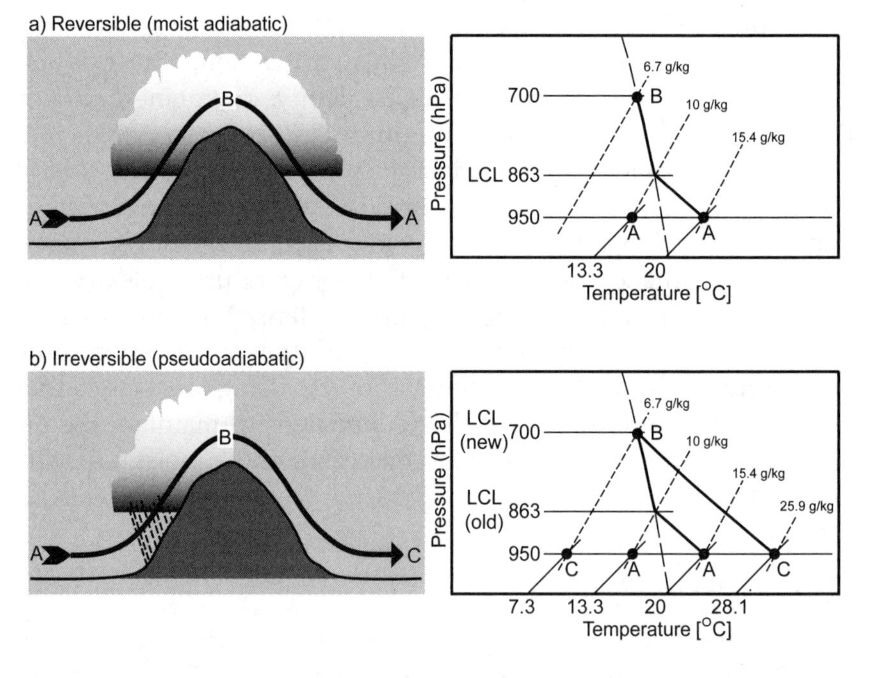

Fig. 7.23: Schematic depiction of (a) moist adiabatic and (b) pseudoadiabatic ascent and descent of air across a mountain barrier. Letter labels A, B, and C indicate the correspondence between the air parcel trajectory (left) and the temperature, dewpoint, and pressure on the skew-T diagram (right).

follows the same moist and then dry adiabats on descent as it did on ascent, with no net change in the properties of the parcel at any particular level.

A completely reversible moist adiabatic process of the type just described occurs most often in shallow wave clouds arising in fairly smooth (laminar) airflows. If the cloud becomes too deep, then precipitation becomes likely; if the cloud is too turbulent or convective, then dilution by environmental air at higher levels is likely. The wave clouds depicted in Fig. 7.12 are good examples of a reversible moist adiabatic process.

Pseudoadiabatic case

At the opposite extreme from the ideal reversible case just described is the irreversible *pseudoadiabatic* process in which all condensate is assumed to immediately fall out as precipitation. Thus, the condensed water mixing ratio $w_l = 0$, and the vapor mixing ratio $w = w_{\text{tot}}$ can never be larger than the lowest saturation mixing ratio encountered at any point in the parcel's history. The new LCL of a parcel of descending air on the leeward side of the ridge corresponds to the highest altitude achieved by the parcel. The parcel therefore follows a dry adiabat during its entire descent.

By the time it reaches its original level, it is both warmer and drier than it started out. The degree of warming and drying is a function of how much precipitation falls out on the windward side, which is in turn a function of how far the air ascends above its original LCL.

An example of the complete process is depicted in the right panel of Fig. 7.23b. In this example, air originating at low levels with a pressure of 950 hPa, a temperature of 20°C, a vapor mixing ratio of 10 g/kg, and a relative humidity of 65% is lifted to a pressure of 700 hPa. Upon return to its original pressure level, its temperature has warmed to 28.1°C, and its mixing ratio is 6.7 g/kg, corresponding to a skin-chapping relative humidity of 26%.

The precipitation that is deposited on the windward side of a mountain ridge, incidentally, is called **orographic precipitation.** The dry leeward side of such a barrier is called a **rain shadow**. Most of the wettest places on earth are found on the windward side of mountain barriers. Some of the driest places on earth are found on the lee side of the same topographic features.

Some regions of the world regularly experience episodes of warm, dry downslope winds as a result of the above process. The best known of these include the so-called *föehn* wind in the lee of the Alps in Europe and the *chinook* ("snow-eater") wind on the eastern side of the Rocky Mountains in the United States.

Problem 7.21: Consider a situation in which moist air from the Pacific Ocean is advected over the Rocky Mountains and undergoes an irreversible pseudoadiabatic process during the ascent. The surface pressure on the western side is 800 hPa, the temperature is 20.6°C, and the dewpoint is 15.7°C. The minimum pressure at the summit is 610 hPa, and the surface pressure in Denver, Colorado is 830 hPa. Compute the following based on the assumption that the equivalent potential temperature given by (7.55) is conserved:

a) The initial mixing ratio and relative humidity of the air before ascent.

b) The final temperature, dewpoint mixing ratio, and relative humidity experienced in Denver, given that the minimum temperature achieved at the top of the ascent is 6.7°C.

c) Check your answers graphically using a skew-*T* diagram.

Hybrid case

The two cases just considered are idealizations. In the first, no condensate whatsoever is lost to precipitation; in the second, all of it is lost. Not surprisingly, the reality often falls somewhere between these two extremes.

The important point is that as long as any condensate remains with the parcel, the parcel descent will follow a moist adiabat until the total mixing ratio w_{tot} equals the saturation mixing ratio w_s. The pressure level at which this occurs is the parcel's new LCL. Thereafter, it will follow a dry adiabat.

Problem 7.22: Where appropriate, use a skew-*T* diagram to solve this problem. A parcel of air has a temperature of 23°C, a relative humidity of 78%, and a pressure of 1000 hPa. It is then lifted adiabatically (first dry, then moist) over a mountain range to the 760 hPa level, at an altitude of approximately 3 km. It then descends again to its original pressure level on the other side of the mountain range. Determine the following quantities:

a) the initial dewpoint of the parcel,

b) the Lifting Condensation Level (LCL) of the parcel,

c) the temperature and dewpoint of the parcel at the LCL,

d) the temperature and mixing ratio of the parcel at its maximum altitude,

e) the amount of liquid water condensate by the time the parcel reaches the above altitude, expressed as a mixing ratio in grams water per kilogram air,

f) the same quantity as in (e), but expressed as a density in grams per cubic meter,

g) the temperature, dewpoint, and relative humidity of the parcel after it returns to its original pressure level, assuming that all but 0.3 g/kg of the condensed water in (e) is rained out and therefore permanently removed.

Conserved properties

In both the pseudoadiabatic and hybrid cases just discussed, the final temperature and humidity properties of the air have changed, possibly radically, from their initial values. One might conclude that the air on the lee side of the barrier is not recognizably related to the air that began the ascent on the windward side. However, a couple of key properties of the air are indeed preserved for the entire spectrum of possible scenarios ranging from reversible moist adiabatic to fully pseudoadiabatic—in particular, the equivalent potential temperature θ_e. Because there is a one-to-one relationship between θ_e and the wet-bulb potential temperature θ_w, it follows that the latter is conserved as well. Finally, at any given pressure level, the actual wet-bulb temperature T_w will not have changed (recall that a particular value of θ_w is associated with a unique T_w at any particular pressure, according to Normand's rule).

7.10.5 Mixed layers in the atmosphere

A number of atmospheric processes are associated with chaotic mixing of air, also known as **turbulence**. For example, when the wind flows over rough terrain or around obstacles, such as buildings or trees, eddies and whirls form in their wake. There is a natural tendency for large turbulent eddies in a fluid to break up into ever smaller eddies until the fluid is thoroughly blended. You can observe this process when you pour milk into a cup of coffee and then stir.

In addition, turbulent mixing can occur when air is heated from below, so that the environmental lapse rate becomes greater than the dry adiabatic lapse rate and convective overturning takes place (see Chapter 8).

What are the characteristics of a **well mixed** atmospheric layer? We expect one or more properties to be uniform, but which ones? Logically, it should be those properties that are conserved for moist and/or dry adiabatic processes.

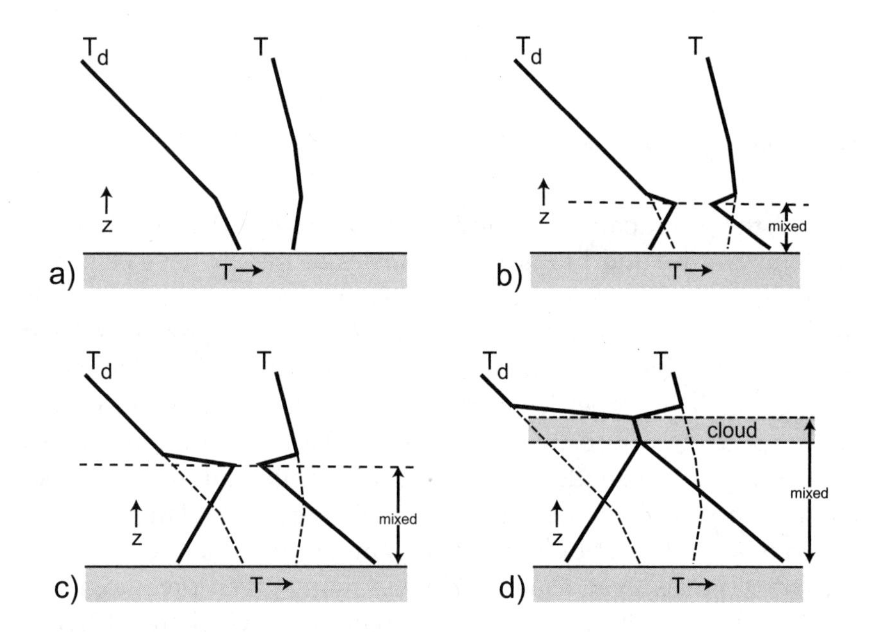

Fig. 7.24: Illustration of the evolution of a surface mixed layer resulting from surface heating and/or mechanical turbulence.

Unsaturated mixed layer

Let us first consider a layer of air that is relatively dry — that is, there is no likelihood of saturation being reached within the layer. In that case, we know that potential temperature θ is the thermodynamic variable associated with temperature that is conserved for adiabatic processes; therefore, we expect a blend of air parcels initially having different properties to wind up exhibiting uniform potential temperature. In the absence of solar (or other) heating, the final value will reflect a mass-weighted average of the initial values in the layer.

Likewise, before mixing there is a certain total mass of water vapor present in the layer and a certain total mass of dry air. The subsequent mixing of the air does not change these proportions overall but leads to a uniform mixing ratio throughout the layer that reflects those original proportions, as shown in panels (a)–(c) of Fig. 7.24.

> **Key fact:** An unsaturated atmospheric layer that is **well mixed** will exhibit uniform potential temperature θ and uniform water vapor mixing ratio w throughout its depth. The equivalent potential temperature θ_e and equivalent wet-bulb temperature θ_w are, of course, also uniform because they are also conserved for dry (as well as moist) adiabatic processes.

Cloud-topped mixed layer

If the layer being mixed is deep enough and/or moist enough, a layer in which θ and w are both uniform throughout will reach saturation at the level corresponding to the LCL of the mixture. Above that level, enough condensation will take place to eliminate any supersaturation. We now have a layer that is characterized by a more or less continuous horizontal sheet of cloud above the LCL.

In the presence of condensation and the associated latent heat release, θ is no longer uniform, as potential temperature is conserved only for dry adiabatic processes. But θ_e is conserved regardless of any condensation. Within the cloud layer, therefore, the temperature profile follows a moist adiabat, as shown in panel (d) of Fig. 7.24.

Key fact: A well mixed atmospheric layer exhibits uniform θ_e throughout its depth and uniform θ and w below the LCL. That is, the temperature profile corresponds to a dry adiabat below the LCL and moist adiabat above, and w is constant below the LCL. Although w decreases above the LCL due to condensation, the *total* water mixing ratio, consisting of the mass of vapor *plus cloud water* per unit mass of air, is uniform throughout the layer's depth, as long as there is no precipitation.

Fig. 7.25: Stratocumulus clouds such as these often occur at the top of a humid mixed layer. Typically, there will be a temperature inversion at the top of the cloud layer. The strength of the inversion helps control the degree to which the cloud layer can thicken by additional turbulent mixing. *(Courtesy of the NOAA Photo Library. Photo by Ralph F. Kresge.)*

Mixed layer as idealization

It is important to recognize that a perfectly well mixed atmospheric layer is an idealization. There are always processes at work that are conspiring to introduce non-uniformities into the temperature or moisture structure of a layer of air. Whether a layer exhibits the properties expected of a well mixed layer depends on whether the mixing occurs at a rate that overwhelms those other processes. Strong near-surface winds interacting with terrain facilitate rapid mixing. Hence, the planetary boundary layer—that is, the lowest kilometer or two of the atmosphere—is where one most often finds the characteristics described above.

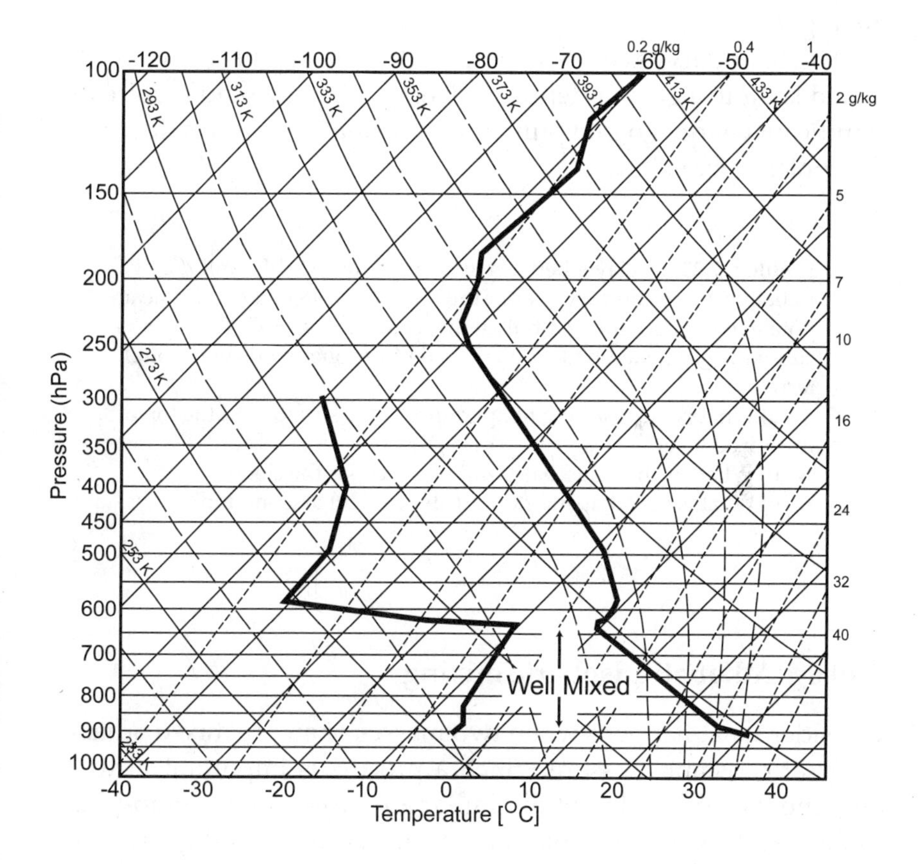

Fig. 7.26: Example of an actual sounding exhibiting a deep surface mixed layer, presumably driven by intense solar heating of the surface. Note the shallow superadiabatic layer right at the surface.

Even when a layer is almost perfectly mixed, radiosonde instruments are imperfect, so actual soundings may often reveal profiles in which θ and w are both *almost* uniform, suggesting that the layer is probably turbulent and therefore well mixed (e.g., Fig. 7.26).

Boundary layer inversion

An almost inevitable result of mixing of near surface air, as described in the above examples, is the appearance of a **boundary layer inversion** at the top of the mixed layer. This feature is seen in both Fig. 7.24 and Fig. 7.26. It is the natural consequence of the steepening of the lapse rate that occurs within the layer undergoing mixing.

The boundary layer inversion tends to resist the growth of the mixed layer to a greater depth, as deeper mixing would require that significant energy go into pulling warm air at high levels down into the cooler layer below.

Problem 7.23: A layer between the surface at 1000 hPa and 770 hPa initially has a mean water vapor mixing ratio of 18 g/kg and a mean potential temperature wet-bulb temperature θ_w of 26°C. The layer is subsequently mixed by turbulence due to strong winds over rough terrain.

a) What is the resulting temperature at the surface and the top of the mixed layer?

b) Where is the cloud base, and how deep is the cloud?

c) What is the adiabatic cloud water content at cloud top?

7.10.6 Adiabatic, isobaric mixing

Consider what happens when two masses of air are mixed adiabatically at constant pressure. Such a process is important virtually anytime there is mixing of dissimilar air masses in the atmosphere, as long as the vertical displacements involved are negligible.

If we start with a mass m_1 of air having temperature T_1 and specific humidity q_1 and a mass m_2 of air having temperature T_2 and specific humidity q_2, conservation of mass tells us the total mass of the system after mixing is

$$m = m_1 + m_2 \quad . \tag{7.60}$$

Moreover, by the same principle, the specific humidity of the mixture must be

$$q = \frac{m_1 q_1 + m_2 q_2}{m} \quad . \tag{7.61}$$

Finally, because the mixing is isobaric *and* adiabatic, the total enthalpy of the system is conserved. Thus

$$c_p m T = c_p m_1 T_1 + c_p m_2 T_2 = c_p (m_1 T_1 + m_2 T_2) \quad , \tag{7.62}$$

where we have assumed that the specific heat capacity c_p may be taken to be approximately that of dry air (i.e., differences in c_p due to water vapor are assumed small). Solving for the final temperature, we have

$$T = \frac{(m_1 T_1 + m_2 T_2)}{m} \quad . \tag{7.63}$$

Finally, by using the approximation

$$q \approx \frac{\epsilon e}{p} \tag{7.64}$$

and noting that p is the same for both air masses, we can write

$$e \approx \frac{m_1 e_1 + m_2 e_2}{m} \quad . \tag{7.65}$$

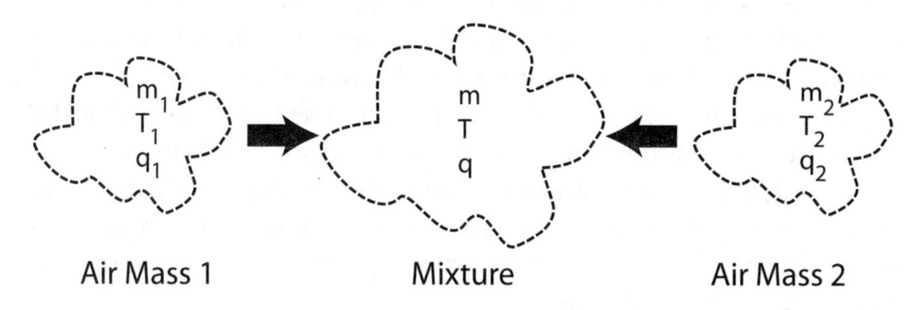

Fig. 7.27: Schematic depiction of the adiabatic, isobaric mixing of samples of air from two dissimilar air masses, each having the indicated mass, temperature, and specific humidity.

It is clear that depending on the ratio m_1/m_2 of the two initial air masses, it is possible to obtain for a final value of T any temperature that falls between T_1 and T_2. The same holds true for the final vapor pressure e. However, the final value of e and of T both depend in a fixed way on the proportion contributed by each initial air mass, so the final value of e is uniquely determined by the final temperature T. We can therefore combine the formula above for T with the formula for e and eliminate m_1 and m_2 as variables. The result may be written

$$e = e(T) = \frac{T - T_1}{T_2 - T_1}(e_2 - e_1) + e_1 \quad . \tag{7.66}$$

If you plot this equation on a graph with T on the horizontal axis and e on the vertical axis, you find that this is a straight line connecting (T_1, e_1) and (T_2, e_2). *An arbitrary mixture of the two air masses will always give rise to a final (T, e) that falls on this straight line between the points defining the two initial air masses.*

If we plot the saturation vapor pressure $e_s(T)$ on the same graph (Fig. 7.28), it is strongly curved (recall the exponential form of the Clausius-Clapeyron equation we have been using). Lines of constant relative humidity on the chart may also be easily drawn by simply plotting a curve of $e(T)$ that is a constant fraction of $e_s(T)$. *It is easy to see that a mixture of two air masses with dissimilar initial temperatures and/or vapor pressures can often lead to a final mixture with higher relative humidity than that of either of the two initial air masses.*

It is possible for the straight line connecting (T_1, e_1) and (T_2, e_2) to intersect the function $e_s(T)$. If that occurs, then any combination of the two air masses that happens to fall above the e_s curve will be supersaturated, and condensation will occur. In any real encounter between two air masses, all possible proportions of each will occur during the resulting mixing process. Therefore, the intersection of the straight line with $e_s(T)$ may be regarded as the criterion for the occurrence of condensation in an adiabatic, isobaric mixing process.

Examples of where adiabatic, isobaric mixing may commonly lead to condensation include the formation of contrails[16] from high-flying aircraft (Fig. 7.29), the appearance of fog in your breath on a

[16]The forecasting of upper level conditions favorable for contrail formation has long been, and still remains, a significant operational concern for military meteorologists. No amount of expensive stealth technology will prevent a bomber from being detected if if leaves an easily visible contrail.

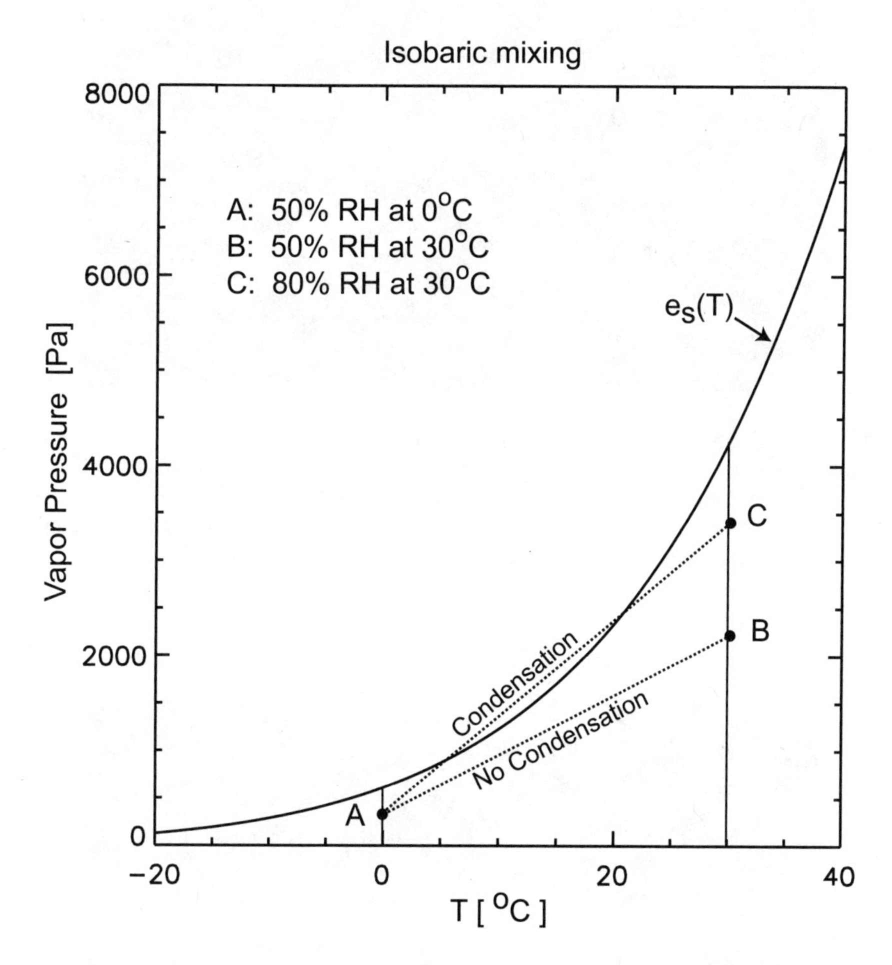

Fig. 7.28: Graphical determination of the occurrence of condensation from the mixing of two dissimilar (but unsaturated) air masses. Mixtures of air masses A and B never produce condensation, whereas mixtures of A and C do for proportions falling roughly between 1:3 and 3:1.

Fig. 7.29: Contrails produced by a jet airliner flying high over London, England. Hot jet exhaust contains water vapor. When it mixes with the cold air at high altitudes, the mixture becomes supersaturated and visible condensation forms. If the ambient air is sufficiently cold and close to saturation with respect to ice, the initial contrail may persist and grow into an extensive cirrus cloud. *(Photo by Adrian Pingstone)*

Fig. 7.30: Early morning steam fog on a southern lake. The mechanism of formation in this case is adiabatic, isobaric mixing of the warmer saturated air at the surface of the water with the overlying colder air. When a similar (though more intense) phenomenon is observed over ice-free water in the far northern or southern oceans, it is often referred to as *sea smoke*.*(Courtesy of the NOAA Photo Library. Photo by Ralph F. Kresge.)*

cold day, and the occurrence of so-called **steam fog** (also known as **sea smoke** or **arctic smoke**) when cold air overruns warmer water (Fig. 7.30).

Problem 7.24: Two different air masses are blended adiabatically and isobarically. The blend consists of a fraction f (by mass) of Air Mass 1 and a fraction $1 - f$ of Air Mass 2. The air masses have initial temperature T_1 and T_2, and relative humidity RH_1 and RH_2, respectively.

For each of two cases given below, do the following:

a) Starting with a copy of Fig. 7.28 or similar, mark the graph with points representing Air Masses 1 and 2 and connect them with a straight line.

b) Based on your graphs, estimate the minimum and maximum fraction f for which condensation occurs. In other words, how much does Air Mass 1 have to get diluted by Air Mass 2, or vice versa, before any condensation evaporates completely?

Case 1: Air Mass 1 is the air you exhale, which typically has a relative humidity of 95% and a temperature of 35°C (i.e., slightly below normal body temperature of 37.0°C). Air Mass 2 is ambient air with a temperature of 10.0°C and a relative humidity of 20%.

Case 2: Air Mass 1 is a warm frontal air mass sweeping into the northern Midwest from the Gulf of Mexico, with temperature 25°C and dewpoint 20°C. Air Mass 2 is the residue of a pool of polar air hanging over Madison, Wisconsin, following a cold-air outbreak, with temperature −5°C, and dewpoint −10°C.

Problem 7.25: Although it might not normally occur to us, it is theoretically possible for our breath to fog not only when it encounters *colder* air but also when it mixes with *warmer* air.

a) For the properties given for human breath in the previous problem, use a suitable graph of $e_s(T)$ [which you might have to sketch yourself, using Eq. (7.18), for example] to estimate the minimum relative humidity that would be required in order for your breath to fog in ambient air having a temperature of 60°C (140°F).

b) From your result for (a), find the dewpoint (you can do this graphically with the same diagram). What practical problem or inconvenience might you experience personally demonstrating the fogging of human breath in, say, a sauna having the required temperature and humidity?

CHAPTER 8

Atmospheric Stability

Now that we understand how the temperature of a parcel changes in response to adiabatic ascent or descent, we can look at the implications of those changes for atmospheric **stability**. Stability (or the lack of it) is implicated in a tremendous variety of atmospheric phenomena ranging from the gentle thermal updrafts exploited by soaring birds on a fair summer day to violent supercell thunderstorms with their attendant hail and tornadoes.

There are three basic types of stability we will consider here:

Local stability: The stability of atmospheric layers with respect to *small* vertical displacements of air parcels within the layer. This kind of stability depends only on the local environmental lapse rate and not on the properties of the atmosphere at higher or lower levels.

Potential instability: The phenomenon in which a previously stable *layer* (according to the definition given above for *local* stability), becomes unstable as the result of large-scale forced lifting of the entire layer. Although the term "convective" instability is frequently used for this condition, it is a bit of a misnomer, as *parcel* stability (below) is more directly associated with the actual occurrence of convection, while potential instability may be a mere precursor.

Parcel (or non-local) stability: The stability of the troposphere with respect to *large* vertical displacements of air parcels, often (though not always) assumed to originate at or near the surface. This kind of stability is directly related to the occurrence of convective clouds ranging from fair weather **cumulus** to deep **cumulonimbus** clouds.

Any discussion of atmospheric stability requires that we first take a critical look at the fairly bold assumptions we will make concerning how parcels of air from various levels in the atmosphere move around and how they interact with their environment.

8.1 The Parcel Method

Our discussion of dry and saturated adiabatic lapse rates and of conserved and non-conserved moisture variables has implicitly been geared toward the thermodynamic behavior of an isolated "parcel" of air—i.e., an idealized blob of air which we assumed could experience changes in pressure (e.g., by moving around in the atmosphere) without mixing with its environment or otherwise losing its identity. This idealization is a very useful one, and we will now begin to extend the so-called **parcel method** to relate the behavior of individual parcels of air to the vertical temperature and humidity structure of the atmosphere.

When using the parcel method, one typically starts with a hypothetical parcel of air taken from an arbitrary level in the atmosphere and then move it adiabatically up or down relative to the environment in order to examine the energetics of such vertical motions. According to the parcel method, one assumes that

- there is no mixing between the parcel and its environment, and
- the vertical motion of the parcel through the environment does not lead to any alteration in the overall characteristics of the environment, for example, via compensating downward motion.

The first assumption requires the parcel to be relatively large compared to the vertical distance it travels; the second, on the other hand, requires it to constitute a small fraction of the total mass of the layer from which it originates. Neither requirement is fully met for most real-world convection.

Nevertheless, the parcel method provides a very convenient starting point for understanding the effects of a given vertical temperature and moisture profile on the behavior of the atmosphere, provided one keeps its limitations in mind. For example, the energetics of thunderstorm updrafts are often analyzed using the parcel method even though, in reality, considerable mixing with the environment occurs, as well as compensating downward motion.

Generally speaking, the non-ideal processes taking place in the real atmosphere serve to *reduce* the effects of instability and to *dilute* the properties of a moving parcel of air, reducing the contrast between its temperature and that of the surrounding air. The parcel method, therefore, yields a theoretical *upper limit* on energy that is available to drive a thunderstorm updraft, for example.

8.2 Stable and Unstable Systems

In a very general sense, a system is **stable** if in response to a small perturbation it tends to return to its initial state. A system is **unstable** if in response to a similar small perturbation it tends to accelerate irreversibly away from its initial state.

As a simple example, consider a marble resting in the bottom of a round bowl. Left to its own devices, it will remain at the very lowest point in the bowl. If you gently nudge it away (and uphill) from the bottom, it will roll back toward its starting point, oscillating back and forth until friction brings it back to rest at the lowest spot in the bowl. This system is stable. The characteristic property of a *stable* system is that a small displacement gives rise to a force that acts to *return* the system to its original state.

Now consider a marble that has been carefully balanced on top of a globe. If you leave it alone, it could conceivably stay there forever. However, if you disturb it even slightly, it will accelerate downhill away from its starting point and never return without outside intervention. This system is unstable. The characteristic property of an *unstable* system is that a small displacement give rise to a force that tends to *magnify* the displacement.

Next, consider a marble resting on a large, flat, level table. If you give it a nudge, it will move away from its starting point, but it will not pick up speed, nor will it show any tendency to reverse direction and return to the starting point. If there is no friction, it will continue rolling without changing speed; if there is friction, it will eventually come to a stop at a new location that is no better or no worse than the original location, as far as the marble is concerned. This system is an example of *neutral* stability.

If we allow our system to be perturbed more strongly, we may have any of the three stability conditions already described. However, there is also a fourth possibility, namely the **metastable** case. A system is metastable if it is *stable with respect to small displacements but unstable with respect to large displacements.* Using the same analogy as before, imagine the marble resting in a local depression that holds it in place despite a nearby ledge. As long as the marble experiences only small perturbations, it is stable. But if it is perturbed enough to overcome the energy barrier between it and the ledge, it will permanently leave its initial position and plunge into the abyss. The greater the energy barrier, the less likely it is that the instability will be released. This case is exactly analogous to *parcel* stability in the atmosphere, as it relates to the potential for thunderstorm formation.

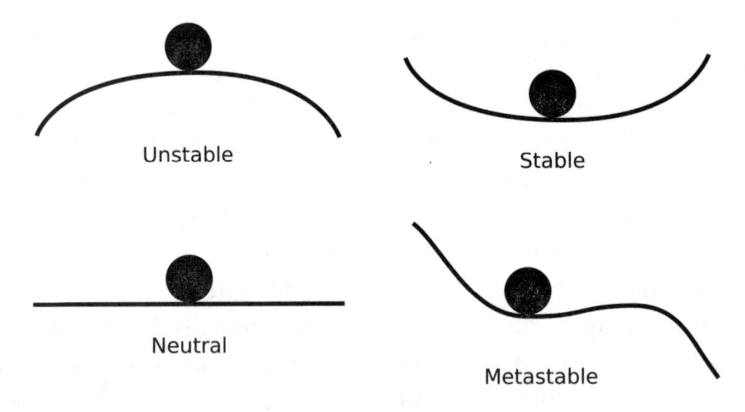

Fig. 8.1: Schematic depiction of the four kinds of stability, as represented by a marble resting on a smooth surface.

8.3 Local (Static) Atmospheric Stability

Consider a certain parcel of air in the atmosphere that is initially at rest and has the same temperature as the environment at that level. Imagine that it is given a mild push upward, so that it moves slightly away from its starting location. After traveling a short distance upward, its temperature falls somewhat, owing to adiabatic expansion. There are now three distinct possible outcomes of this experiment:

1. the parcel might become denser than the environment at its new level (stable case), in which case buoyant forces eventually overcome its upward momentum and send it back toward its starting point;

2. it might turn out instead that the parcel finds itself less dense than its new surroundings (unstable case), in which case it will continue to accelerate upward, away from its starting point;

3. there might be no difference between the new temperature of the parcel and that of the environment (neutral case), in which case it will continue upward until friction brings it to rest at a new level.

How do we determine which outcome will result in any given environment?

8.3.1 Dry static stability

Local lapse rate

In the simplest scenario, both the environment and the parcel are dry, so that changes in parcel temperature due to its vertical motion correspond to the dry adiabatic lapse rate $\Gamma_d = 9.8$ K/km. Under which conditions will an upward-displaced parcel of environmental air find itself colder than its surroundings and thus return to its starting point? Clearly, this occurs whenever the environmental lapse rate Γ at that level is less than the dry-adiabatic lapse rate Γ_d. Likewise, if $\Gamma > \Gamma_d$, then an upward displacement of environmental air will lead to the displaced air being warmer than its surroundings, in which case it will continue to accelerate away from its starting location. Both scenarios are depicted in the following cartoon

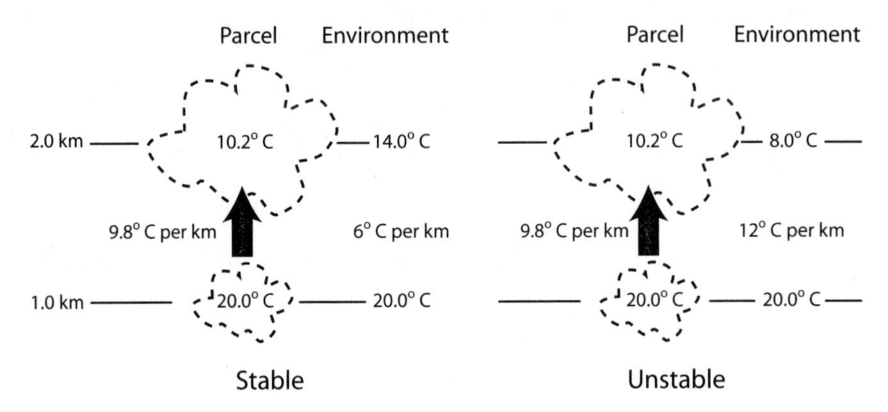

in which the parcel itself experiences the same evolution of temperature, but the environment in which it finds itself is stable or unstable. The same process can be illustrated using a graphic representation of the lapse rates as seen on a skew-T diagram,

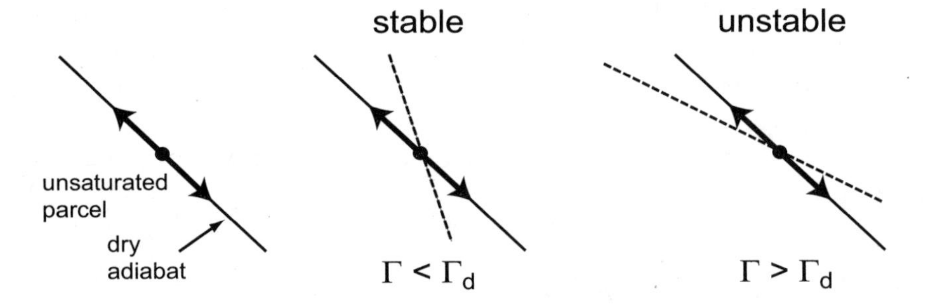

You should be able to convince yourself that the criterion for stability for upward displacements is the same as that for downward displacements. We therefore have the following stability conditions for dry air:

$\Gamma < \Gamma_d$	STABLE
$\Gamma \approx \Gamma_d$	NEUTRAL
$\Gamma > \Gamma_d$	UNSTABLE

Potential temperature

If the local lapse rate Γ is equal to the dry adiabatic lapse rate Γ_d, that is equivalent to saying that the temperature profile follows a dry adiabat. That is, in turn, equivalent to saying that the profile of potential temperature θ is constant with height. We can therefore rephrase the above stability criteria as follows:

$$\frac{\partial \theta}{\partial z} > 0 \qquad \text{STABLE}$$

$$\frac{\partial \theta}{\partial z} = 0 \qquad \text{NEUTRAL}$$

$$\frac{\partial \theta}{\partial z} < 0 \qquad \text{UNSTABLE}$$

8.3.2 Consequences of local instability

If the environmental lapse rate within a layer of the atmosphere fulfills the criterion for instability, then even slight vertical motions within the layer will likely amplify into large vertical motions, with individual parcels of air accelerating away from their point of origin. The net result is usually an overturning, or turbulent mixing, of the layer in question, usually leading to a *well mixed* atmospheric layer exhibiting more or less uniform potential temperature θ and mixing ratio w throughout, as discussed in Section 7.10.5. In other words, an unstable layer generally tends toward neutral stratification unless the instability is continuously sustained by heating from below or cooling from above.

A layer in which $\Gamma > \Gamma_d$ and that is therefore absolutely unstable is called **superadiabatic.** Because of their inherent instability, genuine superadiabatic layers are rarely observed in the free atmosphere, except perhaps very close to ground level when there is strong surface heating. Their appearance elsewhere in a radiosonde report is usually cause for questioning the validity of the data near that level, especially if the apparent superadiabatic layer occurs just above or below an inversion.

8.3.3 The Brunt-Väisäila frequency

In contrast to an unstable layer, a stable atmospheric layer will tend to resist overturning. Instead of leading to convective updrafts or downdrafts, any disturbance may produce **gravity waves** within the stable layer as parcels of air bob up and down about their respective equilibrium points. If the vertical amplitude of the oscillation is large enough, the affected parcels may reach their LCL and form a visible **wave cloud** (Figs. 7.12 and 8.2).

The characteristic angular frequency of oscillation of the parcels in a stable layer is a function of the degree of stratification—the more stable the layer (i.e., the more rapid the increase of θ with height), the more rapid the oscillation. The frequency of oscillation is called the **Brunt-Väisäila frequency.** We will now derive an expression for that frequency in the dry adiabatic case.

Equation (3.59) gave the vertical acceleration of a parcel of air due to buoyancy as

$$f_B = \left[\frac{T_{v,\mathrm{par}} - T_v}{T_v} \right] g \quad ,$$

where $T_{v,\mathrm{par}}$ is the virtual temperature of the parcel, and T_v is the virtual temperature of the surrounding environment. Let us ignore

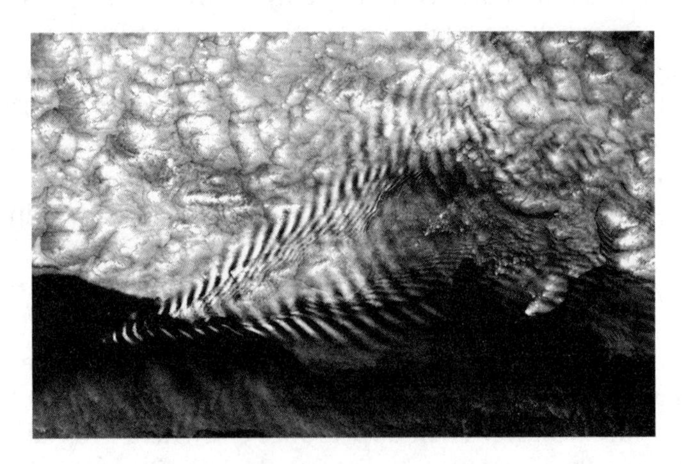

Fig. 8.2: Satellite image of a series of wave clouds forming in the wake of Amsterdam Island in the far southern Indian Ocean on December 19, 2005. (*From the MODIS imager on board the NASA Terra satellite.*)

differences in the specific humidity q of the parcel and environment, in which case we can write

$$f_B = \left[\frac{T_{\text{par}} - T}{T}\right] g \quad . \tag{8.1}$$

Also, because the parcel and the surrounding environment have the same pressure, the above is equivalent to

$$f_B = \left[\frac{\theta_{\text{par}} - \theta}{\theta}\right] g \quad , \tag{8.2}$$

which we may rewrite as

$$f_B = \left[\frac{\theta_{\text{par}}}{\theta} - 1\right] g \quad . \tag{8.3}$$

Let us now consider a parcel at $z = 0$ with potential temperature $\theta_{\text{par}} = \theta$ embedded in an environment whose local stability is characterized by $\partial\theta/\partial z$. If we displace the parcel upward or downward adiabatically by a very small amount z, its potential temperature θ does not change. But the potential temperature θ' of the environment at the parcel's new level *is* different and is given by

$$\theta' = \theta + \frac{\partial \theta}{\partial z} z \quad . \tag{8.4}$$

Substituting into (8.3), we have

$$f_B = \left[\frac{\theta}{\theta + \frac{\partial \theta}{\partial z} z} - 1\right] g \quad . \tag{8.5}$$

By requiring the displacement z to be very small, we may use the following approximation (see Section C.3)

$$\text{for } x \ll 1: \qquad \frac{1}{1-x} \approx 1 + x \tag{8.6}$$

to write

$$f_B = -\left(\frac{1}{\theta}\frac{\partial \theta}{\partial z}\right) g z \quad . \tag{8.7}$$

If the environment is stable, we see that f_B is a restoring force — the parcel accelerates in the direction opposite to its displacement.

Moreover, the restoring force is proportional to both the stability and the magnitude of the displacement. The equation of motion of the parcel may be written

$$\frac{d^2z}{dt^2} + N^2 z = 0 \quad , \tag{8.8}$$

where

$$N^2 = \left(\frac{1}{\theta}\frac{\partial \theta}{\partial z}\right) g \quad . \tag{8.9}$$

For the case that the environment is stable, $N^2 > 0$, in which case you will probably recognize (8.8) as the differential equation for a simple harmonic oscillator whose solution for a parcel with initial displacement z_0 and zero vertical velocity is

$$z = z_0 \cos(Nt) \quad . \tag{8.10}$$

The angular frequency of oscillation N is the Brunt-Väisäila frequency.

If the environment were unstable rather than stable, then we would have $N^2 < 0$, in which case the Brunt-Väisäila frequency would be imaginary. The solution to (8.8) would not be sines or cosines but rather exponentials—that is, the displaced parcel would accelerate exponentially away from its starting point rather than returning.

Problem 8.1: Wind flowing over a mountain peak gives rise to a train of stationary wave clouds that are separated horizontally by a distance L. Each cloud represents the location of maximum upward displacement of parcels of air oscillating vertically in a stable environment. A radiosonde measures the potential temperature profile $\theta(z)$ at the altitude of the clouds. From θ, $\partial\theta/\partial z$, and L, find an expression for the wind speed U at the level of the clouds.

Problem 8.2: Rewrite (8.9) to give N^2 in terms of the temperature T and lapse rates Γ and Γ_d instead of θ and $\partial\theta/\partial z$.

Problem 8.3: A layer of air has a temperature T_0 of 30°C at ground level and a lapse rate Γ of 20°C/km. A parcel originating at the surface is displaced upward with velocity v_0 of 1 m/sec.

a) Ignoring friction and assuming dry adiabatic ascent, find expressions for the altitude $z(t)$ and velocity $v(t)$.

b) Find the time that it takes for the parcel to reach an altitude z_f of 500 m and determine its upward velocity at that point.

8.3.4 Conditional instability

Now what if the layer in question is saturated? In that case, a parcel displaced upward will not cool with the dry adiabatic lapse rate but rather with the moist adiabatic lapse rate Γ_s. Therefore, the layer will be unstable under the condition that $\Gamma > \Gamma_s$.

We also know that $\Gamma_d > \Gamma_s$, so it is apparent that values of the environmental lapse rate Γ exist for which stability depends on whether or not the air is saturated. Therefore, for the general case in which the air may either be saturated or dry, we define the following stability regimes:

$\Gamma < \Gamma_s$ ABSOLUTELY STABLE

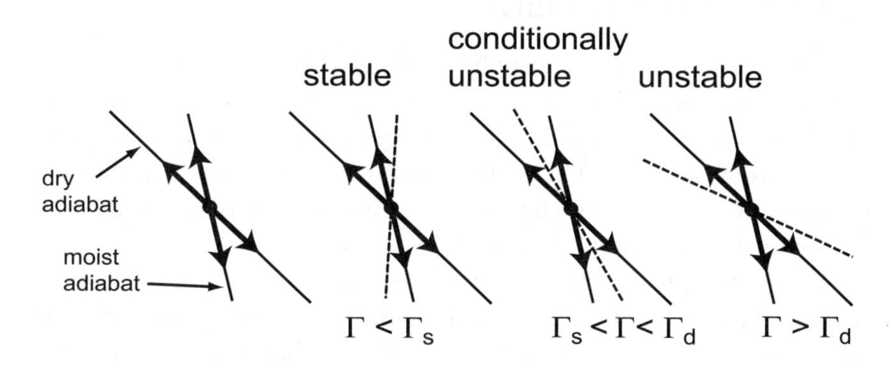

Fig. 8.3: Illustration of the three types of local stability when condensation is possible. Solid lines with heavy arrows illustrate the possible paths that a parcel may follow, depending on whether it is unsaturated or saturated. Dashed lines represent different environmental lapse rates.

$\Gamma = \Gamma_s$	SATURATED NEUTRAL
$\Gamma_s < \Gamma < \Gamma_d$	CONDITIONALLY UNSTABLE
$\Gamma = \Gamma_d$	DRY NEUTRAL
$\Gamma > \Gamma_d$	ABSOLUTELY UNSTABLE

Caveat: In situations where condensate forming in a rising parcel subsequently freezes, the additional release of latent heat may further reduce the effective moist adiabat lapse rate of the rising parcel. Hence, a nominally stable environment according to the normal criteria may in fact be unstable in the presence of freezing. Note, however, that freezing does not occur automatically just because the condensation takes place at temperatures colder than 0°C. On the contrary, cloud water can, and often does, remain **supercooled** for some time even at temperatures approaching −40°C.

Problem 8.4: Obtain a paper copy of Sounding 1 (see Appendix F). Mark all pressure levels where the stability switches from one of the above five types to another. Label the layers between the marked pressure levels with the appropriate stability type and turn in your labeled sounding.

8.3.5 Potential instability

Let us now consider the situation depicted in Fig. 8.4. A layer is bounded by the pressure levels $p_1 = 750$ hPa and $p_2 = 600$ hPa. The lapse rate Γ within the layer is less than Γ_s, so that the layer is absolutely stable. That is, the initial temperatures T_1 and T_2 at the bottom and top of the layer define an environmental profile that slopes to the right of the moist adiabats.

What happens when some process (e.g., an approaching weather system or sloping terrain) causes *the entire layer* to be lifted adiabatically by a substantial amount, so that the layer is now bounded by the pressure levels p_1' and p_2'? Both the bottom and top pressures decrease by the same amount, and the difference between the two remains the same, because the mass of the layer does not change.

The temperature T_1 at the base of the layer will evolve according to the usual rules—dry adiabatic to its LCL, then moist adiabatic. The same is true for the temperature T_2 at the top. However, let us assume that the air at the base of the layer is more humid than it is at the top—that is, the dewpoint depression is smaller at the bottom than at the top. In that case, the bottom of the layer will reach its LCL much sooner than will the top, implying that it spends much of the ascent cooling at the slower moist adiabatic rate. The air at the top of the layer cools much more sharply because it takes longer to reach its LCL.

The outcome in this example is that a stable layer becomes conditional unstable in the course of being lifted. Moreover, because it reaches saturation, conditional instability translates into actual instability. The scenario in which a stable layer can become unstable due to lifting of the entire layer is known as **potential instability** (sometimes called **convective instability.**)

While it is clear that potential instability is associated with decreasing relative humidity with height, we would like to develop a more definitive test for this condition. We note that potential instability is realized whenever the air from the bottom of the layer lands

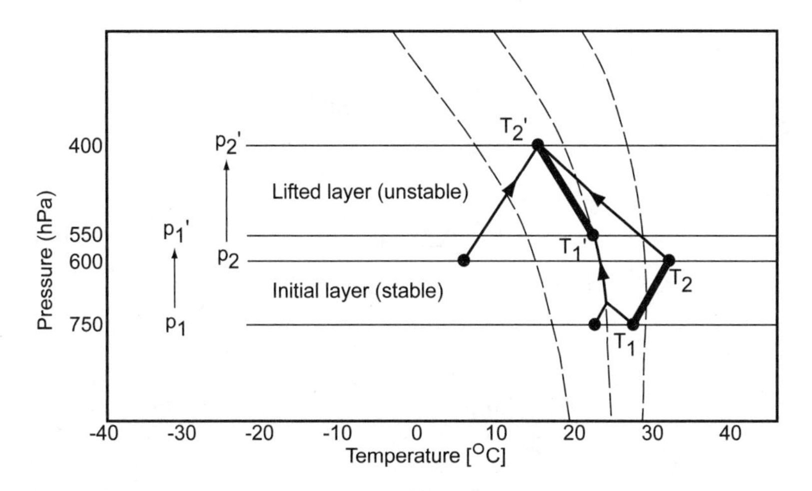

Fig. 8.4: Example of a case of potential instability, in which a stable layer that is lifted adiabatically becomes an unstable layer. The humid bottom of the layer follows a moist adiabat soon after ascent begins; the drier top of the layer follows a dry adiabat for a much greater distance.

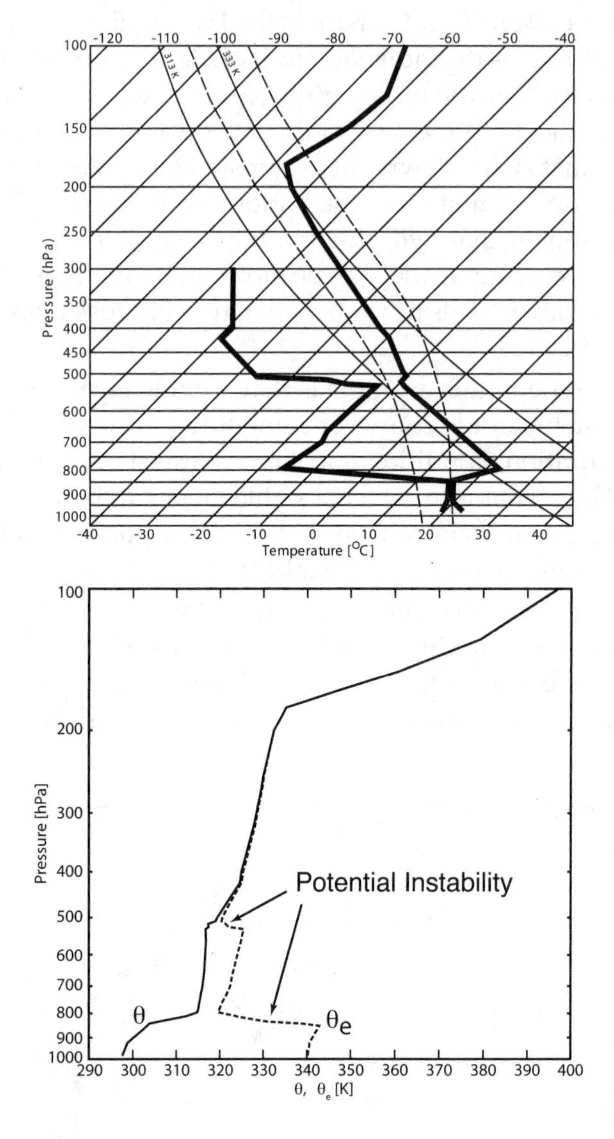

Fig. 8.5: Example of an actual sounding exhibiting significant potential instability near 850 hPa and 530 hPa, in both cases as the result of a sharp decrease in relative humidity immediately above those levels. Top: The standard skew-T representation, with selected dry and moist adiabats for reference. Bottom: Profiles of potential temperature θ and θ_e. Note that θ almost never decreases significantly with height in any sounding, as this would imply a superadiabatic lapse rate and absolute instability. θ_e, on the other hand, is seen to decrease very sharply at the two above-mentioned levels.

on a moist adiabat that is warmer than that associated with the top of the layer. Moist adiabats are lines of constant equivalent potential temperature θ_e, so we have the following:

$$\frac{\partial \theta_e}{\partial z} < 0 \qquad \text{POTENTIALLY UNSTABLE}$$

$$\frac{\partial \theta_e}{\partial z} > 0 \qquad \text{POTENTIALLY STABLE}$$

Figure 8.5 gives an example of a sounding exhibiting considerable potential instability.

Before we move on, I would like to remind you once again that the definitions of local static stability and potential instability introduced so far depend *only* on the *local* temperature lapse rate (or equivalent potential temperature lapse rate) *at* the level of interest and *not* on the temperature or moisture profile significantly above or below that level. We will now consider larger parcel displacements of the type relevant to deeper atmospheric convection.

Problem 8.5: Soundings 1 and 2 (see Appendix F) each depict moist air at the surface capped by warmer, drier air aloft. For both soundings, graphically determine whether potential instability exists within the inversion layer that marks the transition between the two air masses.

8.4 Parcel Stability and Atmospheric Convection

We now turn to the important question of what happens when a parcel is displaced upward a significant distance from its starting point, perhaps even through most of the depth of the troposphere. We know, for example, that thunderstorms originate with deep, intense convective updrafts that sweep near-surface air to great altitudes. Our analysis of **parcel stability** will reveal both the conditions under which free convection is likely to occur, as well as the source of the energy that drives thunderstorms and makes large hail and even tornadoes possible.

I will emphasize once again that the so-called parcel method is an idealization: we don't consider the effects of the mixing of the parcel with its surrounding environment as it ascends. Our stability analysis will therefore generally *overestimate* the energy available to drive convective updrafts, much as the Carnot heat engine overestimates the amount of mechanical work that can be produced by a real-world engine with friction and other losses.

8.4.1 Thermal updrafts and cumulus formation

Before we tackle more dramatic convective phenomena, let us start with the mundane. Imagine a spring or summer day when there are no large-scale weather disturbances (fronts, low pressure systems, etc.) in the vicinity. At sunrise on such a day, the sky might be quite clear. Over the course of the day, the sun beats down on the ground and warms it. The warm ground, in turn, warms the air in contact with it. A superadiabatic lapse rate is established just above the surface, and because it is unstable, the air mixes, so that the warming is distributed over a somewhat deeper layer. As this process continues, larger "bubbles" of warm air, or **thermals**, start to rise. As they rise, they cool adiabatically; therefore, they follow a dry adiabat on a thermodynamic diagram.

The thermals will continue to rise until their temperature matches that of the environment. The level at which this occurs is called the **equilibrium level**, or **EL**, also sometimes known as the **level of neutral buoyancy**. At that point, they may overshoot a bit, becoming colder than the environment and ultimately falling back to their EL.

In the absence of condensation, the above process is usually invisible to the eye. But the rising currents of air may be exploited by soaring birds and even glider pilots to help stay aloft for long periods of time. If the thermals are especially deep and strong, the inrush of swirling air below them may give rise to towering **dust devils**. Dust devils are a common occurrence in the desert regions of the world.

If the rising thermals have any humidity at all and rise a sufficient distance, then there is some point at which visible condensation will occur. The level at which this occurs is, of course, the parcel's LCL *after* allowing for the maximum temperature it reaches before it starts to rise. Furthermore, the maximum distance the parcel *can* rise is governed by the equilibrium level (EL) at whatever temperature it starts out with.

We therefore define the **convective condensation level** (CCL) as the lowest level at which a heated parcel from the surface can rise via free (unforced) convection to achieve saturation. The temperature to which the parcel must be heated in order for this to occur is called the **convective temperature** T_c.

Key fact: Graphically, the CCL is located at the intersection of the saturation mixing ratio line corresponding to the surface dewpoint with the actual temperature profile. Following a dry adiabat back to the surface gives the convective temperature T_c.

Problem 8.6: For Sounding 1 (see Appendix F), find the CCL and convective temperature for a parcel lifted from the surface.

Stable case

We can apply the above definition to the example profile shown in Fig. 8.6. We see that the environment is absolutely stable at the CCL; that is, $\Gamma < \Gamma_s$. Therefore a parcel heated to T_c (and with fixed mixing ratio w) will reach its condensation level at exactly the same point where it also reaches its equilibrium level. We thus expect a cloud base to form at that level, but with very little penetration of the parcel above that level. The visible result of this process is a flattened cloud known as **fair weather cumulus** (Fig. 8.7).

Generally speaking, **cumulus** clouds are characterized by flat bases (representing the condensation level) and cauliflower-like tops that reveal the presence of buoyant updrafts. Glider pilots view

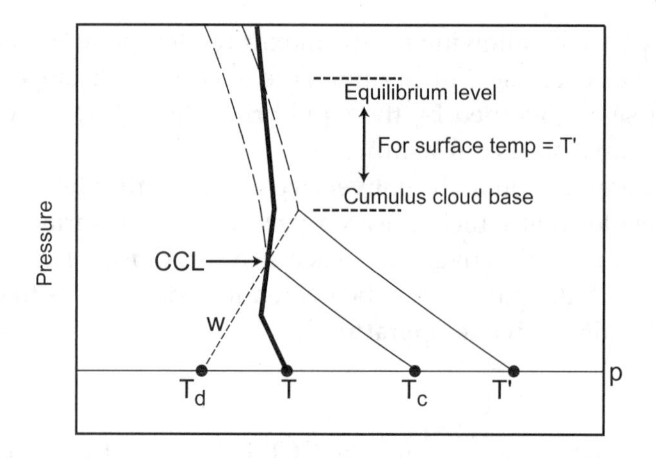

Fig. 8.6: The Convective Condensation Level (CCL) is defined by the intersection of the surface mixing ratio line with the temperature profile. The convective temperature T_c is obtained by following a dry adiabat from the CCL back to the surface. If the surface air is heated to a temperature $T' > T_c$, parcels will ascend to a new, higher condensation level, and the resulting cumulus clouds may achieve significant vertical development.

Fig. 8.7: Fair weather cumulus (*cumulus humulis*) on a December day in Florida. These clouds occur when surface air is heated to its convective temperature T_c, as defined in the text. The cloud base is at the convective condensation level (CCL). Because the environment at the CCL has a stable lapse rate, clouds are shallow and flattened. If the lapse rate at the CCL were conditionally unstable, one would instead observe cumulus of considerably greater vertical extent or even cumulonimbus. *(Courtesy of the NOAA Photo Library. Photo by Ralph F. Kresge.)*

cumulus clouds as markers of the tops of thermal updrafts that can be exploited for soaring.

What happens in this example if we heat the surface parcel to a temperature significantly greater than its convective temperature T_C? In that case, it will still reach a condensation level, though at a slightly higher altitude than the nominal CCL. Moreover, it now has enough buoyancy to rise somewhat beyond the condensation level before reaching its EL. We then expect cumulus clouds exhibiting somewhat greater overall vertical depth.

The textbook scenario for the evolution of cumulus clouds on a pleasant sunny day looks like this:

1. At sunrise, the sky is cloud-free.

2. As the sun rises in the sky and heats the ground, invisible thermals develop, mixing the near-surface air.

3. When the convective temperature T_c is reached in the surface air, the first small, highly flattened fair-weather cumulus clouds appear in the sky.

4. With continued surface heating, the cumulus clouds become more numerous and vertically thicker.

5. As the sun goes down and surface heating ends, the updrafts responsible for cumulus formation subside. There may be lingering remnants of the clouds for a while in the form of *stratocumulus formed by the spreading of cumulus*. Eventually, these clouds dissipate as well.

How much vertical extent one can expect in any given case depends on the details of the environmental profile. If an inversion is present above the CCL, for example, it may be difficult for any parcel with reasonable starting temperature to overcome it. An inversion therefore commonly functions as a "lid" on convection; the tops of all visible convective clouds (if any) will be found near the inversion height.

Conditionally unstable case

As noted, the example profile shown in Fig. 8.6 depicted an absolutely stable environment in the vicinity of the CCL. If instead the environment is *conditionally unstable* ($\Gamma > \Gamma_s$) at the CCL, then the parcel will *not* achieve equilibrium at that point; rather, its vertical momentum will carry it beyond the CCL following a moist adiabat, and that moist adiabat will maintain the parcel at a temperature warmer than the surrounding environment for some distance.

In the presence of conditional instability, the visible result of surface heating may be a cumulus cloud that is not at all flattened but rather deep. Cumulus clouds of moderate vertical development — that is, about as tall as they are wide—are known as **cumulus mediocris**. Very tall cumulus clouds are known as **cumulus congestus** or **towering cumulus** (Figs. 8.8 and 8.9). In extreme cases, the clouds transform into **cumulonimbus** clouds associated with thunderstorms. We will now discuss basic parcel stability concepts relevant to thunderstorm occurrence.

8.4.2 Deep convection

Imagine a situation in which a parcel of air near the surface is forced to rise by an approaching front, by wind flow over a low mountain peak, or by some other mechanism. We know by now that the parcel will first follow a dry adiabat until it reaches its LCL and follow a moist adiabat thereafter.

Assume that the lapse rate near the surface is less than the dry adiabatic lapse rate. The surface is then stable with respect to dry adiabatic motions. Energy must therefore be supplied to lift the negatively buoyant parcel through the layer above it.

Even after it reaches its LCL and begins to follow a moist adiabat, it may remain colder than the surrounding environment. If that is the case, and if whatever mechanism was forcing it to rise ceased, the parcel will simply sink back to the surface.

The Level of Free Convection (LFC)

Under certain circumstances, however, a parcel lifted sufficiently far above the surface may encounter a level at which it ceases to be colder and denser than the surrounding air and instead becomes positively buoyant. On a thermodynamic diagram, this occurs when the moist adiabat being followed by the parcel crosses from the cold side of the environmental profile to the warm side.

Fig. 8.8: This towering cumulus cloud developed in a conditionally unstable environment on a summer afternoon in Madison, WI.

Fig. 8.9: These *cumulus congestus* (towering cumulus) clouds were observed over the Wyoming plains. The top of the cell on the far right is showing hints of glaciation, in that it is losing the "hard" cauliflower appearance and is instead becoming smooth and fuzzy. It is therefore on the verge of becoming a *cumulonimbus calvus*. Once a fully developed anvil has appeared, it will be classified as *cumulonimbus incus*. *(Courtesy of the NOAA Photo Library.)*

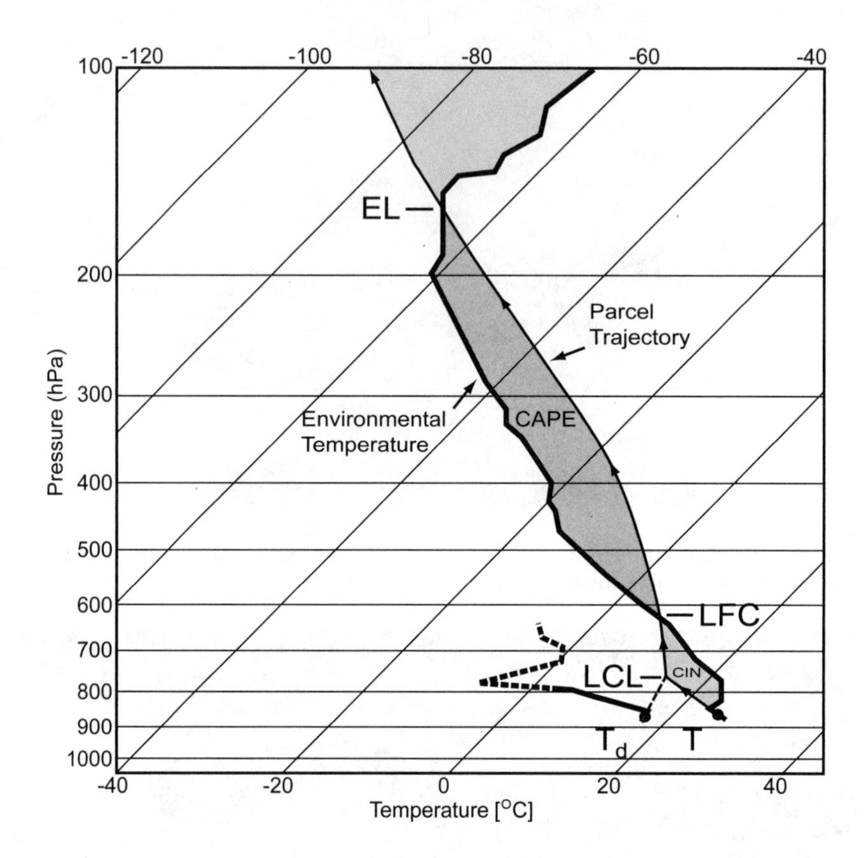

Fig. 8.10: Example of a sounding typical for strong thunderstorm development. Parcels lifted from near the surface rise dry adiabatically to their lifted condensation level (LCL). If forced to continue rising, they reach their level of free convection (LFC), after which the parcel becomes warmer than its surroundings and gains kinetic energy as it rises. The shaded area labeled CIN (convective inhibition) is proportional to the energy required to force a parcel to its LFC. The shaded area labeled CAPE (convective available potential energy) is proportional to the energy the parcel may gain as it ascends through the depth of the troposphere. The equilibrium level (EL) is where the parcel again assumes the same temperature as its surroundings. Although it may initially overshoot this level, it will then fall back to the EL and spread out horizontally, giving rise to the classic "anvil" top of a cumulonimbus tower.

Fig. 8.11: This classic photo of a fully developed cumulonimbus tower with characteristic anvil top (*cumulonimbus incus*) was taken from an aircraft. To the right is a vigorously growing *cumulus congestus*. It is not yet a cumulonimbus because it still has the hard-edged "cauliflower" top and does not yet show signs of glaciation (conversion to ice), which occurs at temperatures approaching −40°C. Note the small pileus (cap) cloud just above the most vigorous updraft; this feature is caused by the layer of moist air just *above* the cumulus top being pushed upward past its LCL. *(Courtesy of the NOAA Photo Library.)*

The level at which this crossover occurs is called the **level of free convection** or **LFC**.

Thus, if the parcel is forced upward and reaches its LFC, no further input of energy is required. Rather, the parcel now ascends freely, accelerating as it goes. It will continue to ascend until the moist adiabat associated with the parcel again crosses to the cold side of the environmental temperature profile, as it ultimately must. As we already saw, this new crossing point is called the equilibrium level, or EL. In some situations, the parcel's EL may be far above its LFC — that is, the parcel might freely ascend through a very substantial depth of the troposphere before coming to rest again.

The above process, and the locations of the LFC and EL, are illustrated for a real temperature profile in Fig. 8.10. In this instance, the LFC occurs at 620 hPa, or around 2.7 km above the surface level of the sounding. The EL is found near 160 hPa, which corresponds to an altitude near 13 km, or approximately 40,000 feet! In fact, the EL in this case is found above the tropopause at 200 hPa!

Fig. 8.12: A time exposure captures multiple cloud-to-ground lightning strokes during a night-time thunderstorm in Norman, Oklahoma. *(Courtesy of the NOAA Photo Library and the National Severe Storms Laboratory. Photo by C. Clark.)*

Assuming then that an external mechanism is capable of forcing near-surface air to rise a mere one kilometer in this particular scenario, we can expect a convective updraft to result that will carry that air to an altitude near 13 km before it reaches equilibrium and spreads horizontally, like steam from a pot of boiling water reaching the ceiling of the kitchen (Fig. 8.11).

As the air ascends, most of the water vapor the parcel started out with is wrung out of it by condensation. Much of this condensate is subsequently converted to frozen precipitation—snow, graupel and even hail—which subsequently falls to lower, warmer altitudes where it (usually) melts to reach the surface as rainfall.

Other microphysical processes in the upper portion of the convective tower, not all of which are fully understood, conspire to separate positive from negative electric charge, setting the stage for the occurrence of the powerful electrical discharge known as lightning (Fig. 8.12). Lightning in turn instantaneously heats the channel of air through which it passes to 10,000 K or more; the resulting explosive expansion of air is heard as thunder. A thunderstorm has been born!

CIN and CAPE

The mere existence of an LFC and a much higher EL neither guarantees the occurrence of a thunderstorm, nor does it give much insight into the likely intensity of any thunderstorm that might actually develop. We therefore now turn to an examination of the energy budget of the process just discussed.

We already saw that mechanical energy had to be supplied to the surface parcel to enable it to reach its LFC. The *amount* of energy required is called the **convective inhibition** or **CIN** (pronounced "sin"). It is usually given in joules per kilogram.

Because work corresponds to force times distance, CIN can be expressed mathematically as

$$\mathrm{CIN} \equiv -\int_{0}^{z_{\mathrm{LFC}}} f_B(z)\, dz \quad , \tag{8.11}$$

where $f_B(z)$ is the upward buoyant force acting on the parcel at level z. In keeping with (3.59), but ignoring the usually small distinction between temperature and virtual temperature (which is harder to track on a thermodynamic diagram), we have

$$f_B(z) = \left[\frac{T(z) - T'(z)}{T'(z)}\right] g \quad , \tag{8.12}$$

where $T(z)$ is the temperature of the rising parcel and $T'(z)$ is the temperature of the environment at the same level. Thus,

$$\mathrm{CIN} = -g \int_{0}^{z_{\mathrm{LFC}}} \left[\frac{T(z) - T'(z)}{T'(z)}\right] dz \quad . \tag{8.13}$$

Between the limits given, the buoyant force is negative by definition; hence, the minus sign in front of the integral ensures that CIN is a positive quantity. By invoking the hydrostatic approximation and the ideal gas law, the above integral can be rewritten to give

$$\boxed{\mathrm{CIN} = R_d \int_{p_0}^{\mathrm{LFC}} \left[T(p) - T'(p)\right]\, d\ln p \quad ,} \tag{8.14}$$

where p_0 is the surface pressure in the sounding.

Once the parcel has overcome the energy barrier represented by its CIN and thus reached its LFC, we may now look at how much energy may be *released* by the resulting buoyant ascent. This energy (again expressed in joules per kilogram) is called the **convective available potential energy** or **CAPE.** Completely analogous to CIN, we have

$$\boxed{\text{CAPE} = R_d \int_{\text{LFC}}^{\text{EL}} \left[T'(p) - T(p) \right] \, d \ln p \quad .} \tag{8.15}$$

An LFC has to exist in order for either CIN or CAPE to be calculated. For very many soundings, no LFC exists, and there is no possibility of free convection for parcels originating at the surface. In such cases both CIN and CAPE are undefined.

Key fact: CIN represents the energy *barrier* to the initiation of free convection. CAPE represents the maximum possible energy that can be *released* (e.g., converted to kinetic energy) by the parcel after the CIN barrier has been overcome.

In order to have any chance of thunderstorm occurrence, CAPE must be present. The more CAPE, the more likely it is that any thunderstorm that does develop could be severe. However, before a thunderstorm can occur as a result of mechanical lifting, whatever CIN is present must be overcome. The larger the CIN, the less likely it is that external forcing will be sufficient to initiate convection.

On the other hand, a moderate amount of CIN is needed in order for CAPE to build up in the first place. In the absence of much CIN, any CAPE that develops is readily released (and thus eliminated) via frequent but relatively weak showers or thundershowers. This is in fact the situation that prevails throughout much of the tropics, especially over ocean. Hence, showers are frequent, but truly violent thunderstorms are rare, unlike the case for many continental regions in the midlatitudes, especially the Midwestern United States and parts of Asia and Australia.

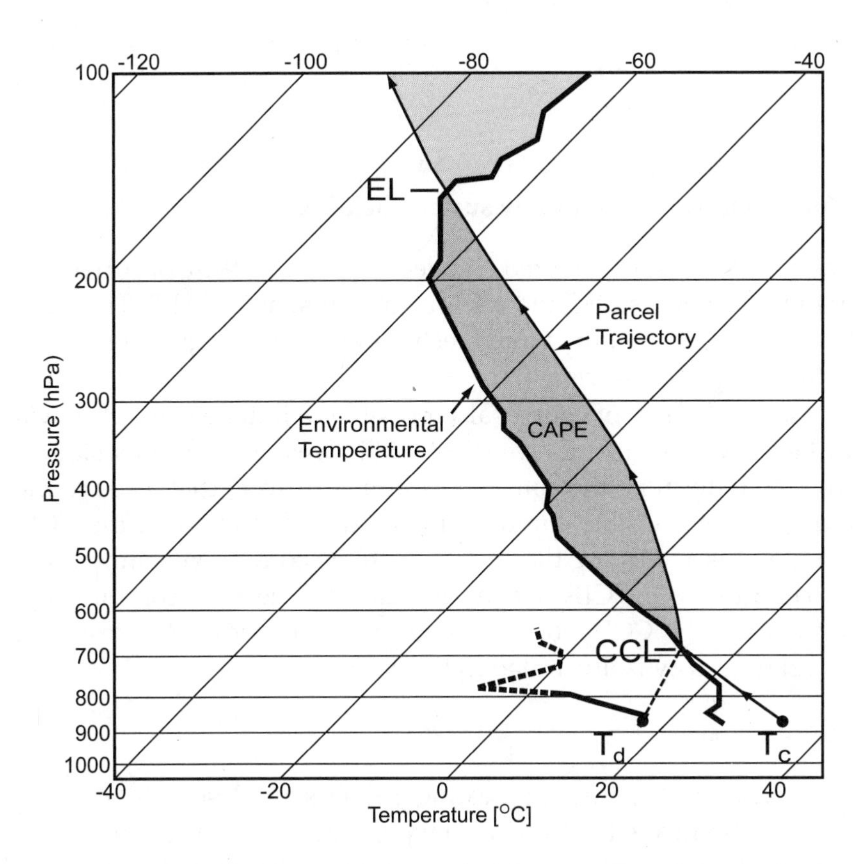

Fig. 8.13: Same as Fig. 8.10, except this time surface air is heated during the daytime to the convective temperature T_c, causing it to rise spontaneously. Not only is there now no convective inhibition (CIN), there is also significantly greater CAPE and a somewhat higher equilibrium level (EL).

Key fact: On a skew-T diagram, CIN and CAPE are exactly proportional to the *areas* bounded by the environmental and parcel temperature profiles, as indicated, for example, in Fig. 8.10.

Thunderstorm initiation by surface heating

The scenario just considered entailed the forced lifting of surface air until it reached its LFC and released any available CAPE. The more CIN that is present, the more mechanical work is required in order to overcome that barrier.

However, it is, of course, also possible to initiate convection via surface heating. Just as we did for fair weather cumulus clouds, we may determine the convective temperature T_c that leads to the formation of a visible cumuliform cloud with its base at the CCL. In many cases, heating the surface air to its convective temperature also eliminates the CIN barrier, especially if the air is conditionally unstable at the CCL. For the same profile as above, the resulting parcel trajectory is illustrated in Fig. 8.13.

Key fact: Surface heating reduces (and sometimes eliminates) CIN while also increasing CAPE. It follows that thunderstorms are usually more likely *and* more powerful in the afternoon and early evening hours.

Nighttime surface cooling, on the other hand, tends to stabilize the lowest layers of the atmosphere and increase CIN, though it is sometimes still possible for thunderstorms to be initiated via the lifting of parcels originating above the cool surface layer.

Problem 8.7: Obtain two paper copies of Sounding 1 (see Appendix F). Analyze the first assuming that an air parcel originating at the surface is mechanically lifted, the second assuming that the same air parcel is heated to its convective temperature. For both soundings, sketch the appropriate parcel line from the surface to the top of the sounding. Mark the LFC and EL, as well as the areas of CAPE and CIN. Based on the U.S. Standard Atmosphere, estimate the altitude in kilometers of the top of the thunderstorm anvil in each case (ignore overshoot by the rising parcel).

8.5 In Practice

8.5.1 Stability indices

Before the widespread availability of computers and numerical weather prediction models, operational forecasters required simple rules of thumb to help them quickly evaluate the potential for severe weather from more-or-less raw real-time weather data. One important example can be found in the development of various **stability indices** that could be readily calculated from a few of the mandatory level values found in any complete radiosonde report.

Regardless of the formulation, the purpose of a stability index is to distill down to a *single number* some measure of the overall stability of the atmosphere. By its very nature, a stability index cannot account for all of the details of a complete sounding; therefore, its interpretation is bound to be misleading in certain cases. Moreover, even a complete sounding does not provide information on how the local atmosphere will evolve in subsequent hours, nor can it account for the influence of external disturbances, such as approaching cold fronts. Last, but not least, geographical location, time of year, and other variables affect the interpretation of any given index. Forecasters therefore commonly made minor adjustments to the basic rules given below in order to improve their utility at their locale.

Notwithstanding the obvious limitations of stability indices as predictors of thunderstorms and/or severe weather, a concise overview[1] of the best-known stability indices seems worthwhile. Not only will this review help reinforce the critical role of atmospheric stability in the threat of severe weather, it will also help illustrate a few of the secondary factors that forecasters often consider important for thunderstorm development. The physical basis for some of those factors, such as the wind terms appearing in the SWEAT index discussed below, will not be apparent until you have had more advanced meteorological coursework.

[1]The stability index descriptions and interpretations that follow were adapted in part from documents published by the National Weather Service, especially `http://www.srh.noaa.gov/ffc/html/gloss2.shtml`, `http://www.crh.noaa.gov/crh/?n=tsp10-sevwea-stab`, and `http://www.crh.noaa.gov/lmk/soo/docu/indices.php`.

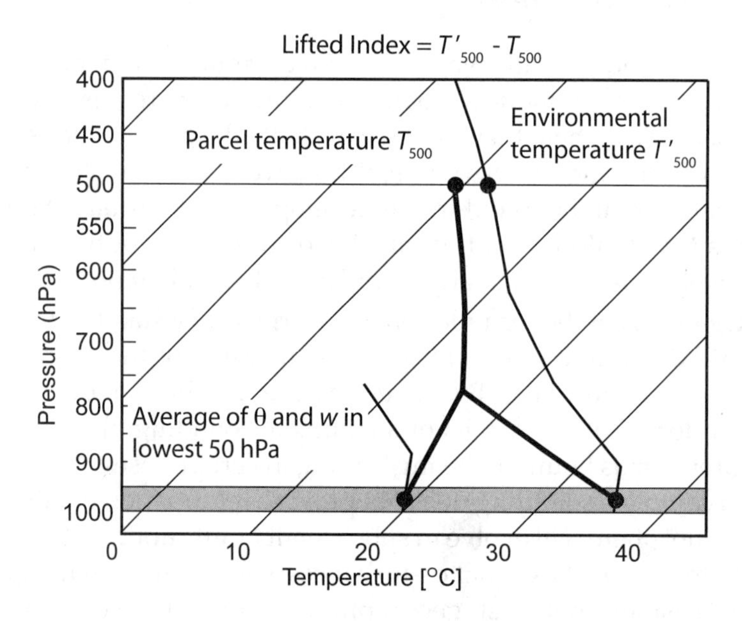

Fig. 8.14: Schematic depiction of the procedure for finding the Lifted Index (LI), based on a parcel representing the average potential temperature and mixing ratio of the lowest 50 hPa of the sounding. The thin, irregular lines represent the environmental temperature profile (right) and dewpoint (left). However, only the parcel's starting temperature and dewpoint and the environmental temperature at 500 hPa are required in order to find the LI.

Lifted Index (LI)

The Lifted Index (LI) is a popular and intuitively appealing stability index that represents the difference between the temperature of a parcel lifted from near the surface to 500 hPa and the environmental temperature at 500 hPa. It thus takes into account near-surface moisture and overall lapse rate (static stability). LI values do depend on the precise level (or layer) from which a parcel is lifted and cannot account for details in the environmental temperature curve above the LCL and below 500 hPa. The original version of the LI (assumed here) utilizes a parcel representing the *average* of the moisture and temperature of the lowest 50–100 hPa of the sounding (Fig. 8.14).

Formally, the Lifted Index may be written

$$LI = T'_{500} - T_{500} \quad , \tag{8.16}$$

where T'_{500} and T_{500} are the environmental and parcel temperatures, respectively, at 500 hPa. The difference, therefore, becomes more positive with increasing stability. The following table gives representative interpretations of LI falling in different ranges:

> 3	Stable.
1 to 3	Weak convection possible if strong lifting is present.
0 to -3	Marginally unstable.
-3 to -6	Moderately unstable.
-6 to -9	Very unstable.
< -9	Extremely unstable.

Showalter Index (SI)

The Showalter Index (SI) is very similar to the LI but is based on lifting a parcel from the 850 hPa level rather than from near the surface. That is,

$$SI = T'_{500} - T_{500} \quad , \tag{8.17}$$

where the variables are the same as for the LI except that the parcel is drawn from the 850 hPa level rather than the lowest 100 hPa layer.

The SI may be better than the LI in revealing instability aloft given a shallow low-level cool air mass near a frontal boundary. However, the SI is considered inferior to the LI in showing instability if the low-level moisture does not extend up to the 850 hPa level.

A drawback of the SI relative to the LI is that it does not account for variations in the altitude of the station. At a station near sea level, the 850 hPa level may be found well over a kilometer above the surface, in which case it could fail to detect instability associated with a fairly deep moist layer residing entirely below this level. On the other hand, at a high altitude station such as Denver, Colorado, the 850 hPa level is usually found at or below the surface of the Earth, in which case the SI cannot be computed at all!

For the SI, the risk of severe weather activity is defined as follows:

> 3	No significant activity
1 to 3	Showers possible with other source of lift
-2 to 1	Thunderstorms possible (generally weak)
-3 to -2	Thunderstorms more probable (possibly strong)
-6 to -4	Strong or severe thunderstorms possible
< -6	Any thunderstorms likely to be strong or severe

Total Totals Index (TT)

The Total Totals Index consists of two components, the Vertical Totals (VT) and the Cross Totals (CT). The VT is designed to capture the overall static stability (lapse rate) between 850 and 500 hPa and is given by

$$VT = T_{850} - T_{500} \quad . \tag{8.18}$$

where T_{850} and T_{500} are the temperatures at 850 and 500 hPa.

The CT accounts for low-level moisture and is defined as

$$CT = T_{d,850} - T_{500} \quad , \tag{8.19}$$

where $T_{d,850}$ is the dewpoint at 850 hPa. The Total Totals Index is then defined as

$$TT = VT + CT \quad . \tag{8.20}$$

Thus, TT accounts for both static stability and 850 hPa moisture. It has the convenient property that it can be calculated directly from data at the two levels without the need for adiabatic lifting of parcels.

Like the Showalter Index, TT is unrepresentative in situations where low-level moisture resides entirely below the 850 hPa level, and it is completely undefined if 850 hPa falls below ground level. In addition, convection may be inhibited despite a high TT value if a significant capping inversion is present.

The risk of severe weather activity for a given value of TT is defined as follows:

44 to 45	Isolated moderate thunderstorms
46 to 47	Scattered moderate / few heavy thunderstorms
48 to 49	Scattered moderate / few heavy / isolated severe thunderstorms
50 to 51	Scattered heavy / few severe thunderstorms and isolated tornadoes
52 to 55	Scattered to numerous heavy / few to scattered severe thunderstorm / few tornadoes
> 55	Numerous heavy / scattered severe thunderstorms and scattered tornadoes

K Index (KI)

The K index is similar to Total Totals except that it takes into account the presence of moist air at 700 hPa as a factor contributing to air mass thunderstorm development. The K index is defined as follows:

$$KI = T_{850} - T_{500} + T_{d,850} - (T_{700} - T_{d,700}) \quad . \tag{8.21}$$

The risk of air mass thunderstorms is defined as follows:

< 15	0% Air mass thunderstorm probability
15 to 20	<20% Air mass thunderstorm probability
21 to 25	20 to 40% Air mass thunderstorm probability
26 to 30	40 to 60% Air mass thunderstorm probability
31 to 35	60 to 80% Air mass thunderstorm probability
36 to 40	80 to 90% Air mass thunderstorm probability
> 40	>90% Air mass thunderstorm probability

SWEAT (Severe Weather thrEAT) Index

This is a fairly elaborate index developed by the U.S. Air Force that takes into account thermal instability, low level moisture content, vertical wind shear,[2] and horizontal wind speeds. The SWEAT index is defined as follows:

$$SWEAT = 12T_{d,850} + 20(TT - 49) + 2f_{850} + f_{500} + 125(s + 0.2) \quad , \tag{8.22}$$

where $T_{d,850}$ is the 850 hPa dewpoint, TT is the total-totals index defined above, and f_{850} and f_{500} are the wind speeds in knots at 850 and 500 hPa.

The shear term s is the sine of the angle between the wind directions at 500 hPa and 850 hPa (thus representing the directional shear in this layer). It is set to zero if any of the following criteria are *not* met:

1. the 850 hPa wind direction ranges from 130° to 250°,
2. the 500 hPa wind direction ranges from 210° to 310°,
3. the 500 hPa wind direction minus the 850 hPa wind direction is a positive number, and
4. both the 850 and 500 hPa wind speeds are at least 15 kts.

No term in equation defining SWEAT may be negative; if so, that term is set to zero.

The interpretation of SWEAT is as follows:

< 300	No activity expected
300 to 400	Isolated moderate to heavy thunderstorms
400 to 500	Severe thunderstorms and tornadoes probable
> 500	Severe thunderstorms and tornadoes likely

Wind shear in particular has been shown to play a crucial role in the organization of intense, long-lived thunderstorms known as *supercells* (Figs. 8.15–8.17).

[2]Change of wind vector with altitude.

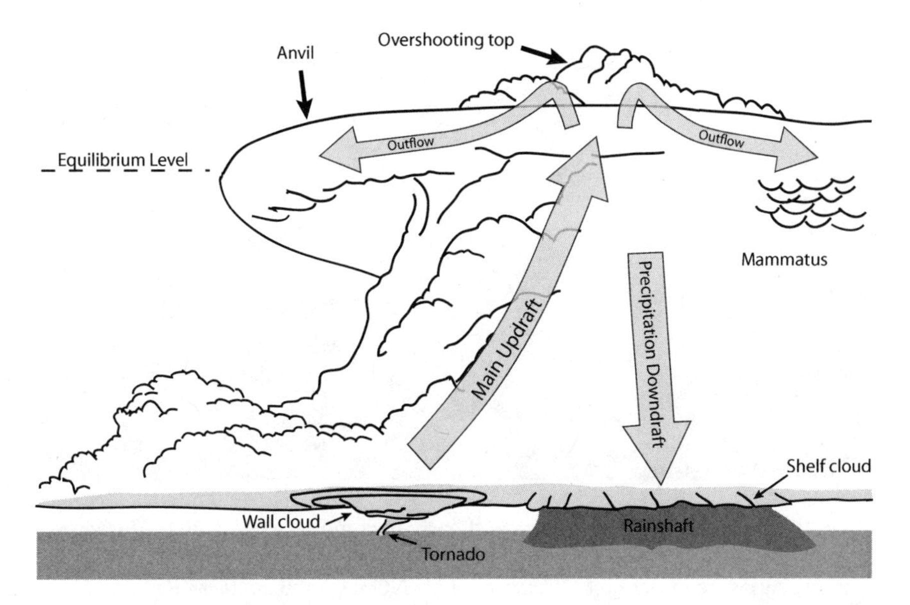

Fig. 8.15: Highly simplified depiction of the updraft and downdraft structure of a tornadic supercell. The intense updraft is powered by the conversion of large amounts of CAPE in the environment to vertical kinetic energy. Strong inflow into the updraft region interacts with rotational motion in the environment to "spin up" the tornado vortex and associated mesocyclone. The updraft also facilitates the formation of large hail. Momentum carries the rapidly ascending air well past the equilibrium level (EL), giving rise to an overshooting top that can often be seen in satellite images (Fig. 8.17). As the air settles back downward, it spreads outward into a characteristic anvil cloud (Fig. 8.16). Mammatus clouds may sometimes be seen on the underside of the anvil of powerful thunderstorms (Fig. 8.19). Heavy precipitation formed in the updraft drags air downward to create a strong downdraft and gust front at the surface (Fig. 8.18). In a supercell thunderstorm, vertical wind shear separates the updraft from the downdraft so that the two act in concert rather than interfering with one another.

Fig. 8.16: During the late afternoon and early evening of April 3, 2004, this supercell thunderstorm dropped two-inch-diameter hail over Chaparral, New Mexico, causing widespread damage. *(Courtesy of the NOAA/NWS Southern Regional Headquarters; photo by Greg Lundeen.)*

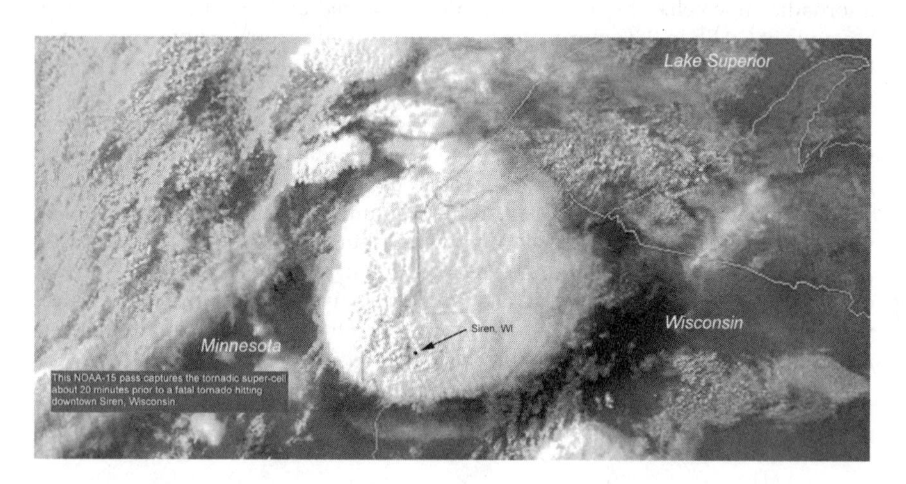

Fig. 8.17: A satellite image of a supercell captured 20 minutes before a tornado devastated downtown Siren, Wisconsin, on July 19, 2001. *(Courtesy of NOAA.)*

Problem 8.8: This exercise uses Soundings 1, 2, and 3 (see Appendix F). (a) For each sounding, determine the LI, SI, TT, and KI indices. (b) Determine the SWEAT index for Sounding 1 only (wind data are provided at each mandatory pressure level). (c) Summarize your results from (a) and (b) in tabular form (one table per sounding), also quoting the potential for thunderstorm activity inferred from each index. (d) The vertical structure of Soundings 1 and 3 are essentially identical except that Sounding 3 has been shifted downward (toward higher pressure) as if the surface pressure had been 20 hPa higher on the day the sounding was taken. The actual stability structure of Sounding 3 is negligibly affected by this change, but what does it do to each of the four stability indices? What do you conclude about the wisdom of relying on a single index as a measure of overall stability?

Convective Available Potential Energy (CAPE)

We already encountered the definition and physical interpretation of CAPE in Section 8.4.2. Like the indices defined above, CAPE can be viewed as a single number that conveys information about the overall stability of the atmosphere. In fact, it is in many ways superior to the other indices because it is not based on information obtained at only a few discrete levels in the sounding but rather considers the complete profile.

The drawback, of course, is that CAPE can't be computed numerically from a simple formula. It is usually calculated using a computer program. Alternatively, one may estimate CAPE by eye from the graphical area on a skew-*T* diagram.

Whatever the means used to obtain CAPE for a particular sounding, here are the conventional interpretations:

< 0	Stable
0 to 1000	Marginally unstable
1000 to 2500	Moderately unstable
2500 to 3500	Very unstable
3500 to 4000	Extremely unstable

The above values are based on the lifting of a parcel having the average temperature and moisture content of the lowest 50 to

Fig. 8.18: Approaching thunderstorm with lead gust front. Dense rain-cooled air within the storm creates a downdraft that spreads outward ahead of the storm once it reaches ground level. It wedges under the warm moist air ahead of it, forming a flat "shelf cloud." This so-called *outflow boundary* not only often produces the strongest gust of wind associated with the arrival of a thunderstorm, it also often provides the lifting mechanism needed to initiate new thunderstorm cells. *(Courtesy of the NOAA Photo Library and the National Severe Storms Laboratory.)*

Fig. 8.19: Mammatus clouds, also known as mamma, are dramatic pouch-like formations that are sometimes observed on the underside of the anvil of vigorous cumulonimbus clouds, though they sometimes occur in conjunction with other cloud types. A number of thermodynamic and dynamic mechanisms have been proposed for their formation, none of which is yet considered definitive. Some of the more widely accepted explanations invoke evaporative cooling at the base of the anvil resulting in destabilization of the layer directly beneath it. *(Courtesy of the NOAA Photo Library and the National Severe Storms Laboratory.)*

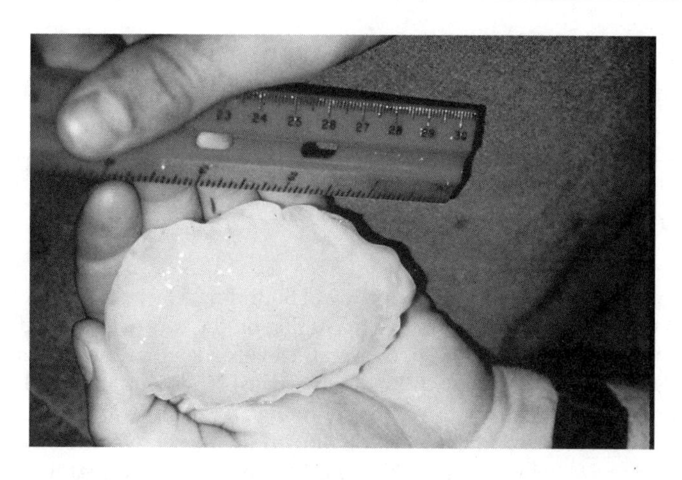

Fig. 8.20: Baseball-sized hail recovered after a severe thunderstorm in Texas. The formation of such large hail requires convective updraft speeds that significantly exceed the terminal fall speed of the hailstone through still air. Such updrafts in turn depend on the presence of large CAPE values. *(Courtesy of the NOAA Photo Library and the National Severe Storms Laboratory.)*

100 hPa layer (i.e., the boundary layer). The value of CAPE is dependent on the level from which a parcel is lifted. Parcels lifted from the surface level usually exhibit a higher (sometimes significantly higher) CAPE value than those lifted based on an average of the entire boundary layer.

The theoretical maximum updraft speed in a thunderstorm W_{max} at the equilibrium level can be calculated by assuming that the entire CAPE is converted to kinetic energy, in which case

$$W_{max} = \sqrt{2(CAPE)} \quad . \tag{8.23}$$

For example, a range of CAPE of 1500-2500 J/kg gives a w_{max} range of about 50-70 m/s (100-140 kts). However, the real-world maximum is considerably lower than the theoretical maximum, owing to the effects of water loading (i.e., the weight of condensed water), mixing, entrainment, and evaporative cooling. The real-world w_{max} is therefore often estimated as about one-half of the theoretical maximum calculated above.

CAPE alone does not tell the whole story. The *shape* of the positive area is also important. Given the same CAPE value in each of two soundings, the longer, narrower profile implies slower updraft acceleration but taller thunderstorms, which is better for high precipitation efficiency. A shorter, fatter profile implies more rapid vertical acceleration, which can enhance the potential for updraft rotation within the storm and, consequently, of supercell and even tornado development.

Problem 8.9: Obtain a paper copy of Sounding 1 (see Appendix F). (a) With the help of (5.95), sketch a region on the sounding bounded by two temperatures and two pressure levels such that the enclosed area corresponds to 1000 J/kg of energy. (b) Now plot a parcel line from the surface to the top of the sounding and identify areas of CIN and CAPE. (c) Using the area you plotted in (a) as a reference, visually *estimate* the values of CIN and CAPE in joules per kilogram. (d) Compute the real-world (not theoretical) maximum updraft speed expected for this sounding.

APPENDIX A

Further Reading

Some of the following textbooks offer more advanced treatments of many of the topics introduced here, as well as providing comprehensive bibliographies. Others give the broader meteorological context. The keys appearing at the beginning of each entry below are used to cite these works throughout this book.

BA98 Bohren, C.F., and B.A. Albrecht, 1998: *Atmospheric Thermodynamics.* Oxford University Press, USA, 416 pp. (ISBN-13: 978-0-19-509904-1)

CW99 Curry, J.A., and P.J. Webster, 1999: *Thermodynamics of Atmospheres and Oceans.* Academic Press, 471 pp. (ISBN-13: 978-0-12-199570-6)

RY89 Rogers, R.R., and M.K. Yau, 1989: *A Short Course in Cloud Physics (3d Ed.).* Butterworth-Heinemann, 304 pp. (ISBN-13: 978-0-75-063215-7)

S96 Salby, M.L, 1996: *Fundamentals of Atmospheric Physics.* Academic Press, 627 pp. (ISBN-13:978-0-12-615160-2)

T07 Tsonis, A., 2007: *An Introduction to Atmospheric Thermodynamics (2nd Ed.).* Cambridge University Press, 198 pp. (ISBN-13: 978-0-52-169628-9)

WH06 Wallace, J.M., and P.V. Hobbs, 2006: *Atmospheric Science: An Introductory Survey (2nd Ed.).* Academic Press, 504 pp. (ISBN-13: 978-0-12-732951-2)

APPENDIX B

Physical Problem Solving: A Tutorial

Homework sets requiring you to solve physical problems are an essential teaching tool in any upper-division physical science course. If you are like most students entering a junior-level course in atmospheric physics, you have had few opportunities yet to *apply* the concepts and techniques of calculus and physics to real-world problems like those encountered in meteorology.

It is easy to overlook the range of distinct learned skills that must be brought to bear in the solution of almost any problem. If you are still weak in any one or more of these skills (and who among us is fortunate enough to be *born* with any of them?), then the whole process will become an ordeal—an exercise in frustration rather than learning.

I have found that most students at this level have also not yet become accustomed to working with physical quantities *symbolically*, rather than numerically. And, sadly, many students (including the author) manage to get through their undergraduate years without developing a real appreciation for the power of *dimensional consistency* as a tool in the construction and debugging of problem solutions.

The purpose of this appendix is to serve as a brief tutorial on how experienced scientists and engineers attack physical problems.

I will highlight specific strategies that you would do well to adopt as habits not only for the problems you encounter in this course but in your future work as well. My insistence on symbolic rather than numerical problem-solving is a good example: my goal is not to make life more difficult but rather to make it *easier* in the long run! You will make fewer "dumb" mistakes, you will use your calculator less, your reasoning will be clearer, and—maybe most importantly, at this level at least—it will be easier for your instructor to spot what you did *right* in your homework and exam solutions! The only thing "hard" about symbolic problem-solving is that you have probably spent much more time doing things the other way.

Before we examine the mechanics of the physical computations, let us first review the entire process of solving a problem that might be given to you in a homework set or on an exam.

B.1 Five Steps to Success

The solution of any homework or exam problem, regardless of the details of the problem, invariably entails (or should entail) the following steps, the first of which has ideally been completed before you even see the problem:

1. Knowledge—learning the relevant facts and theory.
2. Analysis—applying familiar facts to an unfamiliar problem.
3. Execution—the mechanics of working and verifying your solution.
4. Validation—convincing yourself that your answer is correct.
5. Understanding—drawing the appropriate lessons from the exercise.

If you struggle with any of the first three, then your success in obtaining a solution at all may be in doubt. If you don't bother with the fourth, then you won't know until you get your homework or exam back whether your solution was correct. Finally, if you don't follow through with the fifth step, then the effort will be at least partly wasted, even if your solution is correct.

Let us review each of these steps in turn.

B.1.1 Acquiring relevant knowledge

The primary purpose of your instructor's lectures and your textbook is to impart *knowledge* of the subject matter of your course. Knowledge includes (among other things) *observed facts* (e.g., the composition of the atmosphere) and *governing principles* (e.g., the Ideal Gas Law). Problem sets are usually designed to give you practice *applying* the knowledge you have gained and, in some cases, to cultivate deeper insight into How Things Work.

It is not enough to just memorize a vast hoard of facts; you also must understand how they are interconnected. For example, knowledge of the composition of the atmosphere is essential for the computation of the relevant gas constant in the Ideal Gas Law. Knowledge of the characteristic motions in the atmosphere is what justifies our use of the Hydrostatic Relation.

In both your lectures and your reading, you must therefore pay close attention not only to the facts presented to you but also to the *context* in which they are presented:

- *Why* is the instructor or author making a particular point? Is it just knowledge for knowledge's sake, or is it an important brick in a larger wall?

- *What process or situation* does a particular equation describe? Knowing an equation by heart is of no value if you don't know what it is good for.

- *What assumptions* were used to obtain a particular equation? Even if that equation seems to describe something you need, such as the relationship between pressure and altitude, it is worse than useless if its underlying assumptions are invalid for your particular problem.

Actively answering *all* of the above questions in your own mind is an essential part of *studying*. If you passively read your textbook as if it were a mere recitation of disconnected facts, you will not be prepared to correctly *apply* your knowledge. The same warning applies if you read a homework problem first and then dive into your textbook on a scavenger hunt for the one key fact or formula needed to solve it.

B.1.2 Analyzing the problem

The next step is to work out a complete and continuous pathway from the knowledge at your disposal to the desired solution. Typically, your job is to select from your storehouse of facts some sturdy links that can be assembled into a continuous, logical chain leading from your givens to your solution. If any link is missing, then the chain is incomplete and therefore worthless – you will need to take stock and see if there's another piece of information that you overlooked. Sometimes that missing information is not a textbook formula or fact but rather a reasonable assumption, also known as "common sense." *Don't underestimate the power of common sense to help you hack your way through a vast thicket of facts and equations that might seem superficially relevant to your problem!*

If any step in the process takes you down a blind alley, you must recognize that and back up. Do not make unwarranted "leaps of faith" from that blind alley to your solution and hope that the grader won't notice!

Also, there are often both short and long routes to any given destination. When driving from Los Angeles to San Diego, it is theoretically possible (and technically not incorrect) to take a detour through New York, but I don't recommend it! The more complete your grasp of the "big picture", the more likely it is that you will recognize the shortest and simplest path. In my experience, it is very common for students to overlook a quick and easy pathway and pursue a complex, time-consuming one that leads to an identical answer, but with far greater investment and far greater risk of a mechanical breakdown.

Regardless of the path you take, you need to ensure that it is complete and valid. Every step must be logically correct, and every step should take you demonstrably closer to where you want to go. It may sometimes be helpful to write out (if only for your own benefit) what each step in the solution does for you — what did you know when you started, what do you know now, and how does that get you closer to your desired solution? If you can't answer those questions (especially the last one), then you are not *solving*, you are *groping!*

A key test of the validity of your path is that it satisfies the requirement for *dimensional consistency*. Physical calculations inevitably involve not only numbers but also physical dimensions such as length, mass, time, etc. There are strict rules for mathematical operations on physical dimensions, and these rules can be powerful tools for uncovering errors in logic. The subject of physical dimensions is reviewed in greater detail in Section B.3.2. I urge you to review it carefully.

To summarize, you should *plan your solution* by answering the following questions for yourself:

1. What information are you being given as part of the problem?
2. What are you being asked to determine or calculate?
3. Which additional observed facts or reasonable assumptions are likely to be relevant?
4. Which governing principles or relationships apply?
5. Most importantly, how do the facts, assumptions, and relationships at your disposal allow you to logically get from your given information (1) to your desired solution (2)?

B.1.3 Executing the solution

Once you have mapped out your strategy for solving the problem, it is time for the implementation. You need to

1. Assign suitable symbols to represent each relevant quantity.
2. Specify values (including units) for those quantities, if applicable.
3. Manipulate the symbols algebraically to obtain the solution to your problem expressed *symbolically* in terms of your givens.
4. Verify the *dimensional consistency* of your solution.
5. Compute a *numerical solution* based on the specified values of the given variables.

All of the above steps are straightforward and can become second nature to any sufficiently motivated student regardless of native aptitude for science. Fluency is acquired not so much by *study* but rather by *practice*. Most of you, in fact, already *know* the relevant operations; it is sheer *repetition* that will make them automatic. There is, however, so much more to say about several of these steps that I have carved out a whole separate section (B.3) for that lofty purpose.

B.1.4 Validating your result

You have arrived at an answer and duly recorded it on your homework sheet. The dimensions work out—the problem asked for a radius, and sure enough, your answer has units of length.

At this point, many students consider their work done, put their pencil down, turn in their answer sheet, and, just maybe, cross their fingers. But it is not necessary to leave everything to chance. You can reduce the chance of turning in nonsense, and possibly getting zero credit[1] for your hard work, by taking a few extra minutes to think about whether your answer makes sense. Here are some examples:

- If your solution consists of a mathematical relationship, what variables appear in it? Are they the variables you expect based on your understanding of the problem? Is the relationship what you would expect it to be—for example, if x increases, should $y(x)$ increase or decrease based on your understanding of the role of x?

- When you substitute reasonable values for the variables in the relationship, can the result be positive, negative, or zero? Is the sign you get what you would expect it to be?

- What magnitude, or range of magnitudes, do you expect your quantity to take on in typical situations? Is the magnitude of your result consistent with the expected range? If the quantity is a vector, is the direction reasonable?

- Is there a special case or a limit for which you *know* what the answer should be (either exactly or approximately), and does your solution yield that answer?

[1]While every instructor has his or her own policies, my own is to give zero credit for an answer that is *obviously* wrong *unless* the student makes clear that they *recognize* that something is wrong!

B.1.5 Understanding your result

Many assigned problems aren't intended merely to test your knowledge or exercise a particular skill but also to drive home a specific point. What role does condensation and precipitation play in the occurrence of chinook winds? How large, really, is the effect of temperature variations on the change of pressure with height?

It follows that if you simply write up your problem solution, convince yourself that it appears to be mathematically and numerically correct, and then (mentally) walk away from it, you are shortchanging your own meteorological education. Your insight into the subject matter will mature more rapidly if you routinely set aside a little extra time to reflect on the following questions:

1. What general principle does the problem demonstrate?

2. To which parameters of the problem is the outcome most sensitive? Examine this question not only in mathematical terms, but also keeping in mind the likely range of parameter values encountered in the real atmosphere. For example, both the acceleration due to gravity g and the temperature T might appear in a particular relationship. While both vary, T at the Earth's surface is likely to vary by a far greater amount than g and therefore to have dominant influence on variations in your result.

3. Are there values for the parameters of your problem for which your solution "breaks," either mathematically (e.g., division by zero) or because some key assumption in its derivation is likely to be violated (e.g., $x \ll 1$)? Could those parameter values actually occur in the Earth's atmosphere? On another planet?

4. In addition to the specific scenario described in the problem, can you imagine other real-world scenarios to which the methods and/or general principles of the problem might apply?

B.2 The Solution Write-Up—Habits to *Unlearn*

B.2.1 Recipe for disaster

The best way to make the case for developing a disciplined and mature approach to your problem write-ups is to demonstrate the clear shortcomings of the alternative approach. The following pretty well captures what I often see on the first homework sets turned in by new students in my own undergraduate courses:

1. Use the numerical values of the given variables in the problem to compute a new, intermediate value. Write down that value with anywhere from 1 to 10 significant figures.

2. Ignore the units and assume that "it will all work out." Or, if unit conversions are required and are, in fact, explicitly worked out, let these appear as long, cumbersome chains of multiplications and divisions reminiscent of high school chemistry.

3. Use the above intermediate values to compute yet another intermediate value. The number of significant figures (i.e., precision) assigned to the new value may or may not have anything to do with the precision retained for the results of the previous steps.

4. Repeat above as necessary until you have a (purported) numerical value for the solution to the problem.

5. Convert to the desired final units. Or not! Or forget to even indicate what the units of the answer are.

It is quite possible, if you are reasonably careful, to obtain the correct answer to an assigned problem using the above procedure. Nevertheless, this *ad hoc, numerically oriented* approach to physical computations is both inefficient and error-prone. Let us look at some of the pitfalls:

- Every time you compute and write down an intermediate numerical value, you are necessarily rounding off the result. Depending on how much you round, the imprecision introduced each time can accumulate to give significant errors in your final answer.

- It can be almost impossible to spot either computational or logical errors when either you or the grader examines the mass of numbers and unit conversions scribbled on your page. Furthermore, the likelihood of a computational error (e.g., dropping a digit or punching a wrong button) increases each time you pick up your calculator.

- A lot of effort often goes into converting units as you go through each step. Much of this effort is wasted, and it increases the likelihood of errors.

- It obscures the underlying general physical relationships governing the variable you are solving for. Does variable x increase or decrease with increases in variable y? Does variable y even matter? If your approach is strictly numerical, you might not notice that y cancels out and is not even a factor in your final solution.

- If you need to repeat the calculation for the same problem but for a different set of parameter values, you have to repeat the entire procedure from scratch, again wasting time and increasing the likelihood of errors.

- It is difficult for an instructor to give partial credit for a problem solved in the above manner if the final answer turns out to be numerically incorrect because it can be impossible to tell whether the error was conceptual (the student didn't know what he/she was doing) or merely computational (the student dropped a sign somewhere).

A few of the hazards mentioned above are illustrated by the example on the next page, which is not at all unusual among the solutions I get from new students in my courses.

B.2.2 A bad example

Problem: Estimate the *total mass* (in kg) of the atmosphere M_{tot}, using the following information: Acceleration due to gravity $g = 32.17\ \text{ft/s}^2$

Radius of the Earth $R_E = 3960$ miles
Average sea level pressure $p_0 = 1013.2$ millibars
Conversions: 1 m = 3.28 ft 1 mile = 1609.756 m

$$\frac{1013.2\ \text{mb} \times 100\ \text{Pa/mb} \times \frac{\text{N/m}^2}{\text{Pa}} \times \frac{\text{kg m/sec}^2}{\text{N}}}{32.17\ \text{ft/sec} \times 1\text{m}/3.28\text{ft}} =$$

$$= 10330.41965$$

$$4\pi(3960)^2\ \text{miles} = 197060797.4\ \text{miles} \times$$

$$1609.756\ \frac{\text{m}}{\text{mile}} \times 10330.41965$$

$$= 3.277013666 \times 10^{+15} \leftarrow \text{ANSWER (Mass of the atmosphere)}$$

The above solution is not only ugly, but anyone else reading it (e.g., your instructor) may have a hard time following the reasoning. Nevertheless, the *reasoning* is, in fact, correct, and the string of numerical calculations is *almost* correct in terms of finding the value of the total mass of the atmosphere. But the numerical result is wildly wrong, and it is due to exactly one fairly trivial error in the computation. But would you notice it if this were your own solution? Would you be able to spot the error if you were the grader and, if not, *would you even consider awarding partial credit?*

Problem B.1: a) Note the clock time as you start this exercise.

b) Find the computational error in the above solution. For reference, use the complete and correct solution found in Section B.3.6.

c) Record the total time it took you to find the error.

d) Multiply the above time by the number of problems on a typical homework set (assume ten unless otherwise instructed) and by the approximate number of students in your class. Express your answer in units of hours.

B.3 The Solution Write-Up—Habits to *Learn*

Let us now look at how to undertake physical calculations and write up problem solutions the way a professional would. The basic ideas can be summarized as follows:

- We begin our solution with *abstract* manipulation of physical quantities with the goal of finding a *symbolic* solution. The calculation of a *numerical* solution follows as the final step.
- We take care to ensure both *dimensional* and *mathematical* consistency at every step.
- We are disciplined in our use of *significant figures*, neither throwing away precision unnecessarily nor attributing more precision to a value than it deserves.
- We write up the solution in a logical, sequential fashion, making sure that the reader can easily see what steps we are taking even if the details aren't spelled out. We don't need to include every step of an integration, for example, as long as the starting and ending points are clear and the intermediate algebra is obvious.

The last of these requires no explanation, so we will focus in the following on the first three.

B.3.1 Symbolic solutions

First and foremost, we want to stay away from *numbers* as long as possible and analyze our problem instead in terms of *variables* (or *parameters*). *Numbers* have meanings that are tied to a specific instance of a problem. *Variables* have meanings that are independent of a specific case. If the physics is the same, then the algebra of computing the mass of the atmosphere of Mars is identical to that for Earth, only the *values* of the parameters R_E, g, and p_0 change. Therefore, it makes sense to solve the problem in general form first before substituting specific values.

We do this by letting *symbols* (often, but by no means always, Roman or Greek letters, sometimes with subscripts, superscripts, or other embellishments) represent all physical parameters, as well as any physical and mathematical constants. Your problem solution is then obtained by manipulating your chosen symbols algebraically until you have found a *self-contained* expression (or small set of related expressions) for the quantity you seek.

There are four main reasons why symbolic solutions, where possible, are preferable to strictly numerical solutions:

1. *They convey physical insight.* You can see at a glance which variables are important (or even present) and how they are related to the desired quantity.

2. You can readily verify *dimensional consistency*, which is essential for any physically valid solution (see Section B.3.2) without working through a mass of unit conversions.

3. *They are easy to validate and debug.* An instructor looking at a string of your numerical calculations cannot immediately discern whether your pathway basically leads to the desired result (especially if there is an error buried in there somewhere). A correct symbolic solution, on the other hand, will look about the same for everyone. If something is wrong, it will usually be very easy to spot what it is.

4. *They are reusable.* If you are asked to solve the same problem for several different sets of conditions, you don't need to rederive the complete solution for each case; you simply plug the new values into your symbolic solution and crunch them through your calculator. You can even code up the expressions as a Fortran, Matlab, IDL, or C++ routines so that you don't need to pick up your calculator at all. And if you do the latter, it becomes a trivial matter to generate the data needed to plot a graph of the output as a function of one or more of the inputs!

B.3.2 Dimensional consistency

It is impossible to overstate the importance of dimensional literacy[2] in physical problem solving. You *cannot* add a length to a mass. You

[2]If you need to review the fundamental physical dimensions and associated units likely to be encountered in a course like this one, see Appendix D.

cannot take a cosine or exponential of a time or of any other quantity with physical dimensions. Any problem solution that violates these and similar precepts *cannot possibly be correct!* Many of the errors I find in homework solutions could have been easily spotted, and presumably fixed, by the student if they had simply checked for dimensional consistency. This section is a brief summary of the relevant rules.

In any valid equation, the physical dimensions of both sides of the equal sign *must* be the same. For example, if A in the equation

$$A = B \cdot C$$

has dimensions of pressure, then $B \cdot C$ must also have dimensions of pressure. If

$$A = B + C \quad ,$$

then A, B, and C must all have the same dimensions. If

$$A = B\exp(C) \equiv Be^{C} \quad \textit{or} \quad A = B\ln C \quad ,$$

then in each case B must have the dimensions of A, and C must be *dimensionless.* It follows that anytime you have expressions like

$$A = \exp(C) \equiv e^{C} \quad \textit{or} \quad A = \ln C \quad ,$$

A *must* be dimensionless.

Dimensions of derivatives and integrals are straightforward. The dimensions of

$$\frac{df(x)}{dx}$$

are the dimensions of $f(x)$ divided by the dimensions of x. Likewise, the dimensions of

$$\int_{x_1}^{x_2} f(x)\, dx$$

are the dimensions of $f(x)$ *times* the dimensions of x.

Key fact: Carefully checking for consistency of dimensions in your computations will greatly reduce the chance for errors. If they don't conform to the above rules, then your calculation is wrong, period!

The flip side of this principle is that examining the dimensions of the given variables in a problem will often give you a clue as to how to combine them in order to obtain an expression for the quantity of interest.

Problem B.2: In the following, give the fundamental dimensions of the indicated quantity, expressing your answer in terms of the *base* dimensions of "length," "mass," "temperature," and/or "time."

a) $a = bC$, where a has dimensions of force and b has dimensions of mass. What are the dimensions of C?

b) $d = F \sin(2\pi M/H)$, where d has dimensions of pressure and M has dimensions of length. What are the dimensions of H? What are the dimensions of F?

c) $U = (1 + aX)V$, where V has units of degrees Kelvin and X is dimensionless. What are the dimensions of a and U?

d) If y has units of pascals and x has units of meters, what are the physical dimensions of $Z = \frac{dy}{dx}$?

e) What are the dimensions of $\int f(x)\, dx$, if $f(x)$ has dimensions of acceleration and x has dimensions of time?

f) In your own words, explain the difference between the *dimensions* of a physical quantity and its *units*.

Apparent Exceptions

Occasionally a formula may be presented to you that *seems* to require some bending of the above rules. For example, take the radar reflectivity equation $Z = AR^b$, where both Z and R have specific meteorological units (mm^6/m^3 and mm/hr, respectively). If b is a non-integer, then it becomes awkward to make any meaningful statement about the dimensions of the coefficient A. The situation becomes even worse when we take logarithms of both sides to get an expression like this:

$$\ln Z = \ln A + b \ln R \quad ,$$

in which case Z, A, and R are not allowed to have any dimensions at all (i.e., they should be "pure" numbers)! The way around this paradox is to think of Z and R not as dimensioned quantities but rather as non-dimensional *ratios* expressing the magnitude of the radar reflectivity factor and rain rate *relative to their respective standard units.*

Dimensions versus units

While it is not physically meaningful to add a length to a mass, it is certainly meaningful to add an inch to a mile. In other words, the requirement for *dimensional* consistency does not necessarily imply that all of your variables have to be specified using the same system of *units.* For example, it is perfectly acceptable to pose the following:

$$1 \text{ inch} + 1 \text{ mile} = ?$$

To find the sum, you must of course choose a single unit of length to represent your answer, and you must then express both of the lengths on the left-hand side in terms of that unit. All of the following solutions are equally valid

$$1.57\overline{82} \times 10^{-5} \text{ mile} + 1 \text{ mile} = 1.0000157\overline{82} \text{ mile}$$

$$1 \text{ inch} + 63360 \text{ inch} = 63361 \text{ inch}$$

$$0.0254 \text{ meter} + 1609.344 \text{ meter} = 1609.3694 \text{ meter}$$

Of course, we have assumed above that we are speaking of adding *exactly* one inch to *exactly* one mile. After you read the section on significant figures, you will understand that if "1 mile" is taken as a *measured* quantity with only one significant figure of precision, then

$$1 \text{ inch} + 1 \text{ mile} = 1 \text{ mile} \quad !$$

B.3.3 Mathematical consistency

Quite often in atmospheric physics, we encounter first-order differential equations of the form

$$\frac{dy}{dx} = f(x,y) \quad .$$

In words, this equation tells us the following: Given particular values of x and y, an infinitesimal change dx in x will lead to an infinitesimal change dy in y; furthermore, the *ratio* of the change dy to the change dx (i.e., the left-hand side) is given by the function $f(x,y)$. In any real problem, the function $f(x,y)$ would be known, and your job would be to find the function $y(x)$—or perhaps $x(y)$—that satisfies the equation.

The standard method of solution is to try to separate variables in the following fashion

$$g(x)\, dx = h(y)\, dy,$$

where

$$f(x,y) \equiv \frac{g(x)}{h(y)},$$

Quantities like dx, dy, and $d\phi$ are known in calculus as *differentials*. It is essential to understand that they represent arbitrary *infinitesimal* (i.e., microscopic) changes in the quantities x, y, and ϕ. These have no specific value on their own and are meaningful only when compared with other differentials.

Furthermore, a differential quantity times anything is still a differential. The entire left- and right-hand sides of (B.3.3) are therefore each differentials in their own right. If we want, we can give them new names, such as

$$dU \equiv g(x)\, dx \quad , \quad dV \equiv h(y)\, dy \quad .$$

In meteorology, we are not normally interested in microscopic changes except as a starting point for our analysis; we want to see what happens in response to a *macroscopic* (finite) change in a variable. The process by which we get from infinitesimal to finite changes is via *integration*. In fact, integration can be thought of as the process of summing up the results of an infinite series of infinitely small steps.

For the separated differential equation given above, we normally want to integrate both sides between some initial state a and some ending state b :

$$\int_{x(a)}^{x(b)} g(x)\, dx = \int_{y(a)}^{y(b)} h(y)\, dy.$$

With luck, we will be able to find closed-form expressions for both sides that don't involve integrals.

The above procedure is straightforward and should be very familiar to you by the time you finish this course. In the meantime, you should carefully pay attention to the following essential rules:

- The *only* valid way to get from differential to macroscopic changes in a variable is to integrate. If any of your differentials mysteriously disappear without the help of a clearly indicated integration, something is wrong!

- If you integrate one side of an equation, you *must* integrate the other side, as well. You should never, *ever* wind up with an equality between a differential quantity on one side and a finite quantity on the other.

- When solving physical problems, your integrals will *always* have explicit lower and upper limits of integration (i.e., no indefinite integrals). These limits represent the starting and ending points of the physical process you are evaluating. If you leave the limits of integration off, then your solution is not mathematically correct and complete.

- The lower limits of integration on each side of the equation *must* be consistent with each other. For example, if your integral on the right-hand side is over time t, and the lower limit of integration is $t = 0$, then the lower limit of your integral over (e.g.) y on the left-hand side must represent the value of y evaluate at time $t = 0$. The same holds true for upper limits.

- When integrating over a particular variable (e.g., t), all other variables (e.g., y) on that side of the equation whose value changes with t must be *inside* that integral. This is true even if y is not already written out as an explicit function of t. If it is not, then you need to figure out how to express it as a function of t so that you can properly evaluate the integral. If you can't, then at least consider the possibility that y might more naturally belong inside the integral on the other side of the equation.

B.3.4 Numerical precision

Exact versus measured values

In the sciences, we distinguish between exact values and measured (or estimated) values. Exact values include theoretically derived quantities, like π and the ratio $4/3$, both of which appear in the formula for the volume of a sphere. Also, an *assumed* (not measured) value for a physical variable may also be treated as exact, in the sense that we can say, "Consider a balloon that ascends to the 500 hPa level..." without anybody worrying about whether we really mean 500.00000 hPa or rather 500.00001 hPa.

Measured values, on the other hand, are inherently approximate. When we read an aneroid barometer, we can be pretty sure of getting a reading that is correct to the nearest hPa. With practice, we can go a step further and *estimate* to the nearest 0.1 hPa. But we can say nothing whatsoever about the correct value of the hundredths place. Our measurement, like all measurements, therefore has a finite *precision*.

Measures of precision

We can express the presumed precision in any value in either of two ways: via the *number of significant figures* and/or the *least significant decimal*.

Significant figure: Any digit that is *not* a leading zero. A number should be rounded or padded with trailing zeros to give it the correct number of significant figures in light of its actual precision.

Least significant decimal: The decimal place that holds the last significant digit. Decimal places are numbered starting at zero for the ones place and increasing to the left. Decimal places to the right of the decimal point are negative.[3]

Key fact: If the least significant decimal is greater than zero, then scientific notation should be used to prevent trailing zeros from being misinterpreted as significant.

Here are some examples of numerical values and their associated precision:

Example	No. Sig. Figs.	Least Sig. Decim.
1.37	3	−2
54.389	5	−3
1010.	4	0
1.01×10^3	3	1
0.000002	1	−6
15.0 million	3	5

The number of significant figures effectively tells you the *relative* (or fractional) uncertainty in the value. For example, a value with three significant figures is believed to be known to within about one part in 10^2–10^3 (depending on the exact value).

The least significant decimal, on the other hand, is a measure of the *absolute* uncertainty. For example, if the least significant decimal is −2, then we believe we know the value to approximately the nearest 0.01, regardless of whether the number has five significant figures (e.g., 529.03) or only one (e.g., 0.05).

[3]In other words, decimal places are numbered according to the base-10 logarithm of the value of the place.

Key fact: When *multiplying* or *dividing* two values, the number of significant figures of your result is the *lesser* of the number of significant figures of your two values.

For example, if x has five significant figures and y has only two, then the values of both xy and x/y have only two significant figures.

Key fact: When *adding* or *subtracting* two values, the least significant decimal of your result is the *greater* of the least significant decimals of your two values.

For example, if x is significant to the tenths place and y is significant to the thousandths place, then $x + y$ or $x - y$ is significant only to the tenths place.

B.3.5 Summary

Let us now quickly recap our guidelines for writing up problem solutions:

1. *Identify* the relevant variables in the problem and *assign symbols* to represent those variables. Also, determine the *physical dimensions* of each variable.

2. Ignoring the *values* of the variables for now, *solve* the given problem *symbolically*. That is, express the answer to the problem mathematically in terms of the symbols representing your known variables (and perhaps any new variables you choose to define).

3. *Verify* that your symbolic solution is dimensionally consistent—that is, that the dimensions of the right-hand side are the same as the left-hand side. If they are inconsistent, you are *guaranteed* to have made an error!

4. *Convert* the numerical values of all given variables to a *consistent set of units.* This will normally be SI. Thus, every variable whose dimensions include a length (for example) should have that length expressed in units of meters.

5. Then—and *only* then—plug the above numerical values into your symbolic solution and crank them through your calculator. There is no need to mess around with units at this point, because if the variables all had consistent units going into the calculator, the numerical result that appears on your calculator *must* be in terms of the same set of units.

6. If required, you may now convert the units of the answer to the final units requested in the problem. Whether you have to do this or not, *ensure that the actual units of your final answer are clearly displayed.* Unless the quantity you have solved for is inherently nondimensional, a numerical value with no units is about as useful as a book with no words.

7. *Persuade yourself* that the numerical result you found makes sense! For example, if you calculate a raindrop radius of 10 meters as the answer to a certain homework problem, you should immediately recognize that something is wrong, either with the problem itself, or (more likely) with your solution. Also check the *sign* of your result and see whether it is consistent with your expectations—probably the majority of computational errors I see involve sign errors.

It is important to recognize that, in the above procedure, your calculator does not come into play at all until step 4. If you have to solve the same problem a second time, say with a new set of values for your given variables, you don't need to repeat the entire derivation; you only need to jump right back to step 4. *Step 2 is the one responsible for most of the thinking work on most homework and test problems.*

B.3.6 A good example

Problem: Estimate the *total mass* (in kg) of the atmosphere M_{tot}, using the following information: Acceleration due to gravity g = 32.17 ft/s^2

Radius of the Earth R_E = 3960 miles
Average sea level pressure p_0 = 1013.2 millibars
Conversions: 1 m = 3.28 ft 1 mile = 1609.756 m

Reasoning:

1. pressure $p_0 = \frac{\text{force}}{\text{area}} = \frac{\text{mass} \times g}{\text{area}} \quad \rightarrow \quad \frac{\text{mass}}{\text{area}} = \frac{p_0}{g}$

2. total mass of atmosphere $= \frac{\text{mass}}{\text{area}} \times$ [surface area of Earth] $= \frac{p_0}{g}\left[4\pi R^2\right]$

Symbolic solution:

$$M_{tot} = \frac{p_0 4\pi R^2}{g}$$

This is the most important part of your solution! If you get this part right, most of your "thinking" work is done. This form does not depend on the actual values of, or choice of units for, the parameters of the problem. You could repeat the calculations below for a different planet without rederiving the above equation!

Next, verify dimensional correctness. The above expression should have dimensions of mass (kg in SI units). If it does not, go back and find the error!

$$\frac{\text{Pa} \cdot \text{m}^2}{\text{m/s}^2} = \frac{\text{N} \cdot \text{s}^2}{\text{m}} = \frac{\text{kg} \cdot (\text{m/s}^2) \cdot \text{s}^2}{\text{m}} = \text{kg} \quad \surd$$

Finally, substitute numerical values of parameters **after** converting to consistent set of units (in this case SI):

$g = 32.17\ \frac{\text{ft}}{\text{s}^2} \cdot \frac{1\ \text{m}}{3.28\ \text{ft}} \quad \rightarrow \quad g = 9.808\ \frac{\text{m}}{\text{s}^2}$

$R = 3960\ \text{mi} \cdot \frac{1609.8\ \text{m}}{\text{mi}} \quad \rightarrow \quad R = 6.374 \times 10^6\ \text{m}$

$p_0 = 1013.2\ \text{mb} \cdot \frac{100\ \text{Pa}}{\text{mb}} \quad \rightarrow \quad p_0 = 1.013 \times 10^5\ \text{Pa}$

Numerical solution: $M_{tot} = \frac{(1.013 \times 10^5) 4\pi (6.374 \times 10^6)^2}{9.808} = 5.27 \times 10^{18}$ kg

1. Note that we didn't need to explicitly compute the units in the final calculation because we had already verified that the *symbolic* solution correctly yielded dimensions of mass. If we then specify the values of all parameters in SI units, the results must also be in SI units!

2. For most problems in this book, three or four significant figures in the final numerical solution is sufficient precision. In this case, we chose three. We therefore don't really need to retain more than four significant figures (one more than the desired precision of our final result) for the value of any parameter going into the problem.

B.4 Checklist for Homework Solutions

- ☐ The symbolic part of the solution *must* take the form of a self-contained formula, or small set of formulas.
- ☐ A box should be drawn around the final solutions (both symbolic and numerical), so that they can be clearly identified when grading.
- ☐ All symbols appearing in the formula(s) *must* represent either (a) parameters given in the original problem, (b) quantities defined inside the solution box, or (c) quantities for which a symbolic expression was provided in a previous part of the same homework problem.
- ☐ Each solution *must* be dimensionally consistent (see Section B.3.2) to receive even partial credit.[4]
- ☐ If the starting point for the solution involves differentials, make certain that any integration is shown explicitly on both sides of the equation, with appropriate (and consistent) limits.
- ☐ There should never appear any *numerical values* in the symbolic formula that represent physical (as opposed to purely mathematical) quantities. Any such value should be replaced with an appropriately defined symbol or combination of symbols.
- ☐ There should never appear any numerical values that are decimal approximations to an exact number. For example, π should always appear in a formula as that symbol, *not* as 3.1416. Even for rational numbers, decimal representations are best avoided: use $5x/4y$ rather than $1.25x/y$.
- ☐ If a physical calculation involves temperature, there's a high likelihood that the temperature should be expressed as an *absolute* temperature. *Verify* that you have converted to Kelvin wherever required. Note: for temperature *differences* it does not matter whether you use Celsius or Kelvin—the *size* of one degree is the same for both.
- ☐ Derived or measured numerical values required as inputs to calculations should normally preserve at least four significant figures of precision, where possible—more if needed to satisfy the requirement below. Assumed values should be treated as exact.
- ☐ Where possible, final numerical values for your solution should be given with a precision of three significant figures, unless otherwise noted. However, the stated precision of the result should not be greater than that justified by the lowest-precision input to the calculation. Possible exceptions: temperatures should normally be given to the nearest tenth of a degree, pressures should be given to *at least* the nearest hectopascal, even when this means four significant figures. Temperature *differences* should be calculated to the nearest tenth of a degree, or to three significant figures, whichever is the greater precision.

---

[4]This may sound draconian, but checking for dimensional consistency is so easy, and so important, that there is never a valid reason to skip this step.

APPENDIX C

Math Review

This appendix reviews a few relevant mathematical relationships that you might have forgotten.

C.1 Basic Identities

C.1.1 Logarithms and powers

These should be very familiar:

$$x^{-a} = \frac{1}{x^a} \qquad (x^a)(x^b) = x^{a+b} \quad ,$$

$$x^a y^a = (xy)^a \qquad \frac{x^a}{x^b} = x^{a-b} \quad .$$

Relationships involving natural (base-e) logarithms[1] and exponentials:

$$\exp x \equiv e^x \qquad \text{Same function, alternate notation!} \quad ,$$

[1]In the sciences, when we write log, we almost always mean *natural logarithm* (often indicated with ln, including on your calculator). On the rare occasions when we use base-10 logarithms, we will usually make this explicit by writing $\log_{10}$.

$$\log(1) = 0 \qquad \log(e) = 1 \qquad \log(e^x) = x \quad ,$$

$$\log(MN) = \log(M) + \log(N) \quad ,$$

$$\log\left(\frac{M}{N}\right) = \log(M) - \log(N) \quad ,$$

$$\log(M^p) = p \cdot \log(M) \quad ,$$

$$\log\left(\frac{1}{M}\right) = -\log(M) \quad .$$

Conversion between natural logarithms and base-10 logarithms:

$$\log(M) = \log_{10}(M) \cdot \log(10)$$

C.1.2 Differentiation and integration

The *derivative* of $f(x)$ is simply the ratio of the small change df in $f(x)$ in response to an infinitesimally small change dx in x. It may thus be interpreted as the tangent slope of the graph of $f(x)$ at x. Mathematically,

$$f'(x) \equiv \frac{df(x)}{dx} \equiv \lim_{\Delta x \to 0} \frac{f(x + \Delta x) - f(x)}{\Delta x} \quad .$$

Note that $f'(x)$ is a synonym for $df(x)/dx$. In this book, we use the latter notation.

Here are the most commonly required identities:

$$\text{Product rule:} \qquad \frac{d}{dx}(uv) = u\frac{dv}{dx} + v\frac{du}{dx} \quad ,$$

$$\text{Power rule:} \qquad \frac{d}{dx}(x^a) = ax^{a-1} \quad ,$$

$$\text{Chain rule:} \qquad \frac{d}{dx}(f(u(x))) = \frac{df}{du}\frac{du}{dx}(x) \quad ,$$

$$\frac{d}{dx}(\ln u) = \frac{1}{u}\frac{du}{dx} \qquad \frac{d}{dx}(e^u) = e^u\frac{du}{dx} \quad ,$$

$$\frac{d}{dx}(a^x) = \frac{d}{dx}[\exp(x \ln a)] = a^x \ln(a) \quad .$$

Integration is the inverse of differentiation:

$$\int du = u + \text{constant} \qquad \int_{u_1}^{u_2} du = u_2 - u_1 \quad .$$

In this book, we are always concerned with definite integrals (i.e., integrals with explicit lower and upper limits of integration); therefore, we use the form on the right (above). Consequently, we disregard the constant of integration in the common integrals listed below.

$$\int x^a dx = \frac{1}{a+1} x^{a+1} \quad ; \quad a \neq -1 \quad ,$$

$$\int \frac{1}{x} dx = \int d \ln x = \ln x \quad ,$$

$$\int e^{ax} dx = \frac{1}{a} e^{ax} \quad .$$

For the more complicated integrals that we encounter in this course, the most common techniques of integration are *substitution* and *integration by parts*. Some excellent tutorial modules on these and other calculus techniques may be found at `http://archives.math.utk.edu/visual.calculus/`.

C.2 Solving Equations

C.2.1 Linear equations

The equation of a line in the x–y plane can be represented as

$$Ax + By = C \quad .$$

Equivalently, we may use the *slope-intercept* form

$$y = mx + b \quad ,$$

where $m = A/B$ is the slope dy/dx and $b = C/B$ is the y-intercept (i.e., the value of y for the case that $x = 0$).

If we know the parameters m and b (or equivalently A and B), then for any x we can solve for the corresponding y, and vice versa.

Sometimes we don't know m and b at the outset and must determine these from information given in the problem, such as the coordinates of two points satisfying the equation. Given a pair of points (x_0, y_0) and (x, y), the slope m and intercept b of a line passing through both are given by

$$m = \frac{y - y_0}{x - x_0} \qquad b = y_0 - mx_0 \quad .$$

C.2.2 Coupled linear equations

Two equations in two unknowns

Some problems lead to two separate linear equations in two unknowns, and our task is to find the single point (x, y) that simultaneously satisfies both. A pair of linear equations in x and y can be written

$$ax + by = c \quad ,$$
$$dx + ey = f \quad .$$

Each equation defines a different straight line. The values of x and y satisfying the pair of equations correspond to the intersection of the two lines. They may be found by multiplying the top equation through by $-e/b$ and adding the result to the bottom equation, yielding an equation in x alone. Solving for x and then substituting back into either of the original equations then yields an equation that can be solved for y.

The above pair of equations has no solution if $ae - bd = 0$. This corresponds to the case that the two equations describe separate, parallel lines with no point of intersection.

Also, there will be no *unique* solution if one equation is a scalar multiple of the other equation. This corresponds to the case that both equations describe the same line, so that there is no unique point of intersection.

Quadratic equation

The quadratic equation $ax^2 + bx + c = 0$ has the solutions

$$x = \frac{-b \pm \sqrt{b^2 - 4ac}}{2a} \quad .$$

The two roots are either both real or both complex. For problems of the type encountered in this book, roots are usually real. Depending on the context, only one of these roots (e.g., the only positive one, if applicable) might be physically meaningful.

Other equations

Sometimes we have to solve nonlinear systems involving two equations in two unknowns. Our job is much simpler if we can find a way to convert the equations from a nonlinear to a linear form. For example, given the nonlinear pair of equations

$$\begin{aligned} Ae^{\alpha x} &= y \quad , \\ Be^{\beta x} &= y \quad . \end{aligned}$$

we may take logarithms of both equations, giving us the equivalent system of equations

$$\begin{aligned} \alpha x - \ln y &= -\ln A \quad , \\ \beta x - \ln y &= -\ln B \quad . \end{aligned}$$

Note that these are now linear in x and $\ln y$.

Approximate solutions

Occasionally we encounter equations that simply cannot be solved algebraically in closed form. Usually, these can be expressed in the form $f(x) = 0$, where $f(x)$ is a nonlinear equation, and we seek the value(s) of x that satisfies this equation. Such equations are best solved either *numerically* or *graphically*.

One numerical method is that of *successive approximation*. While there are many "recipes" for finding x with the fewest average number of keystrokes on your calculator, it is perfectly acceptable to simply plug in a guess for x and adjust your guess "by feel" until $f(x)$ is sufficiently close to zero. If you are clever about it, it shouldn't take you more than a couple minutes to zero in on a root that is accurate to at least two significant figures.

Be aware that there might be multiple roots—that is, multiple values of x satisfying the equation. The first one you find might not be the one you want!

The graphical method is very straightforward and is pretty efficient if you have access to a graphing program. Basically, you plot a graph of $f(x)$ and determine the value(s) of x where your curve crosses the x-axis. As long as you plot $f(x)$ for a wide enough range of x, it is hard to overlook additional roots! Furthermore, you can always fine-tune your estimates of those roots using successive approximation, as described above.

You may, of course, combine the successive approximation method with the graphical method: for each attempt to guess the value of x that solves the equation $f(x) = 0$, plot the point $(x, f(x))$ on a piece of graph paper. The pattern that emerges will help guide your next trial value of x.

C.3 Power Series Approximations

Any continuous function $f(x)$ may be expanded as a so-called *power series* (or *Taylor*[2] *series*) about a specified point $x = c$ as follows:

$$f(x) = \sum_{n=0}^{\infty} a_n (x - c)^n \quad .$$

The coefficients a_n are given by

$$a_n = \frac{1}{n!} \frac{d^n f(c)}{dx^n} \quad .$$

For the special case that $c = 0$, the expansion is sometimes called a *Maclauren*[3] *series*.

The usefulness of power series expansions lies in the fact that, for x not *too* far from c, we may keep only the first N terms and still have a reasonable approximation to $f(x)$. That is,

$$f(x) \approx \sum_{n=0}^{N} a_n (x - c)^n \quad .$$

The smaller $|x - c|$, the smaller N can be without incurring large errors.

---

[2]Brook Taylor (August 18, 1685 – November 30, 1731) was an English mathematician.

[3]Colin Maclaurin (February, 1698 – June 14, 1746) was a Scottish mathematician.

Practically speaking, we are often interested in the case that $c = 0$, in which case we have obtain the Maclauren series for the following common functions:

$$\begin{aligned} e^x &= 1 + x + \frac{1}{2!}x^2 + \frac{1}{3!}x^3 + \cdots \quad , \\ \sin x &= x - \frac{1}{3!}x^3 + \frac{1}{5!}x^5 + \cdots \quad , \\ \cos x &= 1 - \frac{1}{2!}x^2 + \frac{1}{4!}x^4 + \cdots \quad , \\ \frac{1}{1-x} &= 1 + x + x^2 + x^3 + \cdots \quad . \end{aligned}$$

Regardless of the exact form of the power series, note that when $x < 1$, each successive term is at least a factor x smaller than the one before it.

Let us now specifically consider the case that x is *much* less than 1 (the notation we use for this is $x \ll 1$). By "much less," we generally mean at least *an order of magnitude* smaller, where "order of magnitude" generally refers to a power of ten. That is, 0.1 is an order of magnitude smaller than 1, which is an order of magnitude smaller than 10, and so on.

For example, if $x \approx 10^{-1}$, then $x^2 \approx 10^{-2}$, $x^3 \approx 10^{-3}$, etc. This means that, for $x \ll 1$, we can neglect terms of order x^2 and higher and incur an error on the order of 1% or less:

$$\text{For } x \ll 1: \begin{cases} e^x \approx 1 + x \\ \sin x \approx x \\ \cos x \approx 1 \\ \dfrac{1}{1-x} \approx 1 + x \end{cases} \tag{C.1}$$

Often, when we encounter an equation or formula that is difficult to solve or analyze in exact form, we can substitute one of the above approximations in order to obtain a much more convenient form. Of course, we must ensure the approximate form is not inadvertently used beyond the range for which it is valid!

APPENDIX D

Physical Dimensions and Units

Review of Dimensions and Units

When working with equations that describe physical processes, variables will always have characteristic **dimensions**. For our purposes, the important dimensions are

Length, Mass, Time, Temperature, Charge

Various systems of **units** may be used to specify these dimensions. We will normally use the SI[1] system of units, in which

$$\begin{aligned} Length &\rightarrow meter\ (m) \\ Mass &\rightarrow kilogram\ (kg) \\ Time &\rightarrow second\ (s) \\ Temperature &\rightarrow kelvin\ (K) \\ Charge &\rightarrow Coulomb\ (C) \end{aligned}$$

[1]The International System of Units (abbreviated SI from the French *Le Système international d'unités*) is the modern form of the metric system. It is now used almost everywhere in the world, both in science and in commerce. The United States is the sole major economy that persists in using non-SI units in commerce and daily life. The older metric system included several groups of units. The SI was developed in 1960 from the old meter-kilogram-second (mks) system.

The SI system also includes the following derived units:

$$Force \rightarrow newton\ (N) = \left(\frac{kg\ m}{s^2}\right)$$

$$Energy \rightarrow joule\ (J) = (N\ m) = \left(\frac{kg\ m^2}{s^2}\right)$$

$$Power \rightarrow watt\ (W) = (J\ s^{-1}) = \left(\frac{kg\ m^2}{s^3}\right)$$

$$Pressure \rightarrow pascal\ (Pa) = (N\ m^{-2}) = \left(\frac{kg}{m\ s^2}\right)$$

There are a number of non-SI units that are still commonly used in meteorology and in everyday life. Here are the most important conversions:

1 inch = 2.54 cm = 25.4 mm = 0.0254 m

1 foot = 0.3048 m

1 statute mile = 1.609 km

1 nautical mile = 1.852 km

1 mph = 1.609 km/hr = 0.447 m/s

1 knot (kt) = 1 naut. mile/hr = 1.852 km/hr = 0.514 m/s

1 pound (force) = 4.448 N

1 pound (mass) = 0.4536 kg = 453.6 g

1 millibar (mb) = 1 hectopascal (hPa) = 100 Pa = 0.1 kPa

1 atmosphere (pressure) = 1013.2 mb = 29.92 inches Hg

$^\circ$C = ($^\circ$F - 32)$\times$5/9

$^\circ$K = $^\circ$C+273.15

1° (angle) = (π/180) radians = 0.01745 radians

Before you perform any numerical calculations involving physical quantities, you should always convert all values into a common, mutually consistent set of units. Unless otherwise indicated, your final answers should normally be expressed in suitable SI (metric) units. Exceptions may be made when other units are clearly more natural or widely accepted in a specific context, the most common examples being the use of millibars for pressure or degrees Celsius for temperature.

APPENDIX E

Tables and Charts

E.1 Physical Constants

Universal constants	
Avogadro's number (N_A)	6.022×10^{23} mole^{-1}
Boltzmann's constant (k_B)	1.381×10^{-23} J K^{-1}molecule^{-1}
Universal gas constant (R^*)	8314.472 J kmol^{-1} K^{-1}
Astronomical constants	
Average radius of the Earth (r_E)	6371 km
Standard gravitational acceleration (g)	9.80665 m s^{-2}
Air and water	
Standard sea level pressure (p_0)	1.01325×10^5 Pa
Molar mass, dry air (m_d)	28.9655 kg kmol^{-1}
Molar mass, water (m_w)	18.0153 kg kmol^{-1}
Gas constant, dry air (R_d)	287.047 J kg^{-1} K^{-1}
Gas constant, water vapor (R_v)	461.5 J kg^{-1} K^{-1}
Heat capacity at constant pressure, dry air (c_p)	1005 J kg^{-1} K^{-1}
Heat capacity at constant volume, dry air (c_v)	718 J kg^{-1} K^{-1}
Heat capacity, liquid water	4186 J kg^{-1} K^{-1}
Density, pure water (ice) at 0°C	917 kg m^{-3}
Density, pure water (liquid) at 0°C	1000 kg m^{-3}
Density, pure water (liquid) at 100°C	958 kg m^{-3}
Latent heat of fusion, ice (L_f)	3.34×10^5 J kg^{-1}
Latent heat of vaporization, water (L) at 0°C	2.50×10^6 J kg^{-1}
Latent heat of vaporization, water (L) at 100°C	2.27×10^6 J kg^{-1}

E.2 U.S. Standard Atmosphere

Pressure, geopotential height, temperature, and density in the U.S. Standard Atmosphere. Standard pressure levels are highlighted in boldface type.

p [hPa]	Z [m]	T [°C]	ρ [kg/m^3]	p [hPa]	Z [m]	T [°C]	ρ [kg/m^3]
1013.25	0	15.0	1.225e+0	325	8,624	-41.1	4.878e-1
1000	111	14.3	1.212e+0	**300**	9,164	-44.6	4.572e-1
975	323	12.9	1.187e+0	275	9,741	-48.3	4.261e-1
950	540	11.5	1.162e+0	**250**	10,363	-52.4	3.944e-1
925	762	10.0	1.137e+0	225	11,037	-56.5	3.617e-1
900	989	8.6	1.112e+0	**200**	11,784	-56.5	3.215e-1
875	1,220	7.1	1.087e+0	175	12,631	-56.5	2.813e-1
850	1,457	5.5	1.062e+0	**150**	13,608	-56.5	2.411e-1
825	1,700	3.9	1.037e+0	125	14,765	-56.5	2.009e-1
800	1,949	2.3	1.011e+0	**100**	16,180	-56.5	1.607e-1
775	2,204	0.7	9.859e-1	90	16,848	-56.5	1.447e-1
750	2,466	-1.0	9.601e-1	80	17,595	-56.5	1.286e-1
725	2,735	-2.8	9.341e-1	**70**	18,442	-56.5	1.125e-1
700	3,012	-4.6	9.079e-1	60	19,419	-56.5	9.647e-2
675	3,297	-6.4	8.816e-1	**50**	20,576	-55.9	8.018e-2
650	3,591	-8.3	8.550e-1	40	22,000	-54.5	6.373e-2
625	3,894	-10.3	8.283e-1	**30**	23,849	-52.7	4.739e-2
600	4,206	-12.3	8.014e-1	**20**	26,481	-50.0	3.122e-2
575	4,530	-14.4	7.742e-1	**10**	31,055	-45.4	1.529e-2
550	4,865	-16.6	7.469e-1	9	31,758	-44.7	1.372e-2
525	5,213	-18.9	7.192e-1	8	32,548	-43.0	1.210e-2
500	5,574	-21.2	6.914e-1	7	33,453	-40.4	1.047e-2
475	5,951	-23.7	6.633e-1	6	34,509	-37.5	8.868e-3
450	6,344	-26.2	6.348e-1	5	35,777	-33.9	7.281e-3
425	6,754	-28.9	6.061e-1	4	37,353	-29.5	5.719e-3
400	7,185	-31.7	5.771e-1	3	39,429	-23.7	4.189e-3
375	7,639	-34.7	5.477e-1	2	42,440	-15.3	2.701e-3
350	8,117	-37.8	5.179e-1	1	47,820	-2.5	1.287e-3

E.3 Conservation Properties

Common atmospheric variables and the conditions under which they are conserved. "Moist adiabatic" refers to a reversible process in which any condensed water remains with the parcel and reevaporates as needed to maintain saturation. "Pseudoadiabatic" refers to the irreversible process in which condensed water is assumed to be permanently removed.

Variable	Symbol	Dry Adiabatic	Moist Adiabatic	Pseudo-adiabatic
Density	ρ			
Pressure	p			
Specific volume	α			
Temperature	T			
Virtual temperature	T_v			
Wet-bulb temperature	T_w			
Vapor pressure	e			
Saturation vapor pressure	e_s			
Saturation vapor mixing ratio	w_s			
Dewpoint	T_d			
Relative Humidity	RH			
Vapor mixing ratio	w	$\surd$		
Specific humidity	q	$\surd$		
Potential temperature	θ	$\surd$		
Dry static energy	s_d	$\surd$		
Lifting condensation level	LCL	$\surd$	$\surd$	
Total mixing ratio	w_{tot}	$\surd$	$\surd$	
Equivalent potential temperature	θ_e	$\surd$	$\surd$	$\surd$
Wet-bulb potential temperature	θ_w	$\surd$	$\surd$	$\surd$

E.4 Common Symbols

Symbol	Meaning [typical units]
A	Coefficient in Eq. (7.18) [Pa]
A	Area [m^2]
B	Coefficient in (7.18) [K]
C_{water}	Specific heat capacity of water [J kg^{-1} K^{-1}]
c_p	Specific heat capacity, constant pressure [J kg^{-1} K^{-1}]
c_v	Specific heat capacity, constant volume [J kg^{-1} K^{-1}]]
DA	Density altitude [km]
E_k	Kinetic energy [J]
e	Vapor pressure [Pa]
e_K	Kinetic energy (intensive) [J kg^{-1}]
e_i	Saturation vapor pressure, ice [Pa, hPa]
e_s	Saturation vapor pressure, liquid water [Pa, hPa]
e_{i0}	Reference value for e_i [Pa, hPa]
e_{s0}	Reference value for e_s [Pa, hPa]
F	Force [N]
F_B	Buoyant force [N]
f	Fraction []
f_B	Buoyant force (intensive) [N kg^{-1}]
G	Gibbs function (intensive) [J kg^{-1}]
g	Acceleration due to gravity [m s^{-2}]
g_0	Standard acceleration due to gravity [m s^{-2}]
H	Scale height [m, km]
h	Enthalpy (intensive) [J kg^{-1}]
h	Height [m, km]
k_B	Boltzmann constant [J K^{-1}molecule^{-1}]
L	Latent heat (or enthalpy) of vaporization (or condensation) of water [J kg^{-1}]
L_f	Latent heat of fusion of water [J kg^{-1}]
L_s	Latent heat of sublimation of water [J kg^{-1}]
M	Mass [kg]
M_E	Mass of the Earth [kg]
m	Mass [kg]
m	Molar mass [kg $kmol^{-1}$]
$\overline{m}$	Mean molar mass [kg $kmol^{-1}$]
m_d	Molar mass of dry air [kg $kmol^{-1}$]
m_w	Molar mass of water [kg $kmol^{-1}$]
N	Brunt-Väisäila frequency [s^{-1}]
N_A	Avogadro's number [$kmol^{-1}$]

Symbol	**Meaning [typical units]**
n	Quantity of substance in kilomoles [kmol]
p	Pressure [Pa, hPa]
p_0	Sea level pressure; surface pressure; reference pressure [Pa, hPa]
p_d	Partial pressure of dry air [Pa]
p_s	Surface pressure [Pa, hPa]
p_{alt}	Altimeter setting [hPa, inches Hg]
p_{lcl}	Pressure at Lifting Condensation Level [hPa]
Q	Heat added (extensive) [J]
q	Specific humidity [g/kg]
q	Heat added (intensive) [J kg^{-1}]
R	Gas constant (generic) [J kg^{-1} K^{-1}]
RH	Relative humidity [%]
R_E	Radius of the Earth [km]
R_d	Gas constant for dry air [J kg^{-1} K^{-1}]
R_v	Gas constant for water vapor [J kg^{-1} K^{-1}]
r	Distance from the center of the Earth [km]
r_0	Mean radius of the Earth [km]
S	Entropy (extensive) [J K^{-1}]
s	Entropy (intensive) [J kg^{-1} K^{-1}]
s	Supersaturation [%]
s_d	Dry static energy [J kg^{-1}]
T	Temperature [K, °C]
T_0	Initial or reference temperature; surface temperature [K]
T_c	Convective temperature [K, °C]
T_d	Dewpoint [K, °C]
ΔT_d	Dewpoint depression [K, °C]
T_e	Equivalent temperature [K]
T_s	Surface temperature [K, °C]
T_v	Virtual temperature [K]
$\overline{T_v}$	Mean virtual temperature [K]
T_w	Wet-bulb temperature [K, °C]
T_{wc}	Wind chill temperature [°C]
t	Time [s]
U	Wind speed [m s^{-1}]
u	Internal energy (intensive) [J kg^{-1}]
V	Volume [m^3]
v	Velocity [m s^{-1}]
W	Work done (extensive) [J]
W_{max}	Maximum updraft speed [m s^{-1}]
w	Water vapor mixing ratio [g/kg]

Symbol	Meaning [typical units]
w	Work done (intensive) [$\mathrm{J\ kg^{-1}}$]
w_l	Liquid water mixing ratio [g/kg]
w_s	Saturation mixing ratio [g/kg]
w_{tot}	Total water mixing ratio (vapor plus condensate) [g/kg]
Z	Geopotential height [m]
z	Altitude, height, vertical displacement, geopotential height [m, km]
Δz	Layer thickness, vertical displacement [m]
α	Specific volume [$\mathrm{m^3\ kg^{-1}}$]
ε	R_d/R_v []
Γ	Environmental lapse rate [K/m, K/km]
Γ_d	Dry adiabatic lapse rate [K/m, K/km]
Γ_s	Moist adiabatic lapse rate [K/m, K/km]
Γ_{auto}	Autoconvective lapse rate [K/m, K/km]
Ω	Angular velocity [$\mathrm{s^{-1}}$]
κ	R_d/c_p []
ϕ	Geopotential [$\mathrm{J\ kg^{-1}}$]
ρ	Density [$\mathrm{kg\ m^{-3}}$]
ρ_d	Density, dry air component [$\mathrm{kg\ m^{-3}}$]
ρ_l	Density, liquid water [$\mathrm{kg\ m^{-3}}$]
ρ_v	Density, water vapor [$\mathrm{kg\ m^{-3}}$]
R^*	Universal gas constant [$\mathrm{J\ kmol^{-1}\ K^{-1}}$]
θ	Potential temperature [K]
θ_e	Equivalent potential temperature [K]
θ_w	Wet-bulb potential temperature [K]
θ_{lat}	Latitude [°]

E.5 Psychrometric Tables

Table to convert psychrometric readings T and T_w to relative humidity (in percent) at pressures near 1000 hPa.

T_w	$T - T_w$ [°C]																	
[°C]	1	2	3	4	5	6	7	8	9	10	11	12	13	14	15	16	17	18
0	83	68	55	43	32	23	15	8	1	.	.	.	.	.	.	.	.	.
1	84	69	56	45	35	26	18	11	5	.	.	.	.	.	.	.	.	.
2	84	71	58	47	37	29	21	14	8	3	.	.	.	.	.	.	.	.
3	85	72	60	49	40	31	24	17	12	6	2	.	.	.	.	.	.	.
4	86	73	61	51	42	34	27	20	14	9	5	1	.	.	.	.	.	.
5	86	74	63	53	44	36	29	23	17	12	8	4	0	.	.	.	.	.
6	87	75	64	55	46	38	31	25	20	15	11	7	3	0	.	.	.	.
7	87	76	65	56	48	40	34	28	22	17	13	9	6	3	0	.	.	.
8	88	77	67	57	49	42	36	30	24	20	15	12	8	5	3	0	.	.
9	88	77	68	59	51	44	37	32	27	22	18	14	11	8	5	3	0	.
10	88	78	69	60	52	45	39	34	29	24	20	16	13	10	7	5	3	1
11	89	79	70	61	54	47	41	35	30	26	22	18	15	12	9	7	5	3
12	89	79	70	62	55	48	42	37	32	28	24	20	17	14	11	9	7	5
13	89	80	71	63	56	50	44	39	34	29	25	22	19	16	13	11	8	6
14	90	81	72	64	57	51	45	40	35	31	27	24	20	17	15	12	10	8
15	90	81	73	65	59	52	47	42	37	33	29	25	22	19	16	14	12	10
16	90	82	74	66	60	53	48	43	38	34	30	27	24	21	18	16	13	11
17	91	82	74	67	61	55	49	44	40	35	32	28	25	22	19	17	15	13
18	91	82	75	68	61	56	50	45	41	37	33	30	26	24	21	18	16	14
19	91	83	75	69	62	57	51	46	42	38	34	31	28	25	22	20	18	16
20	91	83	76	69	63	57	52	48	43	39	35	32	29	26	24	21	19	17
21	91	84	77	70	64	58	53	49	44	40	37	33	30	27	25	22	20	18
22	92	84	77	71	65	59	54	49	45	41	38	34	31	28	26	23	21	19
23	92	84	78	71	65	60	55	50	46	42	39	35	32	30	27	25	22	20
24	92	85	78	72	66	61	56	51	47	43	40	36	33	31	28	26	23	21
25	92	85	78	72	67	61	57	52	48	44	41	37	34	32	29	27	24	22
26	92	85	79	73	67	62	57	53	49	45	42	38	35	33	30	28	25	23
27	93	86	79	73	68	63	58	54	50	46	42	39	36	34	31	29	26	24
28	93	86	80	74	68	63	59	54	50	47	43	40	37	34	32	29	27	25
29	93	86	80	74	69	64	59	55	51	47	44	41	38	35	33	30	28	26
30	93	86	80	75	69	64	60	56	52	48	45	42	39	36	33	31	29	27

Table to convert psychrometric readings T and T_w to dewpoint depression $\Delta T_d = T - T_d$ at pressures near 1000 hPa.

T_w	$T - T_w$ [°C]																	
[°C]	1	2	3	4	5	6	7	8	9	10	11	12	13	14	15	16	17	18
0	2.6	5.3	8.3	12	15	20	25	33	50	.	.	.	.	.	.	.	.	.
1	2.5	5.1	7.9	11	14	18	23	29	38	.	.	.	.	.	.	.	.	.
2	2.4	4.9	7.5	10	14	17	21	26	32	43	.	.	.	.	.	.	.	.
3	2.3	4.7	7.2	9.9	13	16	20	24	29	36	50	.	.	.	.	.	.	.
4	2.2	4.5	6.9	9.5	12	15	18	22	27	32	40	57	.	.	.	.	.	.
5	2.1	4.3	6.7	9.1	12	14	17	21	25	29	35	43	65	.	.	.	.	.
6	2.1	4.2	6.4	8.7	11	14	17	20	23	27	31	37	45	73	.	.	.	.
7	2.0	4.1	6.2	8.4	11	13	16	19	22	25	29	33	39	48	77	.	.	.
8	1.9	3.9	6.0	8.1	10	13	15	18	20	24	27	31	35	41	49	74	.	.
9	1.9	3.8	5.8	7.9	10	12	15	17	20	22	25	29	32	37	42	50	69	.
10	1.8	3.7	5.6	7.6	9.7	12	14	16	19	21	24	27	30	34	38	43	51	65
11	1.8	3.6	5.5	7.4	9.4	11	13	16	18	20	23	25	28	32	35	39	44	51
12	1.7	3.5	5.3	7.2	9.1	11	13	15	17	19	22	24	27	30	33	36	40	45
13	1.7	3.4	5.2	7.0	8.8	11	13	15	17	19	21	23	26	28	31	34	37	41
14	1.7	3.3	5.1	6.8	8.6	10	12	14	16	18	20	22	25	27	29	32	35	38
15	1.6	3.3	4.9	6.6	8.4	10	12	14	16	18	20	22	24	26	28	31	33	36
16	1.6	3.2	4.8	6.5	8.2	9.9	12	13	15	17	19	21	23	25	27	29	32	34
17	1.6	3.1	4.7	6.3	8.0	9.6	11	13	15	17	18	20	22	24	26	28	30	33
18	1.5	3.1	4.6	6.2	7.8	9.4	11	13	14	16	18	20	21	23	25	27	29	31
19	1.5	3.0	4.5	6.1	7.6	9.2	11	12	14	16	17	19	21	23	25	26	28	30
20	1.5	3.0	4.5	6.0	7.5	9.0	11	12	14	15	17	19	20	22	24	26	27	29
21	1.4	2.9	4.4	5.9	7.4	8.9	10	12	13	15	17	18	20	22	23	25	27	28
22	1.4	2.9	4.3	5.8	7.2	8.7	10	12	13	15	16	18	19	21	23	24	26	28
23	1.4	2.8	4.2	5.7	7.1	8.6	10	11	13	14	16	18	19	21	22	24	25	27
24	1.4	2.8	4.2	5.6	7.0	8.4	9.9	11	13	14	16	17	19	20	22	23	25	26
25	1.4	2.7	4.1	5.5	6.9	8.3	9.7	11	13	14	15	17	18	20	21	23	24	26
26	1.3	2.7	4.1	5.4	6.8	8.2	9.6	11	12	14	15	17	18	20	21	22	24	25
27	1.3	2.7	4.0	5.3	6.7	8.1	9.4	11	12	14	15	16	18	19	21	22	24	25
28	1.3	2.6	3.9	5.3	6.6	7.9	9.3	11	12	13	15	16	17	19	20	22	23	25
29	1.3	2.6	3.9	5.2	6.5	7.8	9.2	11	12	13	15	16	17	19	20	21	23	24
30	1.3	2.6	3.9	5.2	6.4	7.8	9.1	10	12	13	14	16	17	18	20	21	22	24

APPENDIX F

Essential Online Resources

A few especially useful websites are listed here for the convenience of students and instructors. Except for the first, the author is not responsible for either their content or future availability.

- Supplemental resources, including high-quality downloadable skew-*T* diagrams and sample soundings used in exercises are found on the description page for this book at `sundogpublishing.com`

- Basic glossaries of meteorological terms and abbreviations provided by by the National Weather Service: `www.weather.gov/glossary`

- A comprehensive online *Glossary of Meteorology* published by the American Meteorological Society: `amsglossary.allenpress.com`

- A tutorial on the skew-*T* diagram published by the University Corporation for Atmospheric Research (NCAR): `www.meted.ucar.edu/training_module.php?id=225`.

- The University of Wyoming's comprehensive archive of global upper air soundings from 1973–present: `weather.uwyo.edu/upperair/sounding.html`

Index

Ordering Information

Although this textbook may be ordered through bookstores or commercial online vendors in the usual way, you can save 25% off the retail price by ordering directly from the publisher at `sundogpublishing.com`.

Orders may be submitted via the following methods

(1) Online at `www.sundogpublishing.com` (credit card).

(2) E-mail to `sales@sundogpublishing.com` (bookstore purchase orders and instructor requests for examination copies).

Detailed ordering information and other resources may be found on the above website. To allow for the slight possibility of back orders, please submit orders *at least three weeks* in advance of the start date of the course.

A free examination copy may be requested by instructors of qualifying courses.

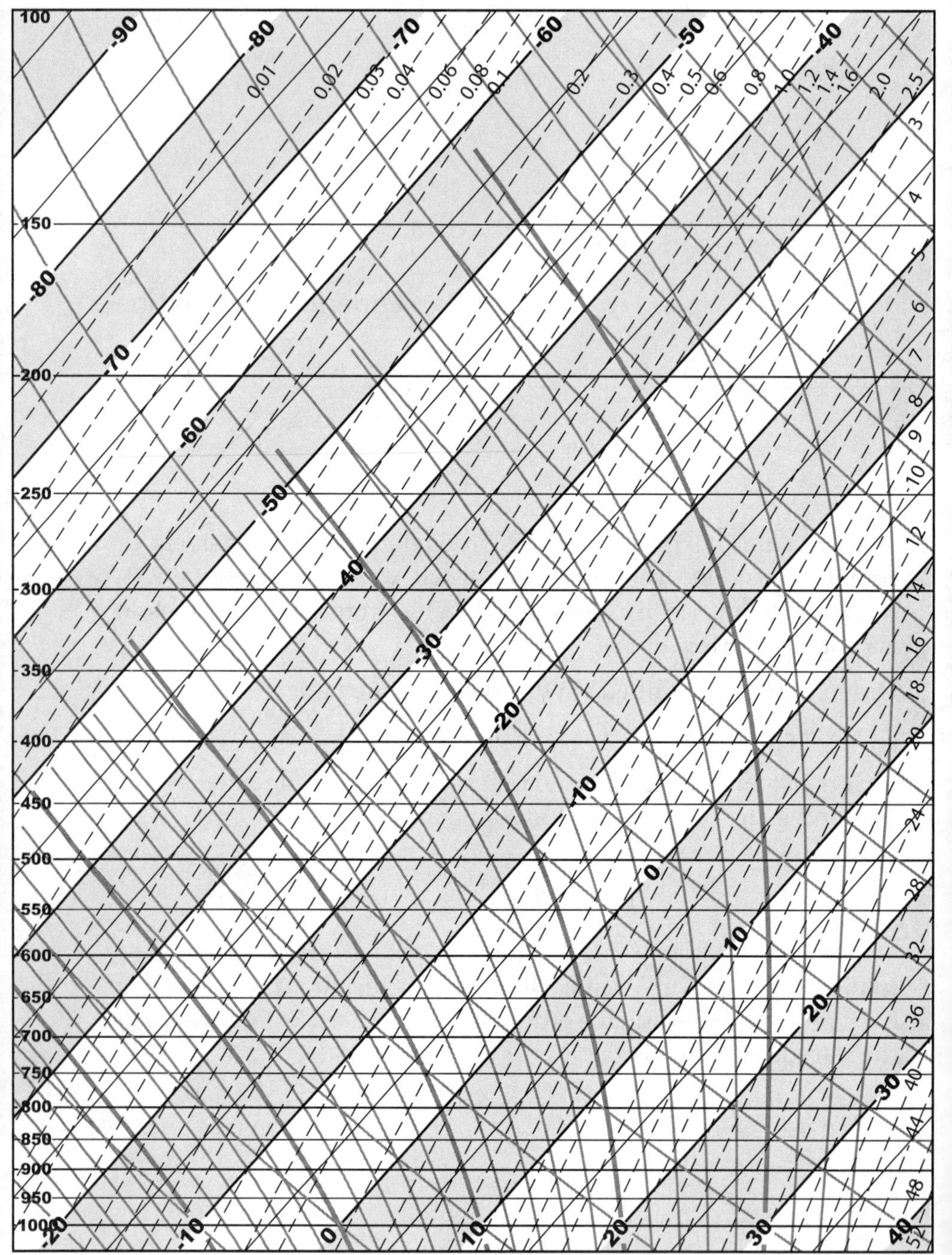

Printable high quality skew-*T* log *p* digrams are available from www.sundogpublishing.com.